THE PRE-COLUMBIAN MIND

D0125902

E
59
.P87
G8

THE PRE-COLUMBIAN MIND

A study into the aberrant nature of
sexual drives, drugs affecting behaviour,
and the attitude towards life and death,
with a survey of psychotherapy, in
pre-Columbian America

by

FRANCISCO GUERRA

M.D., Ph.D., D.Sc.

1971

SEMINAR PRESS · LONDON · NEW YORK

207593

SEMINAR PRESS LTD
24–28 Oval Road,
London, NW1

U.S. Edition published by
SEMINAR PRESS INC.
111 Fifth Avenue,
New York, New York 10003

Copyright © 1971 By SEMINAR PRESS LTD

All Rights Reserved

No part of this book may be reproduced in any form
by photostat, microfilm, or any other means, without
written permission from the publishers

Library of Congress Catalog Card Number: 70–181062

ISBN 0–12–841050–7

Made and printed in Great Britain by
William Clowes & Sons, Limited, London, Beccles and Colchester

PREFACE

Man's increasing awareness of the delicate balance of nature has recently led to a reassessment of the changes introduced in the environment and the role of these changes in the conquest of disease. It has been found that certain diseases occurring in wild life may be transmitted to Man when he intrudes into their territory. In such diseases nature's mechanisms for resistance—commensalism or immunity—acquired after centuries of adaptation always prove to be sounder and more lasting solutions than the attempt to eradicate them by chemotherapy or by suppression of the vectors and reservoirs which complete the cycle of wild life diseases. These discoveries have brought fresh interest to the analysis of disease in historical perspective, by comparing the results obtaining under standard methods of treatment with those which rely on man's self-curative mechanisms and his adaptation to the natural habitat. Although the recovery of a few individuals justifies, in some instances, the retention of standard methods of treatment, the capacity of man for survival by means of adaptation leaves no doubt that man must aim to conquer disease following the self-adjusting methods of nature without interfering with its cycles.

Some of the environmental factors controlling the exchange of disease began to be known in the sixteenth century when the Europeans settled in Africa, South-East Asia and America. The tropical syndromes then imported into Europe had much less epidemic significance than the contagious diseases—smallpox, measles, influenza—which caused havoc among aboriginal populations colonized by the Europeans because they lacked the Europeans' acquired resistance to infection. The introduction of contagious diseases into non-resistant populations resulted in the disappearance of entire civilizations. Medical historians have been conscious of geopolitics of epidemic diseases, but the syndromes of mental distress resulting from acculturation among non-European civilizations have taken a long time to be appreciated. In fact the problem is still discussed in terms of broad cultural effects.

The psychological traumas suffered by the collective consciousness of colonized civilizations or individuals have seldom been studied. As a whole, acculturation seems to receive harsher judgement as the transfer of culture comes closer to our own time. The European culture, despite the fact that it branded as immoral, unlawful or impractical most of the traditional aboriginal values, was not easily grafted on to the native mind, which frequently remained protected by its ancestral, physical and cultural environment. However, in the process of acculturation of native civilizations Europeans eroded, without replacing, the spiritual life these civilizations had developed by means of delicate adjustments best suited to their needs in many civilizations of America, Africa and South-East Asia. The human mind, like the human body, in adapting to physical environmental conditions or organic disease, must maintain a delicate balance with its spiritual habitat. The sudden impact of a new culture, even a more humane and better developed one, could be, and has been proved to be, as distressing to man as a pleasant cool breeze to an orchid, or a temperate climate to arctic wild life, possibly leading to his collapse and spiritual death: imposed cultural values can be as deadly to the human mind as a virulent infectious disease to the human body. At the root of illnesses of acculturation there is always the immense spiritual vacuum left in the aboriginal mind after the rape of its traditional values, which no material gain can ever replace. On the other hand, cultural influences are contagious and operate in both directions; an imported culture might destroy the spiritual life of a colonized people, but likewise environmental and residual cultural factors can also affect and shape to a certain degree the imported tenets and even the importer.

The similarity of this cultural contagion to the processes of organic disease seems to indicate that after the spiritual trauma of a cultural collision, the individual and the collective mind must resort to serious psychological adjustments in order to survive until a balance can be obtained under new conditions. Henceforth, cultural development can be measured by the degree of spiritual harmony reached after acculturation. Communities, like individuals, either survive and flourish after these challenges, or collapse and perish under an alien cultural impact. If it survives, the new society offers a blend of psychological characteristics, and the individual conforms to the imported standards of the Christian European tradition, by submerging or reshaping ancestral aboriginal trends. Despite the external conformity a newcomer can easily detect underlying similarities of religion, language, attire and institutions, clear variants of the cultural tenets in everyone. Food, drink, sexual drives and many other features of behaviour still reflect in some way aboriginal patterns. Two or five centuries of acculturation have not affected the environment, nor have they erased completely more than two hundred centuries of native cultural development in that environment.

Some nations are mature enough to analyse their cultural heritage, discriminating between those factors which should be preserved and nourished, and those which should be discarded in order to achieve balanced progress. Such a moment of reflection took place initially in Mexico early in this century, resulting in the revolt of some Bergsonian philosophers against prevalent Positivism. Lately, another group of philosophers have analysed the Mexican soul under the increasing danger of being engulfed by North American pragmatism. The thesis discussed in 1950 at the University of Mexico by her most distinguished philosophers evolved from Ramos' study of the cultural characteristics of the Mexican mind. The discussions indeed led one to appreciate certain aboriginal elements, but the emphasis of the conclusions was placed on late French cultural influences and the effects of nineteenth century political reforms. At that time I was in the unique position of being a student at the Faculty of Philosophy working for doctorates in History and Philosophy, and at the same time I was Professor of Pharmacology at the Medical School. My biological approach to the analysis of the Mexican mind became more apparent as the studies progressed, particularly under Zea, and at the seminars of Philosophy of History. Ramos, then Dean of Philosophy, with inexhaustible kindness, frequently expounded in our faculty meetings his views about my approach and stimulated my interest in the subject. Shortly before his death, Ramos made clear the difficulties of gaining enough perspective in the survey of the Mexican mind whilst being rooted in Mexico. This point of view was later to be confirmed by Paz's beautiful essay conceived in the United States. Actually Mexico— the New Spain—was repeating the same philosophical quest that the Old Spain had followed in the nineteenth century during the controversies over the decadence of Spanish science and the character of the Spanish mind. Although Menendez y Pelayo, Costa, Saiz Rodriguez and many others offered sound contributions in Spain, Ganivet in Helsinki and Madariaga at Oxford, writing thousands of miles from Spain, were to focus with the sharpest clarity upon the heart of the problem.

Almost a quarter of a century after those seminars at the colonial building of Philosophy in Mexico, an unquenchable thirst for Americana caused me to investigate most of the original texts where the cultural tenets of Mexico were appraised. But despite the vigour of the Mexican subject the problems of acculturation seemed likewise to have affected the rest of the ancient Spanish American colonial dominions, and for that matter any other colonial area. The authors of these texts referred not to the similarities between the Spaniard and the American Indian, but to the differences between their minds. Emphasis had to be given to the aberrant patterns of behaviour which could be grouped under standard psychological headings. It became manifest that my research could not avoid taxing both author and reader with an anthology of primary sources, which give without distortion the honest opinions of the observers. The cosmic force of the pre-Columbian mind was apparent in every line, and without further guidance the study was built around those powerful cultural elements omnipresent in the aboriginal American civilizations. These elements had been argued by sixteenth century theologians as characteristics of irrationality. A comparative assessment of Spanish cultural tenets and the colonial evolution of blended cultural trends was a complementary sequence.

There are many lessons to be learned from the dynamics of the pre-Columbian mind. Those of a medical nature have considerable relevance to ideas about mental health, and also offer much in the understanding of suicide, alcoholism and crime. Psychiatric experiences concerning family life, sexual deviations and the like, can give new insight. Social anthropologists and American historians are provided in the text which follows with a wealth of virgin sources which are waiting to be analysed anew. Medical historians are offered a study where the analysis of the facts has been integrated in order to give cultural interpretations of practical relevance, by following the flow of behavioural patterns of medical significance from the pre-Columbian period, through the colonial society, up to our own time.

Some historians, when they recapture the sadness of the vanquished Aztecs, forget that the abuse they suffered at the hands of neighbouring tribes, or the ignominy of being forced to eat lizards and snakes while cornered at Tizapan, provided them with the necessary stamina for their subsequent military and political hegemony and gained for them the respect of the Conquistadors. The human mind frequently finds its finest hour under the most difficult conditions of endurance, and sometimes, like El Cid, can win battles after death.

September, 1971

F.G.

CONTENTS

MAP OF
PRE-COLUMBIAN
CIVILIZATIONS

1. Eskimo
2. Beothuk
3. Mimac
4. Penobstoc
5. Tlingit
6. Haida
7. Bella Coola
8. Nootka
9. Blackfoot
10. Cheyenne
11. Pawnees
12. Cherokee
13. Natchez
14. Pima
15. Navajo
16. Iroquois

17. Aztec
18. Maya
19. Arawak
20. Carib
21. Chibcha
22. Inca
23. Araucan
24. Tehuelche
25. Puelche
26. Guarani
27. Tupi
28. Mojo
29. Mochica
30. Chimu
31. Toltec

a. Chichen itzá
b. Tikal
c. Yaxchilan
d. Cholula

e. Mexico
f. Teotihuacan
g. Tula
h. Oaxaca

ILLUSTRATIONS

To Francisco and Jaime,
scions of the Old Spain
in the New Spain; may
they love both mothers

CHAPTER I

INTRODUCTION

THE SPIRITUAL NEW WORLD

The discovery of America meant not only the geographical exploration of new lands, but also the unveiling of a spiritual New World, which ranged from primitive communities to highly developed civilizations. It is seldom realized that the pre-Columbian mind appeared so strange in the eyes of the Spaniards that half a century was to elapse before the American Indians were officially declared rational human beings. Then began a controversy on their rationality which remained alive among historians throughout the Colonial period. It has been ignited again in the past century by the growing interest in American archaeology, and has flared up with fury in our own time under the gusts of anthropological storms. It will never end; it will always be relevant, because the life cycle of Spanish America gravitates around behavioural patterns indelibly established in pre-Columbian times, some of which are still alien to traditional European standards.

THE ISSUE OF RATIONALITY

Historians have always reduced to legal terms the problem of the rationality of the American aborigines because of its political and economic implications: if the American Indians were irrational beings, then the Spaniards, and other European explorers who followed them, had the right to their land, to their property, and even to their persons. But, on the other hand, a declaration of irrationality made the American Indians unfitted to receive the Christian faith, and thus left without foundation the spiritual aim in the Conquest of the New World, which was indeed of primary importance.

The issue of Indian rationality was initially avoided when Spain established the right to the American Conquest on priorities of discovery and settlement. This right was laid down in her fundamental statutes *Las Siete Partidas*, issued by Alfonso X *the Wise* (1221–1284), and had been applied in 1417 to the conquest of the Canary Isles without Spain being challenged by any other nation in the world. However, the dimensions of the Western Hemisphere and the fact that its riches were coveted by other nations, moved Spain to secure legal dominion by resorting to the medieval concept of the temporal rule of the Papacy. Thus, a Spanish Pope, Alexander VI (1431–1503) acting as *Dominus Orbis*, on 3rd and 4th May 1493 issued the bulls *Inter cetera* granting Spain sole dominion of the New World, except for certain areas subject to Portugal, with the duty of instructing the American Indians in the Catholic faith. The European reaction was reflected with typically Gallic wit by King Francis I (1494–1547) who wondered what clause in Adam's will allowed the kings of Castile and Portugal to divide the earth between themselves.

The controversy over the American Indians' rationality began to appear anew when the abuses committed by some of the Spanish colonizers were exposed by the missionaries, and the opposition to the legal grounds for servitude of the aborigines began to erode the foundations of the colonial system. The banner of the Indian's rationality was first raised by Fr. Antonio de Montesinos in a sermon shortly before Christmas 1511 at Santo Domingo, when he faced the colonists with the basic questions: "Aren't the Indians men? Don't they have rational souls? . . .", reproaching the colonists for the way in which they were treating the natives. The immediate move of Montesinos to see King Ferdinand the Catholic (1452–1516) in Spain led to the Council of Burgos in 1512, where opinions appeared very much divided, though the report by Matías de Paz was favourable to the Indians. It was followed in 1513 by another Council at Valladolid where Juan Lopez de Palacios Rubios suggested a return to the practice of *Requerimiento* before the Spaniards entered any Indian territory. As in medieval times when facing the infidels, the Spanish Conquistadors had to read out to the Indians the *Request* to accept the Christian faith and the sovereignty of the Spanish Crown. This produced one of the most bizarre conditioned reflexes in the annals of psychological warfare, because the native soon learned that after the reading of the proclamation battle followed, and no sooner had the Crown official taken out the paper of the *Request* in front of the Indian armies, than at the sight of it they fled in fear. In 1517 a Council of theologians also found the Indians rational, and therefore fitted to receive the Christian faith; at the same time pressure grew among the colonizers, and even among certain members of the religious orders with unhappy experiences in their missionary efforts, to abolish the system of servitude on account of the Indians' rationality. They reasoned that only under the immediate care and service of the colonists could the Indians be instructed in the Christian faith.

The issue of the Indians' rationality then became centred upon a thesis taken from Aristotle's *Politica* (Book I, Chapter 1, #2): *Vigentes ingenio naturaliter sunt rectores et domini aliorum . . . deficientes a rationes naturaliter sunt servi* . . . The proposition that . . . "those with superior in-

telligence are by nature the rulers and lords of others . . . [while] those
with deficient judgement are by nature serfs . . . ," and, that it was better for
them to be under servitude, supported the colonial system of *Encomienda,*
or Indian service under the colonist, where they would have the solid
backing of the latter.   This was also maintained by Fr. Bernardo de
Mesa, adviser to the Court, by Fr. Juan Quevedo, bishop of Darien and,
best known of all, by Juan Ginés de Sepúlveda, historian to the Emperor.

In opposition were most members of the Dominican Order, led by
Bartolomé de las Casas, bishop of Chiapas, and the entire Franciscan
Order which, in more peaceful ways, continued to protect the Indians
against abuse.   In 1533 the Franciscan Community of Huexotzingo in
Mexico wrote to the Pope defending the Indians' rationality, as did the
Dominican bishop of Tlaxcala, Mexico, Fr. Julian Garcés, in 1536.   The
letter of bishop Garcés, was carried to Rome by Fr. Bernardino de Miñaya,
another Dominican, and its effect was to produce on 29th May 1537 the
brief of Pope Paul III (1468–1549) to Cardinal Tavera *Pastorale officium*
declaring the rationality of the American Indians and, on 9th June 1537,
the bulls *Sublimis Deus* and *Veritas ipsa* where the doctrine was expressed
in the following words:

> ". . . man is of such condition and nature that he can receive the faith
> of Christ, and whoever has the nature of man is fitted to receive the
> same faith . . .
>
> ". . . some dare to say that the Western and Meridional Indians must
> be subject to our service like animal beasts, using as pretext that they
> are incapable of the Catholic faith . . .
>
> ". . . Considering that those, being truly men, are not only capable
> of the Christian faith, but they approach to it with the greatest desire
> . . . with the Apostolic authority, by the present Letters we resolve . . .
> that the aforementioned Indians and all the other nations which in the
> future come to the knowledge of the Christians, even if they were out-
> side our faith, are not to be deprived, nor fitted to be deprived of their
> freedom, neither of the dominion of their possessions, and must not be
> reduced to slavery . . ."

The doctrine of the rationality of the mind of the American Indians,
clearly established by Paul III in 1537, left without legal foundation the
Spanish colonial system in America. But the bulls *Sublimis Deus* and
Veritas ipsa were in conflict with the powers granted to the Spanish Crown
in 1493 by the *Inter cetera* bulls, and the Pope, by brief of 19th June
1539, had to revoke his previous issues, so far as they were in conflict with
the powers granted to the Spanish King.   In consequence the Council
of the Indies was free to seize for examination the bulls of 9th June 1537
where the Papal doctrine of the Indians' rationality had been proclaimed,
and prevented their distribution in America.

The issue of Amerindian rationality took place in 16th-century Spain,
which was the age of her greatest theologians. It was therefore natural

that after the proclamation of the Papal doctrine, the legal projections of rationality on individual freedom, right to property and sovereignty, fell into the realm of theology, because, as Francisco de Vitoria put it in 1537, legal matters were too important to be left to lawyers. Surveying the views gathered by Esteve Barba (1965), it becomes clear that the thesis of the nature and rationality of the American Indians has always been examined on legal grounds, or at its best from a theological point of view. Even the studies by O'Gorman (1941) and Hanke (1959) have discussed the problem only in terms of 16th-century jurisprudence. It was there that Vitoria excelled among all the others, and though las Casas received laurels of praise when facing the conservative opinions of Sepúlveda, it was Vitoria who brought the rights of Pope and Emperor down to their proper dimensions and lifted the spiritual stand of the American Indians to levels of respect and legal equality. Whatever may have been the cruelty or greed of the Spanish Conquistadors these theologians saved the hour, because, as Hanke (1951) admitted, no other European people before or since the Conquest threw itself into such a struggle for justice as that which developed among the Spaniards shortly after the discovery of America, and which persisted throughout the sixteenth century. It was Vitoria who also discussed the legal position of the American Indians' unnatural behaviour, as measured by Christian standards of natural law. There he came close to the heart of the matter, because the alleged irrationality of the American Indians was not a legal problem, but a biological one.

This matter was thus being appraised according to the canons of Western culture, which in fact represented the classical European tradition shaped into Christian morals. The behaviour and the thought processes of the American Indians were, and have been until now, judged by a positive and natural law which the Christian faith had long identified as her own divine law throughout the Old World, but was completely alien to the environmental and social realities of the pre-Columbian New World. The pre-Columbian mind could be examined within the context of its own world, detached from the morals, philosophy, law, and medicine of 16th-century Europe, but this would be a sterile academic exercise. The tenets and mechanisms of the pre-Columbian mind become relevant to us within the framework of their adaptation into our main cultural stream and their permanence within their own environmental areas. Furthermore they are of paramount importance today in the analysis of national psychologies, as well as in the assessment of psychiatric trends in the individual.

THE GROUNDS FOR IRRATIONALITY

Setting aside the legal and theological discussions, and examining only the biological facts, the American Indians had to be found irrational at the time of the Discovery because they acted against natural law on a number of counts: human sacrifices, anthropophagy, sexual relations of incest and sodomy and abuse of drugs producing inebriation. The reports of explorers and historians on these customs were often biased, but on the whole consistent, though what was true for a single area was often credited to the entire continent. These actions, if executed by human beings, had perforce to be judged by the divine, positive, and natural law as unnatural, and consequently as irrational. From a biological standpoint they are exceedingly important, because they reflect an attitude to life and death, to sexual drives, and towards the customary use of drugs affecting mental behaviour, which was very different from what was held as normal in Europe prior to the discovery of America. In other words, for the purpose of a psychological assessment, the pre-Columbian mind, after centuries of isolation, held values for life, sex, and drugs which were aberrant by the standards of the European cultural tradition. A historical analysis of both the religious and the violent elements of life in pre-Columbian America, as well as the cultural role of inebriating drugs, is important; but personal research over more than a quarter of a century into the primary sources of medicine in the New World has shown that the subject of aberrant sexual drives was that by far the most frequently debated by historians. This heavy psychological burden of the American past was in turn to produce a wealth of psychiatric therapy which has never been properly examined.

It is the purpose of the study to bring to light the historical texts referring to the abnormal nature of the pre-Columbian mind with respect to behavioural patterns towards life and death, sexual drives and drugs affecting mental processes, as well as ritual and techniques of psychotherapy practised in America for the treatment of mental illness and other diseases. Since the spiritual trauma of the American Conquest was followed by the transfer of the Christian culture, it was found pertinent to follow up some of these pre-Columbian patterns during and after the colonial period, because environmental, social and medical conditions did not basically change the way of life of large numbers of the native population. An assessment of the historical sources could provide relevant information concerning the nature of the alleged aberrations among pre-Columbian civilizations, and the problems and solutions affecting them after European acculturation.

There is a warning which must be kept in mind: a medico-historical analysis of aberrant features in the pre-Columbian mind does not set out to promote historical prejudice about the great American civilizations, just as current psychoanalytical views cannot be taken as derogatory to the traditional tenets of European culture. They are biological facts which must be taken into account in a proper historical analysis, and ignored only at considerable risk. In fact, it is by presenting, in contrast with the accepted viewpoint of American historians, the aberrant elements of the pre-Columbian mind, that the riches of psychosomatic medicine and psychotherapy in the New World can be appreciated.

CHAPTER II

THE GREAT
AMERICAN CIVILIZATIONS

THE FORMATIVE PERIOD

The appearance of man in America occurred after the last glaciation, well over 10,000 years ago, when human migrations from northern Asia began to diffuse from Alaska to Tierra Del Fuego, continuing until relatively recent times. Possible trans-Pacific links have been considered, but any contacts between Europe and America by Northmen were culturally irrelevant and the American Indians remained in isolation until the discovery of the New World. The early American man survived by means of palaeolithic techniques—hunting, fishing with net and line, and gathering shellfish. However, he also collected vegetable foods, and this led to the development of agriculture, particularly in Middle America and the Andes, areas where higher civilizations eventually flourished. Their basic staples were corn and beans, though in the colder regions of the Andes the potato supplemented the diet; in the humid tropical regions of Brazil and the Caribbean they relied more on manioc (cassava). American domestic animals were restricted to the hairless dog in Mexico and the guinea-pig in Peru which were both used as food, some fowls, and the llama in the Andes for transport and wool; this limited agricultural growth and large-scale migrations. Indian communities were very much dependent upon environmental conditions, and land exhaustion forced them to introduce crop rotation or to disperse in search of virgin soil. Agricultural advances about the 8th century A.D. made possible settlements in much larger towns in the coastal valleys of the Andes and the high plateau of Mexico.

An understanding of the pre-Columbian mind is only possible if one considers the migrational origin of the American Indians, the environmental conditions affecting their development for over a hundred centuries, the interplay between their groups for survival, and the evolution of their religious beliefs and social structures. However, pre-Columbian history has proved an extremely fluid subject, and archaeological research has progressively added to and corrected previous ideas, and keeps evolving continuously. On the other hand, it is beyond the scope of this study to survey the background of every people settled in the New World at the time of their discovery, and only three major civilizations can be considered: Maya, Aztec and Inca. During the historical research leading to this monograph it was found that, as far as the archaeological and documentary evidence could prove, the aberrant behaviour of these three great pre-Columbian civilizations could be traced to their pre-Classical ancestors: the Toltecs in the case of Aztecs and Mayas, and the Mochica and Chimú for the Inca; some notes about these ancestral cultures have therefore been found pertinent.

In Middle America the basic agricultural techniques, particularly maize domestication, seem to have been introduced during the early years of the first millennium B.C. by the Olmecs. Between 800 B.C. and A.D. 600 they were located in the lowlands of the Gulf of Mexico, in the area of Tabasco and Veracruz. In the colossal carved heads found at some archaeological sites, La Venta and Tres Zapotes, the Olmecs are depicted with pronounced mongoloid features. They were well advanced in agriculture and architecture, and in 31 B.C. left the earliest epigraphic dated records in stelae with the mathematical notation of bar and dot. They were neighbours of the Maya, who began to emerge as a well-defined civilization at Petén, further west, in the fourth century A.D. There was an area in the south of Mexico, extending from the mountains and valleys of Oaxaca to the Pacific shores, where the Zapotec civilization developed from at least 500 B.C. to A.D. 1496, at the same time as the Olmecs and Mayas were also reaching great refinement. The Zapotec religious centre of Monte Alban shows magnificent architecture and city planning, as well as ceramics, jewellery and the beginning of hieroglyphic writing in the Zapotec codices. This latter technique can also be found in the Mixtec civilization flourishing between A.D. 688 and A.D. 1521 in the area between the Olmecs to the north, Zapotecs to the south, Maya to the east and Toltecs to the west. The Mixtec religious centre at Cholula is characterized by one of the largest pyramids; from that area come the finest examples of codices with hieroglyphic writing. The coastal land north of the Olmecs in the Gulf of Mexico was occupied from 500 B.C. to A.D. 1520 by the Totonac civilization, well identified by their laughing head figurines, which seem to indicate a gay and sybaritic people, and the Conquistadors were later to report marked sexual deviations in that area. The high plateau, and particularly the Valley of Mexico, which was to rule the cultural history of Central America, witnessed for almost a millennium (200 B.C.–A.D. 1520) the flow of migrations from the north, in which the Toltec and the Chichimec civilizations, immediately preceding the Aztec, played the most important roles.

In South America the Andean area, where the higher civilizations developed, also witnessed the successive hegemony of different peoples and the fluid movement of migrations. The earliest groups, in about 2500 B.C., were located near the mouth of the Chicama river and were ignorant of maize and pottery. The Chavín civilization developed between 1200 and 400 B.C. in the northern Peruvian highlands, introducing maize agriculture, pottery and architecture, dominated by the jaguar representation, and even weaving and metallurgy. Further south on the coast between 400 B.C. and A.D. 400 the growth of Paracas took place, and at different periods the flourishing of the coastal valleys in Pisco, Ica and Nazca. These peoples have left excellent weaving material and polychrome pottery. However, the peak of civilization in the northern coastal Peruvian valleys was reached by the Mochica between A.D. 400 and 1000, followed by the Chimú in A.D. 1000–1466. All the coastal and highland civilizations were greatly influenced by a migration from the Tiahuanaco empire after A.D. 400. The religious centre of this highland civilization was located at Tiahuanaco, near Lake Titicaca over 4000 m above sea-level, with great megalithic carved stones and monuments, and the religious influence spread over the whole Peruvian area. There, owing to climatic conditions, the staple food was the potato, while the alpaca and the llama were the most important domestic animals. By the middle of the 15th century all these areas and civilizations were subjugated by the Inca, who, descending from the Andean highlands near Cuzco, imposed on them their way way of life and language.

THE TOLTEC

The Toltecs were a migration of Chichimec stock, speaking the Nahuatl language, the first to settle in the Mexican high plateau, in about 200 B.C. Most Mexican chronicles and native documents, though not always in agreement about dates and rulers, are consistent in accepting the Toltec civilization as the most sophisticated of their ancestors. They achieved in definitive form the agricultural techniques of the semi-arid lands in the valley of Mexico, the domestication of maize, and regular crops of beans and chili as well as cotton textiles. All these practical advances were based upon their knowledge in the computation of time and the invention of a calendar system based on the astronomical year of 365+ days, which guided accurately the agricultural seasons.

The legends about the Toltecs mention their arrival from the north guided by a priest astrologer after the destruction of a race of giants in the Anahuac. They were eventually governed by elected kings who ruled in periods of 52 years, and by a powerful religious caste. At the time of their hegemony in the Valley of Mexico A.D. 700–1000 their agricultural system was very much dependent on the slave labour of other Chichimec tribes. The Toltecs were great mechanics and architects, building not just with *adobe* bricks, but using stone masonry and cement on a large scale, with beautiful fresco paintings in some of their temples. Their religious capital Teotihuacan began to be built about A.D. 100 and was reconstructed and enlarged at different periods; even today with its pyramids of the sun and the moon, the citadel of Quetzalcoatl, the temple of agriculture and dwellings for priests, occupies an area of over 15 km² which dwarfs any other religious centre in America. Their political capital, the ancient Tollan (today Tula), built about A.D. 900 and 80 km north of Mexico, still retains its grandiose architectural ideas with monumental porticos and atlantean colonnades.

The discovery of an inebriating drink prepared from agave, *pulque,* was credited to the Toltec queen Xochitl in about A.D. 950. The height of the Toltec civilization was reached during that century under the rule of King Topiltzin, and was immediately followed by its disintegration, due in part to failing crops, pestilences and to internal revolts brought about by moral corruption and sexual depravity. The conflict between the high priest Quetzalcoatl or "feathered serpent" who in Toltec religion represented good ethics, and another priest Tezcatlipoca or "shining mirror" of evil influence, played a great role in the legends describing the fall of the Toltecs and the destruction of Tollan in A.D. 987. Quetzalcoatl, who some accounts identify with Topiltzin, went into exile with some of his followers, promising to return some day. It is accepted that Quetzalcoatl, or Kulkulcan in Maya language, arrived in Yucatan and had considerable influence in the development of the Maya centres at Chichén-Itzá and Mayapan. The Toltec civilization was definitively engulfed by new arrivals in the Valley of Mexico and was finally dispersed by another Chichimec migration from the north about A.D. 1156.

THE MAYA

The Maya civilization occupied an area limited in the south by the highlands of Guatemala, in the north by the coast of the Yucatan peninsula bordered by the Gulf of Mexico and the Caribbean Sea. In the east their territory covered part of Honduras, and in the west extended to the coast of Tabasco and Veracruz, covering an area of some 400,000 km². The Maya land is made up of three different types of country; the Guatemalan highlands, largely of volcanic origin with the flora and fauna of the temperate zone; the central area of Petén, about 150 m above sea-level with a heavy rainfall and luxuriant vegetation; and in contrast, the limestone lowland of Yucatan which is not crossed by a single river—and water is only to be found in wells or *cenotes* which are fed by natural underground currents. The scrub vegetation and limited fauna is a reflection of the thin layer of humus unsuitable for cultivation by the plough.

In the Formative Period the Maya area was populated from the 3rd millennium B.C. up to the year A.D. 300 by some neolithic forbears, who in their last ten centuries, had in common with other American people the domestication of maize and the so-called Mamon monochrome pottery. It was then when some of the first stone buildings, terraces, and low pyramids began to be erected and a more elaborate pottery known as Chicanel was produced. Some Mayan groups migrated north-west to the coast of the Gulf of Mexico to settle down in the Huaxtec, preserving some cultural and linguistic affinities. The Maya Classical Period is accepted to have started in A.D. 320, a date found carved as part of the Maya calendar, on a jade plate now preserved at Leyden. By that time the astronomical year of 365 days had been reckoned, together with the principles of hieroglyphic writing. The building of ceremonial centres began to flourish in the Petén region with Tikal, Uaxactún and other cities, and also farther west in Palenque, where a definite system of town planning can be distinguished. The pottery became polychrome, known as Tzakol during its first phase, and followed after A.D. 633 by the Tepeu style. The Maya Mexican period started in A.D. 987 after the fall of Tollan, the capital of the Toltecs, who dispersed into Maya territory, while the Itzá people invaded Yucatan from the south-west, settling and allying themselves with the most important Maya cities. The invaders influenced profoundly the Maya civilization, introducing many new elements in religion, philosophy, architecture and even weapons; from then on the Maya began to use the bow and arrow as well as the spear. The Mexican period ended in A.D. 1204 when the Itzá tribes were overthrown from the city of Chichen-Itzá, and the city of Mayapan imposed its rule. For two centuries a short renaissance of cultural manifestations and a new style of architecture evolved in the northern area of Yucatan, marking the Neo-classical Period of the Maya which preceded their final decline.

Maya was the basic language of the area at the time of European arrival, and with some variants like the Quiché-Maya and Cakchiquel-Maya; the Yucatec-Maya is still spoken by over two million Indians. They were organized by family clans in city states, and a noble class assisted by religious hierarchies governed the common people; slaves were either captured in war, or were criminals sentenced to slavery. The hereditary family head delegated the administration of the small villages to controllers of taxation, distributing communal land and labour. The peasants worked on the land and also provided building labour, although specialized crafts were also common. Beans, squash and other produce such as cotton were cultivated, but maize represented more than mere food to the Maya; it was a god and the basis of their life, and they believed that man had been created by their gods from maize. The plots where corn was cultivated were reclaimed from the forest by clearing trees and burning the ground; maize was then sown with a stick, and the hole afterwards covered by hand. Maya diet consisted of maize supplemented by fowls, turkeys, pheasants and hens, and other animals such as the hairless dog, fish and deer; honey was also commonly used.

The religious centres of the Maya characterized by temples on stepped pyramids which in a few instances contain burials. The adjacent palaces for the priests were built on terraces and their rooms received light directly through the doors. The ceiling was formed by the typical corbelled vault, and the heavy walls required for that purpose were balanced by a unique blend of sculptural motives and bas-reliefs which lightened the

heavy appearance of the structure. The Maya also used stucco, and developed cements by calcination of stone. Another feature was the use
of mosaics and the technique of mural painting in fresco, the best examples of which are to be found in Chichen-Itzá and Bonampak. This
Mayan architecture with its serene bas-reliefs deserves more admiration
when it is realized that the carving was carried out only with tools made
of other hard stones, the Maya area being devoid of metals. Other buildings were ball courts where rubber balls were used, astronomical observa-
tories and sweathouses where dry heat and steam were used in the
treatment of disease. In Palenque are to be found baths with adjacent
lavatories and sewage system. Some cities in Petén had an adequate water
supply, but in Yucatan water was obtained from the underground wells
or *cenotes*. Causeways through the forest and between cities, such as that
which runs between Cobá and Yaxuná for almost 100 km in a straight
line and about 5 m wide, can still be observed. They emphasize the Maya
trade in metals including gold from South America, jade and obsidian
from the highlands, and pottery from beyond the Mexican high plateau.

Quite early in their evolution the Maya identified their gods with
natural phenomena controlling the agricultural cycle. The world had been
created by Huab, and his son Itzammá was the lord of heaven; Ixchel
his wife was the goddess of floods, pregnancy and medical matters. Ah
Puch was the god of death and accompanied Ixchel in the omens of
pestilence. Suicides by hanging came under the protection of another god.
They believed that their world had been preceded by other ages, the
first occupied by dwarfs, the second by giants and the third by themselves,
and that the world would end by a deluge. The Maya universe was
divided between heavens formed by thirteen layers, of which the earth
was the lowest one, and an underworld which was also divided into nine
layers. To heaven went good people, warriors, women dying in childbirth
and those who committed suicide by hanging. They performed self-
inflicted mutilation as religious practices: blood letting in the ear or limbs,
passing a cord through a hole in the tongue or the penis. The Maya induced cranial deformities during childhood by progressively flattening
the frontal and occipital bones between two flat pieces of wood; another
ideal of beauty was cross-eyes, and mothers used to hang a pendant on
the forehead of their children until cross vision was obtained. Dental inlays
of jade, turquoise and pyrites were frequent and there are many instances
of burials showing special filling of the teeth.

The Maya physician *ah-men* was, and has remained, a member of the
priestly hierarchy, and a product of inherited position and training. They
taught the reckoning of the year, the omen of the days, methods of
divination, prophecies of events, remedies for sickness, their antiquities
and the art of reading and writing their hieroglyphs. The identification of
religion with natural phenomena resulted in the priest having to keep up
a continuous observation of nature. This provided him with astronomical
references that made it possible accurately to determine the seasons and

to establish the length of the tropical year. There is epigraphic evidence that, during the Classical period (A.D. 320–909), every *katun* or period of twenty years, the Maya erected a stele dated according to their chronological system. This chronology is known as the Initial series, meaning that they give the date elapsed since the beginning of the Maya count or zero year, which computed in our Christian era goes back to 3113 B.C. In addition to the astronomical year of 365 days the Maya, like the Aztecs, had another liturgical year, the *tzonkil* of 260 days, which was superimposed on the astronomical calendar in order to regulate their religious life.

The recording of time called for mathematic formulation quite early. Numbers between 1 and 20 were represented among the Maya by dots and bars, five dots being equal to one bar; their system was based on the numbers of fingers and toes and therefore it was vigesimal. The most important aspect of the Maya mathematical system was the establishment of the value of a figure according to its sequence, such as it is used in present-day computation; the figure to the left is ten times higher in the decimal system, but it was twenty times higher among the Maya. There was also a sign for zero.

The highest cultural sophistication of the Maya was hieroglyphic writing. Their hieroglyphs appear in stelae, some pottery, lintel wood, and in the three Maya codices, now at Dresden, Paris and Madrid. These were made by macerating and glueing together the fibres of the inner bark of amatl, a fig tree, and then treating the surface with a smooth white finish. Once the surface was polished the scribe painted the hieroglyphs in colour with a thin brush; the codices were then folded like a Japanese screen. Maya hierogyphs are made of a basic sign, sometimes with infixes drawn inside, and also with prefixes and suffixes which modify the basic glyph. In some cases the signs have a phonetic value, in others they represent ideas, but only a limited number have been deciphered.

THE AZTEC

The Aztecs were a Nahuatl-speaking people from Aztlán, a mythical place in the north, who after wandering for almost a century in search of land reached Tollan at the time of its destruction. They were able, however, to learn from the Toltecs their agricultural systems and technical knowledge before they continued their pilgrimage into the Valley of Mexico. About A.D. 1267 the Aztec migration arrived at the shores of Lake Texcoco, which was already occupied by other Chichimec people, and they had to withdraw their camp to the Chapultepec hill, from where they were expelled by the joint efforts of the Toltecs of Culhuacan and the Tepanecs of Azcapotzalco. As subjects of the latter people the Aztecs were forced to stay for some time in the volcanic area of Tizapan, unsuitable for agriculture, where lizards and snakes were often their food. A.D. 1325 has been accepted as the year when the Aztecs saw their prophecies fulfilled by finding on an island in Lake Texcoco an eagle resting on a nopal, eating a serpent. Then and there they built the first temple to their god and the first dwellings of their capital Tenochtitlan, which afterwards became Mexico city. On the inhospitable island of Tenochtitlan, surrounded by swamps, the Aztecs were able to survive for several generations, enlarging their number unmolested, subject to the Azcapotzalco people, to whom they gave help as mercenaries against their neighbours of Texcoco and Culhuacan. But in 1427, under the rule of their fourth king Itzcoatl, the Aztecs joined their former enemies of Texcoco and Tlacopan to defeat Azcapotzalco and obtain their independence. Thus, on the shores of Lake Texcoco a balance of power remained between the Chichimec people of Texcoco and the Aztec of Tenochtitlan. Their alliance was followed in 1440 by the rule of Moctezuma I with the Aztec expansion over the valley of Mexico and neighbouring areas. Aztec military campaigns reached the Gulf of Mexico and the Pacific coast; Axayacatl in 1469, Tizoc in 1481 and Ahuitzotl in 1486 consolidated their territorial gains. They incorporated new ground into Maya and Zapotec areas during the rule of Ahuitzotl, but the Tlaxcala area in the east and the Tarascan kingdom in the north-west resisted their efforts. The Aztec hegemony over most of the Mexican lands reached its height during the rule of Moctezuma II, their ninth and last king, lasting from 1502 until the Spanish conquest in 1519.

The original area of the Aztecs in the valley of Mexico combined the semi-arid lands of the high plateau, surrounded by volcanoes, with the agricultural lowlands on the shores of a system of lakes and waterways. Their land was divided into hereditary tribal lots called *calpulli*, and the cultivation surface was enlarged by floating in the lakes artificial plots or *chinampas*. Beasts of burden and the plough were unknown, and a long wooden stick was used instead for breaking the ground and planting. Their economy was based on the agriculture of temperate climates, supplemented by the produce of the subjugated lowlands, such as cotton, cocoa beans, feathers, gold, etc., obtained as taxation revenue or in market exchange. The Mexican diet was based on maize, beans and chili, so that, like most American civilizations it was low in protein intake; there were several sources of animal protein, including turkey, hairless dog, fish and game. The intensive cultivation used by the Aztecs in the Valley of Mexico and the well-organized and protected merchants' guild made possible the concentration of population in Tenochtitlan supplied from very remote areas.

The Aztecs were organized as an elected monarchy within a system of social stratification based on the kinship units of *calpulli*, to whom lots of land were allocated. Although there was a certain degree of hereditary nobility and the priestly class was also powerful, the Aztec king was an absolute ruler over an administrative system highly developed for taxation purposes. Their religion was initially centred around the cult of Huitzilopochtli, symbolizing the sun, reborn every day, who had to be sustained by human blood. Their rituals included sacrifices of prisoners or other victims, extraction of their hearts which were offered to the god, and anthropophagy, including over 20,000 victims yearly at Tenochtitlan; but the Aztecs progressively incorporated other gods found among the peoples they conquered, including deified priests such as Quetzalcoatl and Tezcatlipoca. They believed in another life after death, with a heaven, Tonatiuh, in the sun reserved for the heroes, another heaven Tlalocan on the earth, and the abode of rest, the underworld Mictlan, reached by the dead after a dangerous journey. The universe had been created by Tona-catecutli the male god and Tonacacihuatl the female principle. Huitzilo-pochtli was the god for war, Tlaloc for agriculture, Quetzalcoatl for wisdom, Mictlantecutli for death, Tzapotatlena for medicines. Likewise there were special gods for different types of disease: Tlaloc was respons-ible for rheumatic ailments, Xochiquetzal for venereal diseases, Xipetotec for skin and eye ailments, and so on. The Aztecs acknowledged that their scientific tenets and even their medical art had been developed by Toltec wise men who knew the nature and qualities of the herbs and the astro-nomical cycles. They followed a calendar extending over the solar year of 365 days, divided into 18 months of 20 days, plus five complementary unlucky days. In addition there was an astrological or religious calendar *tonalpohualli* of 260 days. The role of the calendar among the Aztecs, as among the Mayas, cannot be over-emphasized, because the fate of the individual in health and disease was determined by it. The Aztecs were usually named after their birthday, and their horoscopes established according to astrological predictions. The names of days and months were represented by ideograms. Although the Aztecs did not possess the hiero-glyphic writing of the Maya, their pictographic characters or rebus writing reached a high degree of perfection, and they recorded events and also taxation in beautiful codices made of vegetable paper or deer-skin folded like a screen. Writing was extended to represent mathematical symbols according to a vigesimal system, the units represented by points, 20 by a flag, 400 by a pine, and 8000 by a bag. Their tools and utensils were made of stone, mainly obsidian, but they also worked some metals including copper, gold and to a lesser degree silver. In metallurgy the Aztecs were less advanced than the Inca, but they knew a casting tech-nique which produced beautiful gold jewellery.

The Aztec used sun-dried mud bricks of *adobe* for building private dwellings; these were easy to manufacture and well suited to the climatic conditions of their environment. The procedure of using a basement of stone filled with soil was followed for the pyramids or religious temples. For important buildings they used stones which diminished in size from the base; and they began to use *tezontli*, the hard porous volcanic stone, binding perfectly with mortar. The roofs were usually flat, supported by wooden beams. Aztecs and Mayas used cements and binding materials such as lime mortar. Stone cutting was performed by special axes made of extremely hard stone. Tenochtitlan, the capital of the Aztecs or Tenochas, built on the island in Lake Texcoco, had a population estimated at around 200,000 inhabitants, and was the largest city in pre-Columbian America. It was reached by three causeways, while a fourth supporting an aqueduct carried the water supply from Chapultepec. The city had a civic centre with the main palaces and religious buildings, twenty-five pyramids with temples at the top, a public market, sport grounds and well defined districts. The great pyramid of Huitzilopochtli had a square base of about 100 by 80 m, was over 30 m high and the platform at the top was reached by 114 steps. At the time of the Discovery the Aztecs had assimilated most of the scientific and technological ideas in the American continent, although they never reached the sophistication of the Maya in mathematics, hieroglyphic writing and architecture, nor the level of the Inca in weaving, smelting and ceramics.

THE MOCHICA

The Mochica civilization developed in the northern coast of Peru between 300 B.C. and A.D. 1000 from the Chicama to the Virú valleys. Little is known of its early history but for its decadence after the Huari-Tiahuanaco invasion about A.D. 1000, when the whole Mochica area was taken over by the Chimú civilization. In A.D. 1370 the Chimú, under the rule of Nanzen-pinco, completed the occupation of the coastal valleys and spread their dominion, but retained most of the cultural elements of the Mochica. The land in this area is extremely dry owing to the calcareous nature of the soil and sand, the absence of rain as a result of the oceanic currents, and the intense heat; nights, however, can be cold, and heavy fog brings enough moisture to provide water in the coastal valleys to support agriculture. The Mochicas also brought water to their land by an elaborate system of irrigation channels, some of them, at the Chicama river, over 100 km long. Their main staples were maize, squash and chili and they also cultivated potato, peanuts, and a great variety of beans; in more humid areas they even cultivated cacao. Coca leaves were obtained from the slopes of the Andes. It seems that in order to obtain higher yields the Mochica began to use on their land a variety of fertilizers: guano from the sea-birds found in huge deposits in the coast, heads of sardines and even human excrement. The Mochica had a few domestic animals: turkeys, guinea-pigs and hairless dogs; llamas were used for transport, and its sun-dried meat was one of their foods. Fish was also very abundant.

The Mochica like the Chimú and other peoples of the coast used the Yunca language as spoken in the valleys. Each of these valleys had a tribal organization with a lord (*cie*) who controlled the family groups (*ayllus*) and allocated the *tupu* (lots of land) and labour, as occurred later under the Incas. Although like the latter they worshipped the sun, the principal Mochica and Chimú god was the moon, and they sacrificed children in its honour; they also revered the water. There are remains of several temples and pyramids built both by Mochica and Chimú with *adobe* brick which was the main material in their architecture; like other ancient people they added wetted grass to the mud to increase its resistance. The magnitude of the Mochica labour force and their ability to use *adobe* can be seen in the pyramid of the sun at the Mocha Valley, almost 115 by 20 m at its base and 35 m high, in which at least 50 million *adobe* bricks were used. There are Chimú cities like Chan-Chan, their capital near Trujillo in northern Peru with well-defined boundaries and dwellings, which like the water engineering projects indicate good use of *adobe* construction. However, the Mochica excelled above any other pre-Columbian civilization by their use of clay for pottery; their polychrome pieces in contrast with the black clay used by the Chimú have no equal. The Mochica potter was the woman and the pottery was produced by moulds. The variety of objects, animals and scenes represented fortunately compensates for the lack of other documentary evidence about Mochica life. Sexual practices and diseases are frequent motifs. As the spouts and handles were cast separately it is possible that this pottery was mass produced. The Mochica weaving was also of the finest quality, using cotton and wool, not from llama, but preferably alpaca and vicuña wool which is finer. Feather weaving, as among the Aztecs, was common. Metallurgy was also an early achievement of the Mochicas, afterwards improved by the Chimús, where gold was one of the articles of taxation. There was a considerable number of utensils and weapons made of bronze, though gold jewellery like pottery has received universal appreciation.

THE INCA

The Inca people originally occupied a very small area in the highlands around Cuzco. Most chronicles agree on a succession of thirteen rulers, the first of them the legendary Manco Capac (fl. 1200); but the Inca civilization reached its height between 1438 and 1471, after the rule of the ninth Pachacutec Inca Yupanqui, who carried out the territorial expansion, completed by his son Tupac Inca Yupanqui from 1471 to 1493. The first Inca neighbours to fall were the Colla and Lupaca in the Titicaca area; afterwards the Chanca in the west. With the fall of Chan-Chan, the capital of the Chimú empire in the north, the Inca territory extended over 4000 km of the Pacific coast; from Colombia to Chile, and reached inland well into the highlands of the Andes. The eleventh ruler, Huayna Capac, completed the subjugation of the people from the Maule river in Chile to the Ancasmayo river in Colombia. He was succeeded in 1525 by his son Huascar, but at the time of the Spaniards' arrival was taken prisoner by his brother Atahualpa who ordered his assassination shortly before he himself was executed by the Spaniards.

Quechua was the language spoken by the Incas and they made it compulsory for the conquered people in the highlands who spoke Aymara, or

Yunga in the Mochica–Chimú area of the coastal valleys. Their social structure was very close to socialism in the sense that cultivated land was public and allocated to *ayllus*, or family clans, according to their size. The peasant was at the bottom of the social scale and his labour made possible the cultivation of maize, potato, squash, tomato, peanuts, chili and manioc as well as cotton. Their domestic animals included guinea-pigs, hairless dogs and ducks for food, and llamas for transport. The crops, however, were not received directly by the worker, but gathered into storehouses; one part was then to be consumed by the peasant himself, but the other two were reserved for the Inca ruler and the religious hierarchies and civil servants. The Inca society was rigidly stratified, the peasants being controlled by local headmen, *curacas*, who in turn obeyed regional rulers, responsible only to the Inca king. The king was considered of divine origin, son of the sun and to be married to another person of divine extraction, his sister, although he also selected other wives among the virgins serving in the temples of the sun. The religion was based in the cult of natural phenomena and the main god among the Inca was the sun; Viracocha, the creator god, was less revered. In the temples there were priests under vow of chastity who performed sacrifices, sometimes of human beings, and made divinations. There were also virgin girls who prepared chicha, an alcoholic beverage obtained by fermentation of maize, and wove the Inca ruler's clothing with *alpaca* wool. But many other things, like idols and burials or ancestor's remains called *huacas*, were the object of religious worship. In pottery, the Incas did not reach the excellence of the Mochicas, but their works of engineering and architecture were outstanding. They built several suspension bridges over rivers and canyons as part of a unique system of roads which connected Cuzco, their capital, with the most remote parts of their territory, from Colombia to Chile. The Incas maintained on these roads a system of relay runners, *chasquis*, who travelled the short distances between stations at high speed carrying messages. Some of the Inca cities, such as Cuzco, alleged to have been designed by king Pachacutec about 1440, were divided in sections with streets allocated to separated *ayllus* or families, and built with stones, sometimes of colossal dimensions, which fitted perfectly without cement. Other Inca cities, like Machu-Picchu, also show a careful arrangement of fortresses and dwellings with the terraces of cultivated land used to their maximum advantage. The labour for these projects and other public works was provided by the *mita*, or compulsory public service of the people, which as in the case of military service in time of war, was commanded by the Inca ruler. The Inca civilization was also outstanding for its weaving techniques, probably the finest among ancient people, and for the quality of metal work in copper, silver and gold. The Incas did not have writing, not even pictographic representation, but they developed a mnemotechnic method of recording quantities on knotted cords called *quipus* which was the basis of their administrative system.

These American civilizations had no knowledge of the plough, wheel, quern or arch, of distillation, smelting of iron or glass, or of stringed musical instruments; in many ways they had not even reached the European Bronze Age, but even so, they mastered huge technological problems in a fascinating way and developed scientific ideas without any contact or influence from the Old World. In a similar way, even without the benefit of the literary tradition of the ancient philosophers, pre-Columbian civilizations had a pattern of moral development very similar in many ways to those found in Europe; however, a hundred centuries of cultural isolation, their struggle for survival and very often hostile environmental conditions, had to develop moral trends, which *a priori* must appear callous, hard, and cruel.

LIMITATIONS OF HISTORICAL SOURCES

The pre-Columbian civilizations have been the subject of many historical monographs in the last twenty-five years. Vaillant (1947) and Caso (1959), among others, have written about the Aztecs; Morley (1956) and Thompson (1956) about the Maya; Bushnell (1956) and Mason (1961) on the Inca; von Hagen (1965) on the Mochica and Chimú, and many more on these and other American civilizations. However, it was pointed out in a study of Maya medicine (Guerra, 1964) that standard textbooks were completely inadequate in their coverage of medical information. The excellent monograph by Morley, for instance, in 500 pages of text only has a few lines on medical matters. The same has been shown in a study of Aztec medicine (Guerra, 1966), and the recent monograph on pre-Columbian medicine (Guerra, 1971). Standard books on pre-Columbian civilization have been produced by archaeologists who based their studies on artefacts and are seldom trained to appreciate medical history. The aforementioned references are useful to obtain a general view, and to place the American Indian in time and space, but fail to give us the image of those human beings as they were, of flesh and blood. Only von Hagen (1965), for example, discusses at any length the meaning of sodomy in Mochica pottery.

It would be useless to search these works for the religious and psychological factors involved in Aztec medicine arising from the social structure of the Mexican civilization, their stern discipline, the close dependence of children upon parents, the complexes of obedience–reward and disobedience–punishment which created a dependence of the individual on the family elders, the tribal leaders and in particular on the gods. These facts are of great importance in the understanding of their anxieties, and indeed of their history and the explanation of their conquest and colonization. It is only when the research is taken back to the original sources, not just archaeological, but documentary, that the true pre-Columbian mind begins to be revealed; to take an example, the primary sources for the study of the Toltecs unveil stories of lust, sexual perversions, and decadence never appearing in textbooks, and we learn of the lewdness of Uemac, the sodomy of Tezcatlipoca and other stories of inebriation and incest never told. Similarly for the Chichimecs: one may look in vain in later sources for the truth about Nezahualcoyotl ridding himself of Quaquauhtzin to win the love of Axcalxochitzin, very much like the biblical story of David and Bathsheba, or years later another Chichimec ruler Nezahualpiltzintli doing away with his wife and her three lovers. Only by going back to the original sources can we find for the pre-Columbian civilizations the opposite numbers of Narcissus, Oedipus, or Jocasta.

The student of human emotions may see from a sample of case histories that the pattern of the pre-Columbian mind, in sex at least, was very much the same as that of the classical tradition. But this is only true up to a point. Sex and its aberrations played a considerable role in shaping the pre-Columbian mind, and so did the lust for power. In a preliminary survey of the American civilizations it must be brought to the attention of the student of human nature that many other elements ruling the motivation of human actions in the European culture are missing among the pre-Columbian civilizations. This applies to money, hereditary property, land ownership, etc. Barter was the usual way of acquiring property among the American Indians, though the use of copper axes and shells as tokens has been mentioned. The closest thing to currency in Pre-Columbian America was cocoa beans, which were widely used among the Aztecs in trade; but this is a "currency" which can be kept only for a limited time, because otherwise it becomes rancid and its value disappears. The status of pre-Columbian ownership of the land has been completely misinterpreted by contemporary social reformers: the Indian peasant before the Spanish Conquest was never the owner of the land he worked. The *calpulli* and *ayllus* or family units among the Aztecs and Incas were the users, never the owners of the *milpa* or *tupu* allocated to them by the rulers every season. Another puzzle for the European mind, deeply committed to hereditary privileges as an outlet for its fears of finitude, was the absence of heritable assets among the Indians. One of the strange findings in this research has been the discovery, in the earliest religious manuals for the natives, of the techniques for making last wills and testaments which were instructed to the Indians like the dogmas of the Catholic faith. The novelties of the human mind to be found in pre-Columbian America were, and indeed still are, surprising.

CHAPTER III

THE PRE-COLUMBIAN MORALS

PRE-COLUMBIAN MORALS

Sources for the analysis of pre-Columbian morals are very limited, as these civilizations lacked written records capable of expressing moral concepts. Evidence of pre-Columbian manufacture on moral ideas in graffiti, jewellery, epigraphy or codices is negative. The codices of Middle America are mostly concerned with calendaric and ritual matters, or the historical sequence of rulers, and like certain epigraphic remains they only give a glimpse of moral ideas when depicting religious rituals. However, the codices of post-Hispanic manufacture are indeed concerned on occasion with moral issues including the education of the youth, punishment of evil, ritual anthropophagy, inebriating drugs, and other subjects. For the Toltecs we have to rely entirely on post-Hispanic sources, but for the Mochicas, at least for their sexual behaviour, pre-Columbian pottery offers the best surviving evidence, despite the fact that because of its very nature most of it came to be destroyed at the hands of missionaries after the Conquest. It is difficult to obtain a clear picture of pre-Columbian American morals because of the great upheavals after the Spanish Conquest, and the cultural variations from one area to another, even within the same area at different historical periods. In fact it can be stated that, as with pre-Columbian medicine, there is not one but many different systems of pre-Columbian morals, as many as pre-Columbian civilizations. Cieza de León (1553) expressed the same idea when he candidly admitted with respect to the main issues—homicide, anthropophagy, inebriation, incest and sodomy—that what was found to be institutionalized and morally acceptable in one area, was forbidden and punished in another.

The Conquistadors and missionaries, on arrival, absorbed an oral tradition in respect of rules for social behaviour which entailed the acceptance of certain moral principles in the three major pre-Columbian civilizations, Aztec, Maya and Inca; much guidance can also be obtained from the American chronicles in general, because the authors in most cases were actually describing in a naïve anthropological fashion the way of life and beliefs of the different peoples of America. A condensed and factual view of pre-Columbian morals can better be grasped by analysing them through the social laws in which they became established in each particular American civilization. As in the Spanish society, or for that matter any other society, customary law, and eventually civil law, reflected the moral and religious principles guiding a nation at every particular period of its history and they could not be in conflict. The problem in pre-Columbian America is that, in the absence of written records, its customary law was culled after colossal social changes had taken place, and at least a generation after the cultural conflict of the Conquest. To make the pre-Columbian appraisal of morals worse, every recorder was either of Indian extraction or a religious missionary trying to protect the Indians, and that tainted the report with considerable bias. The Dominican bishop las Casas (1542) and the Franciscan Torquemada (1615) almost a century after the Conquest, gathered together what previous writers had written about the traditional laws of the Aztecs or Mexicans, the Mayas in Vera-Paz and Guatemala, and the Incas in Peru. Besides them there were individual accounts on localized areas, sometimes showing great differences from las Casas and Torquemada. As in other cultural aspects the information about the Aztecs is richer than that on the Incas; that on the Mayas is comparatively poorer.

AZTEC MORALS

The earliest record of a code of social behaviour which reflects in part the moral ideas of the Aztecs in the pre-Columbian period is a manuscript on the *Laws of the Indians of New Spain* by Fr. Andrés de Alobiz, dated at Valladolid 1543, quoted by Orozco y Berra (1880) in the García Icazbalceta collection. This document after careful analysis seems to be a poor and incomplete copy of a similar text quoted by another Dominican, the celebrated Bishop las Casas in his *Apologética Historia de las Indias* which he wrote (1542) about the same date as Alobiz, at the convent of San Gregorio in Valladolid, Spain. Although las Casas' *Apologetic History* remained unpublished until 1909, it is accepted that his manuscript was studied and copied by other writers. At the end of the 16th century other Franciscan friars also gathered independent versions of the ancient laws of the Mexicans, and the most complete of them was made in Mexico by Fr. Gerónimo de Mendieta (1596), only published in 1870. After him two other members of the Franciscan Order, Torquemada (1615) and Vetancurt (1698) also quoted the ancient Aztec laws. While las Casas' text runs fluently and congruously, the context in Alobiz's is altered, condensed and sometimes confusing. Mendieta's version is also fluent, but it varies considerably from las Casas' text; the versions given by Torquemada and Vetancurt have been glossed and supplied with commentaries and quotations from parallel biblical and classical texts, making their reading difficult.

Apologética Historia, 1909 edition, pp. 562–563; Chapter CCXV

"These are the laws kept by the Indians of New Spain. If the son of a chieftain was a gambler and sold his father's estate, or sold any part of land he died for it being secretly strangled, and if he was a commoner or of lower condition, he was made a slave. If someone took from the agaves, which are a sort of large thistle, or small thorny trees mentioned above in chapter . . . where it was told that it produced twenty useful things, to make honey, if twenty plants, they pay for it with cotton shirting that the judge sentenced and if they did not have them or there were more agaves, then they became slaves. He who asked for cloth or borrowed it and did not pay for it, was made a slave. If some one stole a fishing net, he paid for with cloth, and if he did not have any he became a slave. If someone stole a *canoe* (which is a small boat made of a treetrunk for sailing) they paid with cloth the value of the canoe, and if he did not have it he became a slave. If someone had use of a slave girl before she was of age, he became a slave. If he took a slave girl to be sold at Azcapotzalco where the slave market took place, and the buyer gave clothing for her, and he received the cloth accordingly, if afterwards he regretted it and returning the clothing, he lost the slave. If someone was left when very young and the relatives sold him away, if this was known after he grew up, the judges took some clothing from them, and gave it to the buyer and the one sold became free. If some slave ran away and sold himself to another person, when he was found he was returned to his owner, and the buyer lost what was paid for him. If someone had relations with the slave of somebody else, and she died during pregnancy, the one responsible for her pregnancy became a slave; but if she delivered a child without danger, the child was free and was taken by the father. If someone sold a child for a slave and afterwards it was recognized, all involved in this became slaves, and one of them was given as a slave to the buyer, and the rest were divided between the child's mother and the one who found it. Those who gave potions to someone to die, died themselves by blows, if the dead man was a slave, the guilty one was made a slave himself. If they stole corn cobs, above the number of twenty, he died for it, if less, he was made to pay according to the sentence. Those who pulled up corn before the grain had grown, died for it. Those who stole *yetecomatl*, which is a sort of small gourd, tied up with some red leather by the head, with some feathers at the top used by the chieftains to carry some green powders which they take by mouth with smoke in the Hispaniola island called Tabacos, they died for it by blows. Those who stole some *chalchiuitl*, which is a stone considered precious, and any other jewellery whatever part they stole it, were stoned in the market, because no man of low condition could have it. If people stole something from the market, the people of the market themselves were permitted to stone them to death. Those assaulting in the roads, were publicly stoned to death. They had a law that if the high priest were drunk, wherever he was found drunk he was killed with cudgels. The young man who got drunk to get married was taken to a house called Teocalli and there was killed with clubs. The chieftain who had some position or appointment, if he got drunk, had the position taken from him, and if because of his courage he was considered a true man, which among them was a great honour, it was taken from him. If the father happened to commit sin with his daughter, they both died strangled by the neck with a rope. Those who sinned with their sisters, died strangled; this act was considered among them very loathsome. If one woman committed sin with another they died strangled in the same way. If the high priest was found with some woman, secretely he was killed by strangulation or burned up. It was said that his house was demolished and his estate confiscated, and all those who knowingly had kept silence about it died as well. For conviction for adultery proof was not enough unless those concerned found together and their penalty was to be stoned publicly."

Las Casas' description of Aztec pre-Columbian laws, despite the bias of his *Apologetic History* in favour of the Indians, and his many omissions, indicates that there were a number of moral issues such as incest, inebriation, theft and the like, which in the Indian mind ran parallel with European values. Unusual to European conceptions was the Aztec's concern about the protection of crops—maize and agave, their main staples—and above all the severity of the penalties awaiting those who broke the moral laws. In Aztec life there was seldom opportunity for repentance, the punishment was practically always the same: death. Mendieta's version (1596) of the ancient Mexican laws pays more attention to adultery, incest and other sexual offences.

1870 edition, pp. 136–138; Book II, Chapter XXIX

"Chapter XXIX. Of the penalties given to those guilty and delinquents. They sentenced to death those committing serious and grave felonies, and also the homicides. Anyone who killed another died for it. The pregnant woman who took something for abortion and to expel the child, she and the midwife who gave the potion to expel it, both died for it. Women always cured women, and men cured men. Who raped a virgin by force, either in the field or at the parent's house, died for it. Who gave a potion to another, and caused his death, the homicide and the one who gave the potion to kill, died as well. If a husband killed the wife who committed adultery even if he caught her in the act, he died for it, because he usurped the office of justice, as he should have taken her to the judge and being proved guilty, die after sentence. The woman who committed adultery and the adulterer, caught in the act, or being seriously suspect of it, were taken prisoners, and if they did not confess, they received torment and after confessing the felony they were condemned to death. Sometimes they were killed tied up hand and foot and lying on the ground, with a large round and heavy stone they crushed their temples in such a way, that after a few blows their heads were left like a cake. Others were strangled with some oak sticks. On other occasions they burnt the adulterer, and she was hanged. Other times they were both hanged, and if they were principal people, after hanging their heads were feathered and they put in them small tufts and burned them like that, saying that it was a sign that they felt sorry for them, to burn their bodies in that manner. The judges ordered other adulterers to be stoned and took them to the square where many people gathered and placed them in the middle of the square, they tied their hands, and soon shot stones like rain upon them, and when they fell they did not suffer much because they were soon dead and covered with stones. Those who committed adultery while intoxicated with wine, were not excused on account of their drunkenness but died like the rest. The man who laid down with his stepmother died for it, and she as well if she consented it, and the same if the brother laid with his sister, whether they were brothers of father and mother or only of father, or only of mother. The step father who laid down with the step daughter, both died. All those who committed incest in the first degree of consanguinity had death penalty, excepting brothers and sisters in law; on the contrary, when one of the brothers died, it was customary for another of their brothers to take the wife or wives of the brother, even if he had children, ... The penalty for procuresses was that after they found out her ruin office, she was exposed to shame, and in the square in front of everybody they burnt her hair with a burning torch, until her skull was burnt and thus ashamed and, known by the burnt hair, she left. But if the person procured was honourable and principal, they had a greater penalty and punishment, to lose their lives ... Those who committed the nefarious sin [sodomy], agent and patient died for it. And once in a while the law searched for them and questioned about it to kill and finish them: because they know quite well that such a nefarious vice was against nature, as they did not see it among the animals. But the [vice of] bestiality was not found among these natives. The man who went dressed like a woman, and the woman who went dressed like a man, both had the death penalty. The thief who committed a considerable theft, especially in the temples or the house of the lord, or if he broke into a house when robbing, he was made a slave for the first time, the second time he was hanged. To the thief who robbed something of value in the square or the market, such as cloth, some gold token, or committed petty thefts frequently in the same market ... he was hanged because of his theft and the nature of the place. They considered very serious theft those committed in the square or market. Those who plot or arranged to betray some lord, or tried to take over his rule, even if they were very close relation, were punished with the death penalty ..."

It is strange that Sahagún, to whom we owe most of our knowledge of pre-Columbian Mexico, did not include any version of its laws, although he described (*c.* 1565) Mexican social structure in detail. However, he agreed with other authors and with the pictographic descriptions of the Codices Mendoza and Magliabecchi in respect of inebriation, stating that the penalty for drunkenness was death.

1938 edition, Vol. I, p. 293; Book III, appendix Chapter VI

"Chapter VI. Of the punishments given to those who got drunk. The youth educated in the house of *telpochcali* were in charge of sweeping and cleaning the house; and nobody drank wine, but only those who were already old drank wine in secret and they drank little, without getting drunk; and if a youth appeared drunk in public or if he was found with wine or he was fallen in the street or he went singing, or he was accompanied by others drunk, to this one, if he was *macequal* [peasant] was punished by blows with sticks until he died, or he was strangled in front of all the youth gathered, as an example and to frighten them never to get drunk. If he was of noble birth the one drunk he was secretly strangled ..."

In referring to the youth Sahagún mentioned an interesting fact which has so far escaped previous historians, although it was quoted (Guerra, 1967) in a survey of Mexican drugs producing hallucinations. Sahagún indicated (*c.* 1565) that the youth among the Aztecs also went in search of artificial paradises by taking hallucinogenic mushrooms, which could only be consumed by adults and priests during certain ritual ceremonies, well described by Motolinia (1541), Muñoz Camargo (1576), Duran (1581) and others.

1961 edition, part XI, p. 37, Book X, Chapter II, 2

"The lewd youth is mad. He is a sot who drinks raw wine and becomes drunk, foolish and dejected. He eats mushrooms which make him demented, restless and dissolute. He is shameless, presumptuous, lewd, tattling, wicked, vile, brutish and brazen. He is impudent, vain, proud, debauched, vicious and promiscuous, a libertine who exhausts himself by a life devoted to pleasure."

There is in Sahagún (*c.* 1565) a Book X *On the vices and virtues of these Indian people*, which contains two excellent accounts which are of great interest, relating what the Indian informants considered to be the moral failures of two types of individuals in their society. Sodomites are described in the most despicable terms. Prostitutes, however, are given a more gay and attractive description, and making the chewing of *tzictli* distinctive of the oldest profession. The translation from the Nahuatl version of Sahagún has the repetitive style of the original Mexican language.

1961 edition, Part X, pp. 37–38; Book XI, Chapter XI

"The sodomite is an effeminate, a defilement, a corruption, filth; a taster of filth, revolting, perverse, full of affliction. He deserves laughter, ridicule, mockery; he is detestable, nauseating, disgusting. He makes one acutely sick. Womanish, playing the part of a woman, he merits being committed to flames, burned, consumed by fire, he burns; he is consumed by fire. He talks like a woman, he takes the part of a woman."

1938 edition, Vol. III, pp. 47–48; Book X, Chapter XV

"Of the public women. The whore is a public woman and is like this; she goes about selling her body, starting since young and does not leave it when old, she goes drunk and loose, she is beautiful and polished, and under this without shame; and gives herself to any man, and sells her body, because she is very lewd, dirty and without shame, talkative and very vicious in the carnal act. She arrays herself very much and is so careful in her make up that she looks like a rose after she has fixed herself up, and to embellish herself very well she first looks herself in the mirror, takes a bath, washes herself very well and refreshes her body to please better; she uses to anoint herself with a yellow ointment of this land which they call *axin* to have a nice and shining face, and at the same time she puts on colours and cosmetics in the face because she is dissolute and mundane. She also has the habit of dyeing her teeth with cochineal and let the hair loose to make it more beautiful, and at times she has half of them loose, and the other half upon ear or above the shoulder, and she braided the hair and placed the tail upon the head like little horns and then she walks about showing off, as a bad woman, shameless, dissolute, infamous. She has the habit to perfume herself with nice smelling fumes, and goes about chewing *tzictli* to clean her teeth, she considers it as graceful and while she chews it she makes noises like castanets. She likes walking, or to move about, she is in the street, and in the squares, she goes about walking, looking for vicious people, she goes laughing, she never stops and her heart is always uneasy. And due to the pleasures she is always engaged in she leads the roads of the beats she joins these and those; she has the habit of calling the people; to make gestures, to turn an eye on men, to talk winking the eye, to call with her hand, to move the eye in an arch, to go laughing for everyone, to pick up the one she likes best, and to be wanted, she deceives the young men, or youths, and she wants to be well paid, and she goes procuring these for those and selling other women."

Sahagún also left a most beautiful version of what the Aztec considered the desideratum of moral thoughts in the scholar and the physician. It was pointed out (Guerra, 1966) that both professional concepts overlap in Sahagún's manuscripts (*c*. 1565) and the loftiness of their ethical values is enhanced by amalgamating the Spanish and Nahuatl versions. It is clear that Aztec moral ideas on what makes a good physician came very close, if not equal, to those found in the Hippocratic Oath.

1938 edition, Vol. III, p. 32; Book X, Chapter VIII

"The wise man or scholar *tlamatini* is exemplary, like a beacon, a shining mirror, learned, well-read, keeper of books, bearer of tradition and responsibility, a guide. A good scientist is like a good physician, who takes good care of things, he is a counsellor, a teacher of the true doctrine, worthy of confidence, a confessor, reliable. He shows the way, establishes order, he knows about the land of the dead, he is dignified, unreviled, confided in and trusted, he is very congenial, reassures, calms, helps, satisfies, gives hope, favours with his knowledge, he makes one whole. A bad scientist is like a stupid physician, silly and vain, pretending to be trustworthy and wise, he is a sorcerer, a soothsayer, a deluder, a deceiver, a public robber, he confounds, causes ills, leads into evil, destroys people and kills.

"The physician *ticitl* is a curer of people, a restorer and provider of health. A good physician is a diagnostician, experienced and well versed in the virtues of herbs, stones, trees and roots. He is moderate in his acts, cures people by setting bones, providing splints, knows how to purge and to give emetics and potions, he knows how to bleed, he stitches wounds, makes incisions and revives the sick. A bad physician is a fraud, a half-hearted worker, unskilled, a killer with his medicines because of overdosage, he worses the condition of the sick, endangers others' lives, he pretends to be a counsellor, adviser and chaste. He bewitches, is a sorcerer, a soothsayer, a caster of lots, he seduces women and bewitches them."

Where Aztec morals can be seen at their best is in Sahagún's *History* (*c.* 1565) which contains a Sixth Book *Of the Rhetoric and Moral Philosophy and Theology of the Mexican People....* Some of its chapters are invocations and prayers to the different gods, other chapters deal with polite speeches of leaders accepting office; the most beautiful ideas appear in those chapters of parents addressing their sons and daughters, advising them to follow a life of work, respect for their elders and honesty. Interesting too are the homilies recorded by Sahagún in respect of moral values in marriage, invocations after childbirth and counselling for married life. Some examples suffice to express the main Aztec moral rules, but unfortunately, as they are long-winded and retain the repetitious style of Nahuatl literature it will be wise to present a few of their guiding ideas.

1938 edition, Vol. II, pp. 116–121; Book VI, Chapter XVII

"Chapter XVII. Of the reasoning, full of good doctrine that a lord made to his sons when they had reached the years of discretion, exhorting them to avoid vice and to exercise in nobility and virtue.

"Listen my children what I wish to tell, I your father, who cares and rules this province . . . despite my faults and defects . . . be humble in your heart and have hope in God, because if you lack that he will be angry at you as he can see everything secret, and will punish you, as he will think and please. The second thing you must keep in mind is to be in peace with everyone . . . have respect for everyone . . . do not dare against anyone . . . be silent and if they knock you down do not answer . . . the third . . . do not waste the time that God gave you . . ."

1938 edition, Vol. II, pp. 122–127; Book VI, Chapter XVIII

"Chapter XVIII. Of the language and affection used by the lords in talking and teaching their daughters when they had reached the years of discretion: exhorting them to discipline and internal and external honesty, and to keep in mind their nobility to avoid any action which might affront their family, talking to them with tender words and about very private matters.

You my daughter precious like a drop of gold, like rich feather, which came out of my entrails . . . you are my blood and my image . . . listen . . . that this world is to cry and suffer travails . . . this world is evil and painful . . . look my daughter, my little dove . . . do no dishonour yourself . . . do not sleep too much . . . get up at night and keep vigil . . . remove your clothing, wash your face, wash your hands, wash your mouth, take promptly the broom to sweep . . . After this is done start soon to do your chores, to make cocoa, to grind maize . . . look diligently and with curiosity to learn how to prepare food and drink . . . for your marriage . . . do not give yourself to venereal pleasure; do not throw yourself on the manure and stench of lewdness . . ."

1938 edition, Vol. II, pp. 128–132. Book VI, Chapter XIX

"Chapter XIX. Where in finishing the father exhorting his daughter, then in front of him, the mother took her hand and with loving words she told her to hold in great esteem what her father said and to keep it in her heart as a very precious thing, and afterwards she began to instruct her about the dress she should wear and how she must speak, look and walk, not to care about other people's lives, and never to repeat evil things about others . . .

"My very beloved daughter, my very dear little dove, you have listened to the words that the lord your father has told you . . . your dresses will be honest and clean . . . when you talk do not talk too fast . . . not too loud . . . do not be curious in your conversation . . . when you walk be honest, do not walk too fast . . . do not go with the head too high, because it is a sign of bad manners . . . do not go looking to one side or another . . . do not use cosmetics in your face . . . they are things for harlots . . . be careful . . . do not give your body to anybody . . . be sure that only one man knows you . . ."

1938 edition, Vol. II, pp. 133–138; Book VI, Chapter XX

"Chapter XX. Of the language and affection used by the father, headman or lord, to admonish his son towards humility and the knowledge of himself, to be accepted by the gods and men . . .

"My very beloved and very dear son, take notice of what I am going to tell you . . . the world is very dangerous and very difficult . . . nobody can escape from the ups and downs in it . . . our ancestors . . . lived in great humility . . . but were very much revered and respected . . . they had authority to kill and wage war, they maintained the sun and the earth with flesh and blood of men . . ."

1938 edition, Vol. II, pp. 139–144; Book VI, Chapter XXI

"Chapter XXI. Of the language and affection that the father, principal lord, used to persuade his son in the love of chastity, where it is said how friendly were the gods of the chastes ones, with many comparisons and examples very much to the point in excellent language . . .

"My very beloved son: take good notice of my words . . . leave aside the pleasures of the flesh and do not desire them . . . do not throw yourself to the woman like a dog throws itself to what it is going to eat, do not behave like a dog in eating and devouring whatever is given, giving yourself to women before it is time; even if you want woman resist, control your heart until you are a strong and complete man . . ."

1938 edition, Vol. II, pp. 145–150; Book VI, Chapter XXII

"Chapter XXII. Where it is contained the doctrine that the father or lord gave to his son concerning external things and policy, that is how he should behave in the sleep, eating, drinking, speech, dress, walking, looking and listening and to keep away from eating food prepared by bad women because they use witchcraft . . ."

Mendieta (1596), like Sahagún, reproduced some of these homilies although not in great detail. León Portilla (1963) has glossed Sahagún's chapters on Aztec thought, but it must be kept in mind—and this is the heart of the matter—that they represent only one side of the moral tenets held by the pre-Columbian Aztecs. Sahagún, who loved the Mexican Indians, next to the aforementioned moral values which can be compared with the best in the Christian tradition, had this to say about their morals on homicide, anthropophagy and other vices which pertain to their rituals, and are described further on.

1938 edition, Vol. II, p. 119; Book II, Chapter XX

"There is no need to tell in this Second Book the refutation of the idolatric ceremonies which are reported in it, because they are so cruel and inhuman that anybody listening will be horrified and frightened . . ."

The human sacrifices and anthropophagy which, according to Mendieta (1596), the Mexicans began to practise after they reached Tollan in their pilgrimage *c.* 1057, were one facet of the cruel rituals which pervaded Aztec morals and gave them such a bloody reputation. This cruelty was not only against the enemy or the alien, but was also applied towards the individuals of their own group and, what is more important, against themselves. The ritual mutilations of the teeth, mouth, tongue, ears and limbs; piercing with maguey thorns was the standard punishment for children. Motolinia (1541), like many others, left good descriptions of self-mutilations practised by the youth to assert their courage.

1969 edition, p. 40; Chapter 9

"... They sacrifice themselves many times in different parts of the body ... in that hole they make in the ears or the tongue they passed a cane as thick as a finger of the hand and as long as the arm ... and they got bloody and the blood they could collect in some papers, were offered in front of the idols. In Tehuacan ... they made many cruel sacrifices of captives and slaves; and upon themselves the *tlamagazques* or young priests did one of the most strange and cruel things in the world: they cut and made an incision through the member of generation between skin and flesh and made a large opening to pass through it a rope as thick as the arm around the wrist, and in length according to the penitents devotion; some were ten fathoms, others fifteen, others twenty, and if any of them fainted during that cruel foolishness, they said that the lack of courage was due to having sinned and laid with woman ..."

Besides the punishment to small children depicted in the Codex Mendoza (1542), it is interesting to report, from among many, that recorded by Mendieta (1596).

1870 edition, p. 124, Book II, Chapter XXIV

"... the Indians are now so vicious in lying, though before the parents very much advised their children to tell the truth and not to lie; and if they were vicious about it, the punishment was to cut and to open the lip a bit, and as a result they used to speak the truth ..."

MAYA MORALS

The earliest version of Maya morals was obtained by las Casas while he was bishop of Chiapas. His two accounts (*c.* 1542) in the *Apologetica Historia*, Chapters CCXXIV–CCXLII, did not reflect the more sophisticated morals of the Yucatan Mayas. Bishop Landa, on the other hand, who wrote the fundamental study on the Yucatan Mayas (*c.* 1570), was extremely brief about their moral laws, and those concepts appeared in his work disseminated among other information. There is, furthermore, the brief account by the Mayan native Gaspar Antonio Chi written in 1582, which was quoted by López de Cogolludo (1688). The other author offering a comprehensive view of Mayan customary law, which reflects its morals, was Torquemada (1615), who followed las Casas very closely and annotated the Indian laws with his usual biblical commentaries. Torquemada's version (1615) was published when the Maya area of the highlands and the forest territory of Peten was practically closed to Spanish colonization, and it is based on las Casas. The important thing to notice here is that in contrast to the severe penalties of the Aztecs, the Maya introduced a system of pecuniary punishment for certain faults, elsewhere deserving death, using as a token the precious *quetzal* feathers, a bird only found in Guatemala, and cocoa beans.

1615 edition, Vol. II, pp. 417–419. Book XII, Chapter VIII

"Chapter VIII. Of the establishments and laws of the Indians in the kingdoms of Guatemala and other neighbouring provinces.

"Although these Guatemaltec Indians agreed with the others aforementioned of the kingdoms of New Spain in many of their laws or all of them the punishments and penalties were not the same because it is found they were more lenient and in others more severe in their punishments . . . who killed another died for it . . . If the king's wife committed adultery . . . if he was a noble he was strangled and both died in this manner; but if he was a commoner, a peasant, he was flung.

"If someone had intercourse with some slave, he was punished with some pecuniary fine, and sometimes the man paid as much as the value of the slave with whom he committed the act, or purchased another slave of the same value; but if the offence had been committed against a lord who was known had intercourse with the slave the penalty was doubled, by reason that the offence was greater.

"The thief was punished with pecuniary penalty that went to the king . . . besides he paid the owner everything which seemed to have been stolen. This it must be noticed if he was not a frequent and habitual thief; but if he had it for custom and he could not be corrected he was hanged; but before that his relations, if he had any, were asked to redeem his life paying for him . . .

"To those condemned to death, it was usual and common to confiscate their property and make slaves their wives and children . . .

"To those who fornicated, that is, bachelor and spinster, who are comprehended in fornication, were punished with pecuniary penalty. . .

"Who raped a woman, if the offence was executed, he died for it; but if the act was not completed, he was made a slave, on account of the violence and force he tried to use in it. Who robbed something from the temples, if it was valuable and costly, he died flung, because he dared to go after things they considered sacred and dedicated to their god; if they were less valuable, he was made a slave."

1615 edition, Vol. II, pp. 419–420; Book XII, Chapter IX

"Chapter IX. Where is continued the previous matters. It was an inviolable law among these people of Guatemala to slay and sacrifice to their idols all the noblemen and lords captured in war, and their flesh was then eaten by their kings and victorious lords. The reason they gave not to forgive, and to sacrifice and eat them was to frighten and scare their enemies, so they appreciate them and learn that if they slew and ate the kings they would also kill and eat their vassals, because they had them in less esteem . . .

"The vassal who ran away from his lord . . . was killed . . . Who committed treason against his king . . . was killed, his property confiscated and his wife and children made slaves.

"It was a law that nobody should hunt in alien mountain, or to fish in waters outside his limits . . . The woman who had received a dowry, or had been purchased, as they said, never returned to her parents' home, or among her relatives, but if the husband died, she was married to her in-laws or with the brother of the deceased.

"The woman who for any reason left her husband or went to another, or to her parents' home, did not have any penalty according to the law; but if the husband requested her return and she did not want it, he could marry another because in this case, woman had the right not to stay with their husbands if they did not want to live with them, and the husbands could marry again, because they could not live without woman, on account of the food and other things necessary to life."

1615 edition, Vol. II, pp. 420–422; Book XII, Chapter X

"Chapter X. Of the laws the Indians of Vera-Paz and their provinces had. The people of Vera-Paz and their provinces . . . had laws . . . It was a law, that the sorcerer who made a pact with the devil to harm the republic, died for it strangled or hanged . . . There was not penalty for those who wounded or slew his own slave; because they said it was his property . . . Those who killed another's slave usually was ordered to pay for it . . . Who killed a free man died for it without remission, because this law was inviolable, his death was to be strangled or hanged, which any one of them were the customary kind of death among these people.

"If the husband killed the wife or the wife to the husband they were hanged for it or strangled . . ."

1615 edition, Vol. II, pp. 422–425. Book XII, Chapter XI

"Chapter XI. Of the laws concerning sensuality and lustful people, reporting with what punishments and penalties were punished and corrected. It was a law that the young man who had intercourse with a virgin, marry her and he was forced to do so when he refused, and if the virgin was engaged to another when that offence was committed, this one did not receive her; on the contrary he asked for the return of the dowry or pledge . . . which was paid by the raping youth to the parents of the raped virgin . . . Who committed fornication with widow or slave was condemned to sixty rich feathers [of Quetzal] . . . Who committed adultery with married woman was condemned to the penalty of one hundred feathers; but if the offence was frequent and committed many times, both of them were strangled. The young man free or slave who was found committing adultery with the wife of the lord or headman, was soon dead, usually common dead, although sometimes he was taken to be sacrificed during the day of their festivities. If some slave, bachelor or married, had intercourse with slave woman . . . both were taken out of the village and stoned to death. When a married man committed this offence with a virgin, the family and relatives considered it a great affront, and dissimulated it, to cover the fault . . . If the married man sinned with widow or married woman, punished them once or twice . . . and smoked . . . if they did not mend their ways they paid it with the death penalty. This punishment had to be preceded by the accusation of the husband . . . Some in those provinces were found with the nefarious sin [sodomy], and there was a law which prohibited it . . ."

1615 edition, Vol. II, pp. 425–427; Book XII, Chapter XII

"Chapter XII. It continues the laws of the Vera-Paz Indians, and are noticed those concerning thefts.

"Concerning thefts these people had a variety of laws, because they punished in a different way petty thefts than large ones or of valuable things; it was a law, that whoever robbed a chicken or some maize, or similar things should return them to the owners, and the thief ordered to pay some feathers . . . The thief who robbed something of value and esteem, such as a gold crown . . . was forced to return what he had taken, if by chance he had it . . . but if he had dissipated it or disappeared, he was sold as a slave, and from the price he was sold, the value of the stolen thing was paid. Who killed the bird of beautiful feathers found in these provinces [Quetzal] had death penalty . . .

"Who robbed these feathers in another's mountain was forced to pay for them, with as many more as those in the theft; the same about cocoa and other seeds . . ."

1615 edition, Vol. II, pp. 427–428; Book XII, Chapter XIII

"Chapter XIII. Where it is continued the laws of Vera-Paz, stating those they had about not to lie, or make false statements.

". . . Who lie damaging his neighbour was severely reprimanded and besides he was condemned to fifteen or twenty feathers according to the offence. The woman who accused any man of some offence done to her . . . she was not believed on her only own word . . . to proceed with this case had to be witnesses . . ."

INCA MORALS

The area of Tierra Firme in the northern part of South America was inhabited at the time of the Discovery by Chibcha tribes, which were in the process of evolving into a well integrated and centralized civilization as had the Inca, their southern neighbours, a century earlier. Bishop Fernandez de Piedrahita (1688), who was of Chibcha descent, recorded a few laws thought to be customary among the Indians in the valley of Bogota and Tunja. They are unfortunately not in agreement with the accounts of Cieza de León (1553) who recorded the customs of these Indians at the time that territory was opened by the Spanish Conquest.

1688 edition, pp. 45–48; Part I, Book II, Chapter V

"Chapter V. The Zippa issue laws in their kingdom and get ready for the Tunja war.

". . . those issued by Neméquene are said to be these. He ordered that anybody who killed another paid with his life, even if the wife [of the victim] forgave him.

"If any man raped a woman be killed for the felony if he was a bachelor, but if he was married, his own wife had to sleep with two unmarried men . . . If any man committed incest with his mother, daughter, sister or niece be put in a narrow hole filled up with water and vermin, and covered with a gravestone to perish miserably; and the same penalty to be executed on women.

"For the sodomites he ordered death penalty to be executed immediately with painful torment . . .

"He ordered that if any married woman died during delivery the husband should lose half of his property and be applied to the father or mother in law . . .

"To those who were thieves he ordered to put fire in front of their eyes to blind them . . ."

There are several sources for the study of pre-Columbian Inca laws which are in fairly good agreement among themselves. The earliest ones by las Casas (*c.* 1542) in the *Apologética Historia* (Chapter CCLVIII) and Torquemada (1615) are unfortunately from second-hand information, as neither of them ever visited Peru. An important source is the recension given by the anonymous Jesuit, believed to be P. Valera (*c.* 1594), of Inca descent, where the legal system of the Incas is described in detail:

1968 edition, pp. 177–180

"Laws. If the Peruvians were laudable in anything it was in the laws they had and in the way they kept them. And there were two kinds of laws: Some belonged to their false religion . . . The other type of laws concerning civil and moral matters was highly praiseworthy and many of them are still kept today . . .

First law. All the subjects of the Inca empire must speak the same general language . . .

II. All the villages must have all types of artisans . . .

III. Nobody can be excused at the time of fallowing, sowing . . .

IV. To select the grounds for each seed . . .

V. To learn the ability of the youth and their inclinations . . .

VI. To provide all the provinces with storehouses . . .

VII. To maintain reserves of cattle . . .

VIII. To divide the land in each village . . .

IX. Each person to dress and array according to his rank . . .

X. To be moderate and temperate in eating and much more in drinking; and if anyone gets drunk and loses his senses, the first time should be punished according to the judge's pleasure, the second exiled, and the third time deprived of their offices if they were magistrates, and thrown into the mines. This law was first kept with rigour, but afterwards its practice was so relaxed, that the ministers of justice were the first to drink, and even when they got drunk there was not punishment; because the *amautas*, who were like lawyers and scholars among them, made an interpretation of the laws indicating the differences between *cenca* which was to be high and warmed, and *hatun machay* meaning to get drunk to the point of losing consciousness, and that first condition was what usually occurred among them because they did not act mad, and the latter in few occasions or never took place. This was the cause of their dissolution as we have seen previously.

XI. All types of homicides taken place outside war, were punished with the death penalty in this way: who killed his father or mother, to die and be quartered; the same if he killed his grandparents or children; who killed a boy or girl, to die flung over a cliff or stoned; who killed his lord to die quartered; who killed another in the village, to die by hanging.

XII. Who killed an officer of the king, knowing he was one, or a minister of the gods, or a virgin *aclla*, to die after being dragged and shot with arrows. Who killed his wife out of hate, without her being guilty, or without certainty of her adultery, to die hanged and be quartered; the same to the woman if she killed the husband.

XIII. Who killed the wife being found in adultery to be exiled for a certain period. The same if he killed the adulterer with whom his wife committed adultery, but the time of exile not to exceed one year.

XIV. Who was responsible for the death of miscarriage of a woman after three months pregnancy up, giving her herbs or blows, or in any other manner to die hanged or stoned.

XV. Who killed the king or queen, or prince heir to die dragged and quartered . . .

XVI. The adulterer and adulteress to be punished by death; and the husband finding his wife in such felony to denounce it immediately to

accomplish prompt revenge; and the same for the woman who learnt
or saw her husband with adulteress, to denounce them to be dead.

XVII. Who raped a virgin and dishonoured her to die stoned. And if
she wanted to marry him, he will not die, but must marry immediately.
Who raped a married woman to die hanged. Who committed rape with
young girl if she consented, to be both flogged and shaved and exposed
to public shame, and him to be exiled and sent to the mines and her
to be kept in some temple; and if they want to get married, only to be
flogged and married immediately; but if he is married and has children,
he will be condemned to serve the community with his children and wife,
and her to a temple or with *acllas*.

XVIII. Who had intercourse with his own daughter, both to be flung
over a precipice, and even more if she was a virgin and consented it;
but if she was forced and raped, the father to be dead and her to serve
for ever the *acllas*; and if somebody asked her for marriage, to be
married. If any woman fornicated with her own son, to be both dead
by flunging. Who had intercourse with his sister of father and mother,
or only of mother, to die both of them hanged or stoned, more so if she
was a virgin and consented it; but if she was forced and raped, the
brother to be hanged, and her to serve the *acllas*. Who had intercourse
with his sister, the daughter of his father, if she was virgin or married
and consented, both of them to die stoned; if it was known that she
was raped with violence, the brother to die and her to be placed to
serve the temples.

XIX. Incests with uncles and nephews, or with cousins in second
degree, or first degree kinship, if they were virgins or married and
consenting, both to be punished with death by hanging or stoning.
If they were not virgins or married, both to be flogged, shaved and
taken to the mines, and the woman to keep and serve in the temples.

XX. Who committed the sin of sodomy to die dragged and hanged, and
then burnt with all his clothes, and the same if he laid with some beast.

XXI. If the great lords committed anyone of these felonies deserving
death, the governors and council to investigate and report them, and
the sentence be reserved for the king; and when they die for their
felony, to be cut off the throat in the square or where it pleased the
king; and if they were ladies of distinction or their daughters, and
deserved to die, to have the throat cut inside the prison.

XXII. Who were a procurer in the commission of rapes or incests and
these were committed, to die as a result of it by hanging. The same for
the witch who gave herbs to induce love and lust. Who were a procurer
of adulteries and these were committed, to be sent to life imprisonment,
or condemned to the mines, or to the lands or parts of the community.

XXIII. Who robbed something to eat or dress, or silver or gold, to be
questioned, if the theft was forced by need and poverty, and if it was
found that was the case, the thief not to be punished, but the one who

has the office of purveyor to be deprived of it because he was careless to provide the needed, neither made provision for them; and the thief be given what he needed of cloth and food, and land and house, with the warning that if ever robbed in the future he died. If it was found that he robbed in amount and worth of—*achupallas* [pineapples] and from then on, not for need but for vice, and because he was dissolute and lazy, to die hanged, and if he was the son of a lord, to have the throat cut in prison.

XXIV. In every town to have a judge against idlers and lazy people, to punish them and to make them work."

The Inca laws as recorded by Torquemada (1615) are far less detailed, and like those of the Maya, seem to be taken from the *Apologética Historia* by las Casas (1542).

1615 edition, Vol. II, pp. 428–430; Book XII, Chapter XIV

"Chapter XIV. Of certain laws used by the people of Peru, which ruled and governed those great and powerful kingdoms.

"There was an universal law in all the kingdoms of Peru subject to the Inca kings, that nobody should marry to her sister, cousin, aunt or niece ... but as who makes the law has the power to annul it, these lords and kings ... among themselves tolerate this and married as they pleased.

"It was a law that the adulterers die for the felony they committed, if they executed out of free will ...

"The thief who stole something valuable was killed on the first instance he committed this felony.

"The homicide who slew with violence was punished without remedy with the death penalty.

"Those who lie were punished according to the quality and gravity of the lie; particularly women in whom these laws were executed even if the lies were very light; this severity was not kept for men.

"The wizards and witches who caused sterility to women ... killed with witchcraft ... received the death penalty ...

"The accountants of high and lower office kept the records very faithfully, but if something was missing ... were soon killed."

The ordinances of the Incas in the rendering of Huaman Poma de Ayala (c. 1610) are presented like those of P. Valera (c. 1574) in great detail. Huaman Poma, who was a full-blooded Inca and devoted his life to defending the legal status of his fellow Indians, made a point of presenting the Inca system at its best, and the Colonial administration at its worst. His hate for the Spanish officials and missionaries, who took away from him one of his wives, and in particular for Negroes, mulattos and people of mixed blood, whose excesses he blamed for the Incas' decline, mar his valuable and intimate knowledge of Inca traditions.

1936 edition, pp. 182–193

"Ordinances of the Great Government of the Incas... Topa Inca
Yupanqui and the rest... we order and command in these kingdoms
and dominions to be, kept and obey, under death penalty for those who
disobey and their children and descendants because they will be punished and killed and condemned to death and their generation all
finished, and their villages destroyed and salt spread on them and beasts
will inhabit them... I order this city [Cuzco] to have a chief pope...
Also that in this city should be a royal council... Also an adviser...
Also a viceroy... Also a judge in every province... Also an alderman
... Also a secretary to the Inca... Also a royal registrar... Also high
accountants... Also... that nobody curse the sun my father or the
moon my mother... Also that nobody curse the council... Also that
no woman be accepted as a witness because they are liars, deceitful
and pusillanimous... Also, nobody who is poor to be a witness to avoid
being bribed... Also, no fruit tree or tree... to be burnt or cut down
without licence... Also... not to catch [certain animals] excluding
falcon and fox... Also widows not to show their faces or leave the
house in six months... Also... to bury the dead in graves... and not
inside the houses... with the eating utensils, food and drink and clothing... Also that youth and children be very obedient to their fathers
and mothers and old people... if they do not obey to be flogged for the
first time, and to be exiled for the mines of silver and gold the second
time... Also there will be no thieves in this kingdom or highwaymen
... to be punished with five hundred lashes the first time, and to be
stoned to death the second... Also what was found to be restituted...
Also that after somebody is dead, the wife... or any relation had to
pay his debts... Also those exiled Indians men and women be under
heavy work to receive sorrow and punishment for their offences... Also
nobody in this kingdom to have poison or potion or witchcraft to kill
another... be punished to death... and if it was against the Inca or
lords... to be made drum of his skin, flutes of the bones, necklaces of
his teeth... Also anybody who killed another to die in the same way
... Also women with their menstruation not to enter the temple... Also
woman who killed her son to die and if it was a girl two hundred lashes
and exile... Also the woman who was dissolute or allowed herself to
be corrupted or she was a whore to be hanged by the hair... and let
die... the man who committed rape five hundred lashes and to go
through torment... some die, some remain alive... Also... a woman
widow not to marry again or to be concubine if she has a son... Also
those who have a son be honoured *yupazchasca* and those with two
[more and more honours and land according to the number of sons]...
Also to those lazy and dirty [like] pigs were punished to drink by force
the dirt of the *chacara* [garden] or the house, or the dishes they use
to eat, or from the head, and the hands, and the feet... Also those who

were exiled to bury their dead in their homes with them ... Also that the lords and headmen of the kingdom to have fifty women for their service to increase the number of people in the kingdom ... Also ... nobody to marry his sister, his mother, his cousin his niece or relative or godmother under penalty of taking their eyes out and be quartered and put in the hills for example and punishment, only the Inca can be married to his sister by law. Also we order that the captains be of good blood and extraction ... Also that nobody waste maize or any other food or potatoes or to peel them because if they had feeling they would cry when they are peeled ... Also, that in time of pestilence or sacrifice, tempests, or in time of hunger or thirst or death of the Inca ... not to make festivities or dance, or to play drums or flute or men to touch women nor to eat salt or *aji* or meat or fruit nor to drink *chicha* or eat any food but only white maize ... Also all the officials not to be lazy or idle ... [and to have all sorts of artisans in the kingdom]. Also that in the kingdom be kept plenty of food, plenty of maize and potatoes ... Also that all the houses, dresses and pots and whatever they had worked and raise rabbits ... be inspected twice a year ... for the Inca, the captains and for them ... Also that the barbers and surgeons ... that cure with herbs ... and midwives ... Also that the matrons for orphans be reserved of everything ... Also that no Indian in this kingdom change the dress and attire of his tribe or *ayllu* under penalty of one hundred lashes ... Also ... that the lords, headmen, and all sorts of Indians in every village must eat in the public square, and all the poor, orphans, widows, sick, old, blind, paralytic, pilgrims, travellers, all eat from charity ... Also ... to have for us virgins in the temples ... these must die with their virginity without corruption ..."

MORAL INTERPLAY WITH RELIGION

A cursory recapitulation of the aforementioned accounts of pre-Columbian laws among the major American civilizations seems to indicate that homicide, inebriation, incest, and sodomy, besides adultery, theft and other miscellaneous offences were considered unlawful and punishable by all of them. Furthermore, it must be kept in mind that, if this were true, it was precisely on the grounds of the first group of offences that it was attempted to justify the Conquest and colonization of America. Apparently the only reasons to which the Spanish Conquistadors could resort were the existence of human sacrifices and anthropophagy in certain areas, and the propagation of the Gospel among gentiles. A reminder of the Christian Decalogue brought to the pre-Columbian civilizations by the Spaniards shows that every one of the commandments was included in the basic American religions. (1) The love of God above all things differed among the American Indians in that they accepted certain natural phenomena instead of the Christian tradition. (2) The same reverence existed among them about the name and the invocation to the gods as among the

Christians. (3) They also kept a sequence of religious festivities; for instance the Aztecs had a separate liturgical calendar, *tonalpohualli*, and the Mayas, the *tzonkil*, and among the Incas the religious festivities coincided with the sequence of the agricultural year. (4) Honouring parents and elders was advised among American Indians as much as within the European family. (5) Homicide was indeed forbidden. (6) Fornication, incest, sodomy, rape and other sexual offences seem to have been prohibited. (7) Theft also appears to have been severely punished in every one of the American civilizations. (8) False testimonies were repudiated explicitly by the Maya and the Inca. The curious thing here was that women were considered deceptive by nature and they were not allowed to give testimonies or bear witness. (9) Adultery was included in all customary American laws; but, both the 9th and 10th Christian commandments deserve further comment.

It was noticed by the earliest Catholic missionaries that the pre-Columbian mind showed a considerable divergence from the orthodox theological thought in which the Spaniards had been instructed. The 9th commandment "not to covet thy neighbour's wife" and the 10th "not to covet thy neighbour's property" were alien to the American Indians, because they accepted as immoral and sinful the commission of acts, but not the thoughts or the intention of a sinful action. This concept, as Mendieta (1596) pointed out, was only known to the Indians after indoctrination under the Catholic missionaries. Even more puzzling for the Spanish mind was to discover among pre-Columbian civilizations, not just that the morals of his Decalogue also permeated American morals, but, what was more disturbing to the Catholic priests, to find in the pre-Columbian religions practically all the Sacraments of the Catholic Church which they thought were the means instituted by Christ alone to share His grace. Indeed, outward signs and liturgical ceremonies of Baptism, Confirmation, Holy Eucharist, Penance, Extreme Unction, Holy Orders and Matrimony existed in some of the pre-Columbian civilizations and can be found described in detail by Sahagún (*c.* 1565), Acosta (1590), Mendieta (1596) and other authors. Las Casas (1542) and Acosta (1590) even discussed the parallel between the Catholic festival of Corpus Christi and its Mexican equivalent. This led to speculation that the apostle Saint Thomas, whom some missionaries tried to identify with Quetzalcoatl or Viracocha, had preached the Gospel in America; or if the American Indians were descendants of the lost tribe of Israel. But behind this apparent similarity of Sacraments between the Christian and pre-Columbian traditions existed fundamental differences.

The most important case in point was penance. It is incredible that throughout almost 500 years of American history, it has not been realized that the heterodoxy of the pre-Columbian mind derives from the absence of the concept of hell, which exists in the Christian tradition. Most American civilizations believed in another life after death, they even accepted the existence of different kinds of heaven, but the concept of hell as a place of banishment and pain in punishment for mortal sin did not exist in the American mind. The Incas, like the Mayas and the Aztecs, believed in an underworld, called *mictlan* by the latter, which historians had accepted uncritically as the Christian hell. It was not; it was the place of abode of the dead, not a place of eternal suffering, and something similar to the Christian Limbo. Curiously enough the best understanding of the conflict between the moral and religious issues on this matter comes, not from the three major civilizations, but from the Abipones and Guaraníes in South America; they laughed at the missionaries' threat of the eternal fire of hell for their heathenism. The efforts of the Jesuit missionaries after this experience can be appreciated in the engravings depicting hell prepared for the Guaraní edition of Nieremberg's *Differences between the secular and the eternal* (1705). This doctrine of the absence in the pre-Columbian mind of the fear of hell as eternal punishment, makes it possible to understand certain queries by the earlier missionaries. For instance, Mendieta (1596) reporting the meaning of prayer among the Mexican Indians (1870 edition, p. 93) indicated that:

"... when they prayed they said that they do not ask for pardon of their sins but that these were not to be known or made public ... they only fear the present and secular punishment, not the eternal one in the other world ... they did not know where hell was ..."

The sequence of this doctrine with respect to Penance in the pre-Columbian mind also has important meaning in the interpretation of grace, because confession, which was present in most American civilizations, must be understood in a very different connotation. The pre-Columbian confession was not a ritual to gain grace and forgiveness in order to escape the eternal punishment, but a transfer of moral guilt by a medical practice.

A similar case is the Sacrament of the Holy Eucharist and the different types of pre-Columbian Communion. Homicide appears *prima facie* as immoral and unlawful, but besides the communion of special cakes to obtain grace, it must not be forgotten that the Aztecs practised vicarious communion by sacrificing in Tenochtilan alone over 20,000 victims a year to Huitzilopchtli and eating the flesh of the victims. Religious sublimation can also be used to explain the immoral practice of sodomy existing among the priestly hierarchies in pre-Columbian America or the dynastic incest of the Inca rulers.

CHAPTER IV

ANTHOLOGY OF
CHRONICLES REFERRING TO
PRE-COLUMBIAN ABERRATIONS

THE AMERICAN CHRONICLES

All three great American civilizations flourishing at the time of their discovery—Aztec, Maya and Inca—fell under the impact of the Spanish Conquest. Marginal civilizations, particularly the less culturally important ones of North America, which were later colonized by British and French migrations, had little influence in shaping the pre-Columbian psychology, and their surviving members play negligible roles in contemporary societies. It is among the Indian population of Spanish America, direct heir of the great nuclear American civilizations, where the pre-Columbian mind must be searched for. On the other hand it is their ever increasing numbers and their colossal economic, social and medical problems, which give their historical texts lasting interest. Practically all the primary sources in this study, therefore, belong to the early literature of the ancient Spanish American colonies. The chroniclers are presented in chronological order, but only those who participated, or were intimately connected with the discovery, conquest and colonization of the New World are included. A biographical sketch of the author, his character and reaction to the "unnatural" behaviour of the Indians precedes the quoted text, where the original edition, if extant, has been selected. In the translation of the text, a literal version has been followed as closely as possible; at times this may appear clumsy or obscure, but nonetheless it is more faithful than paraphrased or polished texts, in which the truth of the original is lost or deformed. In the discussion, any usage of medical or psychiatric terms has been avoided in favour of plain language, in order to extend the use of this study to a wider public. It is apparent, as the reader progresses with exploring the texts, that some writers used, copied or glossed earlier authors, making an anthology of this type repetitive; however, it is wiser to quote all available sources, rather than to risk omissions.

Within the limitations of a general statement, and for the benefit of those without first hand experience in Americana, it should be pointed out that the chroniclers of Indian extraction display a natural tendency to extol the virtues of pre-Columbian civilizations, while Spanish writers praise the feats of the Conquistadors and the spiritual values of Christian culture brought into the conquered lands. Both Indians and Spaniards were human beings with virtues and vices, and their reports must be examined impartially.

THE SEMANTICS OF ABERRATIONS

The Spanish terms referring to sodomy found in the American chronicles are not always clear to untrained readers. Most writers of the Conquest use *sodomía* or sodomy to describe sexual intercourse between two men, where the active male introduces his penis into the anus of the consenting one; it is also used for sexual intercourse between a man and a woman in an unnatural manner, that is, the man using the female anus instead of the vagina; in a few instances the term sodomy has been used incorrectly to mean the act of bestiality where the male has sexual intercourse with an animal. *Sodomita* or sodomite comes from the Latin *sodomita* which, like the Spanish *sodomítico* (in Latin *sodomiticus*), draws its origin from Sodom, the ancient city in Palestine, where this sexual aberration was first described. Sometimes this term appears in an archaic form such as *somético* or *sodomético*. A few authors used in this context a word of Moorish extraction, *bardaje*, for the passive and consenting sodomite, which comes from the Arabic *bardaŷ* or *bárdach'* and the Persian *bárdah*, originally meaning in those languages a captive young man.

In certain countries—even today—public houses of *bardajes* can be found where sodomy is practised, as in those which existed in some areas of pre-Columbian America; the term *mancebía* was used in ancient Spanish to mean a public house of prostitution and also a dishonest entertainment. *Manceba* was very widely used at that time to describe a concubine or woman kept for illicit sexual intercourse, but it must be remembered that *mancebo*, or young man, comes from the Latin *mancipium* meaning servant or slave. The use of these terms, therefore, in the literature of Americana points very clearly to homosexuality. There is also the colloquial term of *puto* for the sodomite, meaning a male whore; the word for the female whore or *puta* comes from the Latin *pútida* or fetid; also *amarionado* or *amariconado* from *Maria* or Mary, meaning effeminate. Sodomy is also frequently referred to as the *pecado contra natura* (sin against nature), *vicio nefando* (nefarious vice), *pecado abominable* (abominable sin), and similar obliquous terms. Sometimes in the colonial literature it is referred to as the *inhonesto vicio*, which in colloquial Spanish could be understood as the dishonest vice, but it is actually derived from the Latin *inhonestus* meaning unnatural vice or vice against nature. In the Manuals for Confession in American native languages much coarser expressions are used: *usar el vaso no natural,* to use the unnatural vessel; *entrar a la mujer por detrás,* to enter into the woman from behind, and similar phrases. Certain colloquial expressions in Spanish America are completely misleading, such as for a woman *dar las nalgas* or to surrender the arse, which actually means for a woman to execute normal intercourse; this in fact could be traced to pre-Columbian aberrant practices.

In Europe there were no similar drugs to those used in America to produce hallucinations. The only counterparts were the medieval epidemics of Saint Anthony's fire caused by eating bread contaminated by ergot, and resulting in mass production of hallucinations, religious extasis, and behavioural changes which disappeared when the people ate bread made with flour without ergot. It is now known that ergot contains several derivatives of lysergic acid (LSD), responsible for the mental changes. The chroniclers described the effect of the American drugs as inebriation similar to that produced by alcoholic drunkenness.

Human sacrifices and anthropophagy were repeatedly reported, and even depicted; the similarity in taste between human flesh and pork meat was also described. Field enquiries many years ago on this subject and oral reports comparing the roasting of humans to *chicharrón* or bacon, were too horrible to be considered seriously.

THE TESTIMONY OF THE CHRONICLERS

CRISTOFORO COLOMBO (1493)

The earliest news of the American Indian appropriately came from the discoverer of the New World. Cristoforo Colombo (1451–1506) born in Cogoletto, Genoa, into a family of weavers, went in 1478 to Lisbon as an agent of the Centurione merchants, and there he married Felipa Moriz Perestrelo. Columbus was deeply interested and also very learned in navigation, maintaining that the eastern trading lands of Cipango (Japan) and Cathay (China) could be reached by sailing westwards instead of the known route eastwards; it seems that Toscanelli supported his views. After his projects of navigation were rejected by John I of Portugal and Henry VII of England, Columbus secured the support of Queen Isabella of Castile and King Ferdinand of Aragon. The expedition of three ships led by Columbus as its Admiral discovered on 12th October 1492, San Salvador (Watling Island) and other islands in the Caribbean, particularly Hispaniola (Hayti–Santo Domingo) to which most of Columbus's observations refer. Columbus returned to Barcelona to report his first voyage to Queen Isabella and King Ferdinand, and in a letter addressed to Luis de Santangel, his protector (1493), publicized his discovery. The second voyage of Columbus took 17 ships and nearly 15,000 men to the Antilles in 1493. On the third voyage in 1498 Columbus explored Trinidad and the Orinoco river. The administrative collapse of Hispaniola under Columbus and his family led Comendador Bobadilla to take him back to Spain as a prisoner. After regaining his freedom and authority Columbus in 1502 led his fourth and last voyage to America, exploring the coast of Honduras and Nicaragua, where his efforts ended in disaster. Columbus returned in 1504 to Spain, ill and embittered, and died in Valladolid. Columbus's letter dated 15th February 1493 described the American Indians in the most laudatory terms. He also wrote about the medico-religious ceremony of snuffing *cohoba* and the resulting mental confusion, which was quoted by his illegitimate son, Ferdinand Colombo, in his work on the life of his father the Admiral (1571). This is the first record of the use of hallucinogenic drugs in America.

1571 edition, folio 125, Chapter LXII

"...these *cemies* [priests] by means of a kind of ceremony and prayer which they go to make in it as we go to churches. In this house they have a finely wrought table, round like a wooden dish in which there is some powder which is placed by them on the heads of these *cemies* in performing a certain ceremony: then with a cane that has two branches which they place in their nostrils, they snuff up this dust. The words that they say none of our people understand. With this powder they lost consciousness and became like drunken men."

DIEGO ALVAREZ CHANCA (1494)

He was Columbus' physician during the second voyage to America and a very learned man in medical botany. Diego Alvarez Chanca (fl. 1494) sent a letter to the aldermen of Seville in 1494 which was found by Fernandez de Navarrete among the papers of Fray Antonio de Aspa and was first published in 1825. In describing the islands of Turupueria, Ceyre and Ayay, now identified as Guadeloupe, Maria Galante and Santa Cruz, then inhabited by the Caribs, he wrote:

1825 edition, Vol. 1, pp. 198–224

"To the boys [the Caribs] made captive they cut them off the [virile] members and use them until they become men, and then when they wish to make a feast, they kill and eat them, for they say that the flesh of boys and women is not good to eat. Of these boys three came fleeing to us, all with their [virile] members cut off."

Castration in the male produces a recession of masculine characters and a feminine distribution of the fat in the body, as is well known to every culture. As the final destiny of the young men was to serve as food of the cannibal Caribs, Alvarez Chanca's statement must imply that the captives had all the male organs removed, not just the penis, but the testicles as well. A young man thus emasculated easily develops feminine characteristics and behaviour; therefore the expression that the Caribs "used them" must be understood as meaning that the castrated captives were used in the practice of sodomy, as eunuchs and *bardajes* were among Arabs. The expression "to use" a young man is always found in that context later on in the chronicles.

Alvarez Chanca was also the first to report anthropophagy among the American Indians and the differences in the taste of human flesh according to age and sex. The approach of the Caribs to anthropophagy was quite different from that of a religious nature described in the mainland after the conquest of Mexico.

RAMÓN PANÉ (1496)

Very little is known of the life of Ramón Pané (fl. 1496) who, according to las Casas, was Catalonian by birth; he had entered the Order of St. Jerome and arrived in Hispaniola with Columbus on the second voyage of 1493. By order of the Admiral he wrote, after 1496, a *Relation ... concerning the Antiquities of the Indians*, which has survived until the present day because Fernando Colombo (1488–1539) included its entire text in *The Life of The Admiral Christopher Columbus by his Son*, first published at Venice in 1571 in an Italian version. The original text of Pané has been lost, but it was known to Martire d'Angheria, and of course to las Casas, who arrived in Hispaniola five years after him. Fr. Ramón Pané soon learned the Indian language of the Taíno and wrote a treatise on the Indian customs which has been correctly considered as the first anthropological study of America. It has not been appreciated that Pané is the first to mention the existence of syphilitic ulcers in the Indians (Chapter 6), besides describing the use of the hallucinogenic snuff *cohoba* in medicinal diagnosis and for mental stimulation among the Taíno Indians of Hayti. He also mentioned the magic elements, and the sympathetic relationship between doctor and patient which was one of the bases of success in pre-Columbian medicine.

1571 edition, folio 134, Chapter LXII

"The relation of Fray Ramón concerning the Antiquities of the Indians, which he, knowing their language, carefully compiled by order of the Admiral.

"Chapter XV. Of how the buhuitihus practise medicine, and what they teach the people, and of the deceptions they practise in their cures.

"When an Indian falls sick they bring the buhuitihu to him. This doctor must observe a diet just like his patient and must assume the suffering expression of a sick man. He must also purge himself just as the sick man does, by snuffing a powder called *cohoba* up his nose. This produces such intoxication, that they do not know what they are doing; and they say many senseless things, declaring that they are speaking with the *ceméis* [gods] and that the latter are telling him the cause of the illness ..."

AMERIGO VESPUCCI (1505)

Most historians, particularly Spanish, have always resented the fact that the New World was accidentally named after Vespucci's Christian name, as it first appeared on the Waldseemüller map of 1507; but Amerigo Vespucci (1451–1512) deserves mention for his earliest and excellent description of coca chewing. Vespucci was born in Florence, as a young man worked with the banker Lorenzo de Pier Francesco de Medici, and in 1492 he was at Seville when Columbus first sailed; despite his dedication to the supply of shipping materials, there is no doubt that he became highly knowledgeable in navigational matters. In 1499 Vespucci joined the expedition led by Alonso de Ojeda to South America and explored the River Amazon, the coast of Paria, Venezuela and the Magdalena River. After returning to Spain in 1500, Vespucci offered his services to the Portuguese Crown and in 1501 he left Lisbon to sail the coast of South America, almost reaching the Magellan Strait. In 1505 he returned to Seville where he was appointed chief pilot, and there he died. Many of Vespucci's writings published by Ramusio (1553), such as the *Mundus Novus*, are considered apocryphal, but among his letters, the one sent to Piero Soderini in 1504, published probably at Florence (1505), in which he described the voyage with Alonso de Ojeda and Juan de la Cosa from May 1499 to June 1500, seems to be genuine. There at Margarita Island he made an observation of coca chewing producing mental stimulation.

1505 edition, folio 10, verso

"The customs and manners of this tribe are of this sort. In looks and behaviour they were very repulsive and each had his cheeks bulging with a certain green herb which they chewed like cattle, so that they could scarcely speak, and each carried hanging from his neck two dried gourds, one of which was full of the very herb he kept in his mouth, the other full of a certain white flour like powdered chalk. Frequently each put a certain small powdered stick (which had been moistened and chewed in his mouth) into the gourd filled with flour. Each they drew it forth and put it both sides of his cheeks, thus mixing the flour with the herb which their mouths contained. This they did very frequently a little at a time, and marvelling at such a thing we could not guess this secret nor for what purpose they did so . . ."

The white powdered substance like chalk first described by Vespucci was in fact ground up calcinated shells. When mixed with coca leaves and saliva, the calcium salts favour the slow liberation of cocaine from its natural state in the leaf, and the absorption of the drug. This results in local anesthesia of the gastric walls with control of hunger, and at the same time systemic effects, particularly stimulation of the cerebral cortex, euphoria and disappearance of mental and muscular fatigue. All these techniques in coca chewing, and the effects of the drug were subsequently reported by many other writers.

PIETRO MARTIRE D'ANGHIERA (1516)

The first historian of the New World, Pietro Martire d'Anghiera or *Anglerius* (1457–1526) was also a physician, who, after serving under Louis XI of France and the Roman Curia, was taken to Spain in 1487 by the Count of Tendilla. He was a preceptor at the Court of Queen Isabella of Castile, afterwards Apostolic notary, and Councillor of the Indies. In this capacity he became the best informed man in Europe on news from America, because through his hands passed all the reports of navigators, explorers and Conquistadors, such as Columbus, Magellan and the rest. Anglerius published at Seville in 1511 the *Opera . . . Oceani decas*, better know as the *Decades*, which was followed in 1516 by the second and third *Decades*. All these and subsequent decades, with first-hand news of the progress of the exploration and conquest of America were reprinted, always in Latin, at Alcalá de Henares in 1530 and at Basle in 1533. They were also translated into English, Dutch, French and Italian. The English edition, being the most adequate for reference in this instance, is also interesting for a marginal commentary on sodomy made by the translator Richard Eden (1521–1576), a civil servant of the Treasury and later secretary to Sir William Cecil. Eden prepared his translation of Anglerius's Decades from the Basle edition of 1533 during the reign of Queen Mary, who in 1554 married Philip II of Spain, and this appeared in 1555 including an unaltered version of Anglerius's praise of the Spanish deeds in the New World. In 1557, however, Eden was accused of heresy and went to France, not to return until 1569, under Queen Elizabeth. His text in its Elizabethan English reads as follows:

1555 edition, pp. 89 and 90; Decade III, Book I

"Unnatural Lechery.

"Vaschus [Vasco Nuñez de Balboa] founde the house of this Kynge infected with the most abhominal and unnaturall lechery. For he founde the Kynges brother and many other younger men in womens apparell, smoth and effeminately decked, which by the report of such as dwelte abowte hym, he abused with preposterous Venus. Of these aboute the number of fortie, he [Vasco Nuñez de Balboa] commaunded to bee gyven for a pray to his dogges . . ."

"Naturaull hatred of unnatural sinne.

"When the people had harde of the sever punysshment which our men had executed uppon that fylthy Kynde of men, they resorted to them as it had byn to Hercules for refuge, by violence bryngyng with them al such as they knewe to bee infected with that pestilence, spettynge in theyr faces and cryinge owte to owre men to take revenge of them and rydde them owte of the worlde from amonge men as contagious beastes. This stinkynge abhomination hadde not yet entered amonge the people, but was exercised onely by the noble men and gentlemen."

At this point Eden, the translator, adds a marginal note in italics not to be found in Anglerius's original Latin text:

"Palatini. I wolde all men were of this opinion."

This not only reflects the personal feelings on sodomy of the English translator, but gives a clear indication that sodomy was also practised at the English Court. The following passage from Anglerius is also extremely important because it stresses the extensive belief among pre-Columbian civilizations that sodomy was sinful, displeased the gods, and was the cause of natural disaster of divine origin.

"But the people lyftinge up their hands and eyes toward heaven gave tokens that god was grevously offended with such vyle deeds. Affirmynge this to bee the cause of theyr soo many thunderinges, lyghtnynges and tempestes wherwith they are soo often troubeled: And of the overflowinge of waters which drowne theyr sets and frutes, whereof famenne and dyvers diseases insue, as they simplye and faythfully beleve, although they knowe none other god then the soonne, whom onely they honoure, thinkynge that it dooth bothe gyve and take awaye as it is pleased or offended."

All these events took place at Quarequa, in the Panamá isthmus during the explorations of 1513 by Vasco Nuñez de Balboa (1475–1517); but this account first published in 1516 by Anglerius had less influence upon the reputation of the American Indians than those to follow. Interesting likewise are Anglerius's references to drugs, and of course to anthropophagy among the Caribs.

1511 edition, folio VI, verso

"... when the *cacique* wish to consult the *zemes* [gods], concerning the result of war, about the harvest, or their health, they enter the houses sacred to them and there absorb the intoxicating herb called *Kohobba*, which is the same used by the bovites to excite their frenzy. Almost immediately they believe they see the room turn upside down, and men walking with their heads downwards.
"This Kohobba powder is so strong that those who take it lose consciousness; when the stupefying actions of the power begins to wane, the arms and hands become loose and the head droops. After remaining for some time in this attitude, the cacique raises his head, as though he were awakening from sleep, and, lifting his eyes to the heavens, begins to stammer some incoherent words. His chief attendants gather round him (for none of the common people are admitted to these mysteries) raising their voices in thanksgiving that he has so quickly left the *zemes* and returned to them. They ask him what he has seen, and the cacique declares that he was in conversation with the *zemes* during the whole time, and as though he were still in a prophetic delirium

he prophesies victory or defeat if a war is to be undertaken, or the
enjoyment of health, in a word, whatever first occurs to him."

1555 edition, folio 45

"These preests, are also phisitians ... for they persuade them that
the *Zemes* use to speak with theym familierlye, and tel them of
thynges to come ... for them they drynke the powder of a certeyne
herbe, by whose qualities they are dryven into a furye: At whiche tyme
(as they say) they lerne many thynges by revelation of the *Zemes* ...

"... they enter into the house dedicate to theyr *Zemes,* where
snuffinge up into theyr nosethryls the powder of the herbe cauled
Cohobba (wherwith the *Boitii* are dryven into a furye) they say that
immediatly they see the houses turne topsy turvye, and men to walke
with theyr heeles upwarde; of such force is this powder utterly to
take away all sense. As soone as this maddness ceaseth, he embraseth
his knees with his armes, holdynge downe his heade. And when he hath
remayned thus a whyle astonisshed, he lyfteth up his heade as one that
came newe owt of sleepe: And thus loking up towarde heaven, fyrst he
fumbeleth certeyne confounded woordes with hym self."

1555 edition, folio 3

"... The wylde and myschevous people called Canibales or Caribes,
whiche were accustomed to eate mannes flesshe (and called of the olde
writers, Anthropophagi) molest them excedyngly invadynge theyr
countrey, takynge them captive, kyllyng and eatyng them. As owre men
sayled to the Ilandes of these meke and humayne people, they lefte
the Ilandes of the Canibales in manner in the middest of theyr viage
towards the south."

PASCUAL DE ANDAGOYA (*c.* 1517)

Pascual de Andagoya (1498–1548) was the first to report spiritual catharsis
or confession in America. He was born in Cuartango, Alava, and arrived
in Darien, Central America, with the expedition of Pedrarias Dávila in
1514. Andagoya was one of the founders of Panama and was its mayor in
1527, but earlier, in 1522, he had sailed to the coasts of Peru and had been
inspector of the Indians in the isthmus. Despite the grants received from
the Spanish crown he almost lost his life at the hands of Sebastian of
Belalcazar in 1540. Andagoya accompanied La Gasca in the campaign
against Gonzalo Pizarro and died in Cuzco. His *Relación de los sucesos
de Pedrarias Dávila ... en el descubrimiento de la Mar del Sur y Costas
del Perú y Nicaragua* (*c.* 1539) was first published by Fernandez de
Navarrete (1829) and translated by C. R. Markham (1865). Andagoya's
contemporaries described him as an honest and humane colonist, and
his report on Indian confession, like the accounts of the licentious behaviour of some Spaniards in Peru after the conquest, is candid and

accurate. His observations on Nicaragua took place shortly after his arrival in 1514 and 1519 and are very valuable, as no further explorations of this area were made owing to the indomitable nature of its Indians.

1829 edition, p. 415

"... the Indians made a sort of confession of certain sins which appeared to them heinous, and they thought that, by confessing them to this priest, they were freed from them."

THE ANONYMOUS CONQUISTADOR (*c.* 1519)

The *Account* known under the title *Relación del Conquistador Anónimo* (fl. 1519), refers to the same early expeditions to the Mexican coast as those narrated by Díaz del Castillo, and it was written by another conquistador with Hernan Cortés. Only the Italian text was known until J. García Icazbalceta published its Spanish translation in 1858. However, despite his scholarship García Icazbalceta's Catholic prudery led to considerable alterations in the Spanish text and he entirely omitted the subjects of sodomy, the phallic cult and the sexual excesses of the Mexican Indians. The original Italian text reads as follows:

1858 edition, p. 387

"... in other provinces, and in particular in that of Panuco they adored the [virile] member that men carry between their legs, and they have it in the temples, and similarly placed in the squares, together with images in relief of all manners of pleasure which can be executed between man and woman, and have them depicted with the legs up in different ways. In this province of Panuco the men are great sodomites and very lazy and drunkards, so much so, that when they cannot drink any more by the mouth, they lay down and raising up their legs they ask to have it poured inside with a cane through this end until they cannot stand up ..."

Recent archaeological exploration have confirmed that at least in Uxmal, one of the main Maya centres, there was a large phallus in the square and also reliefs with sexual motifs in some of the surrounding buildings. However, this first report of extensive drunkenness among Mexican Indians before the Conquest is somehow in conflict with certain Mexican codices and chronicles indicating that inebriation was severely punished among them.

HERNAN CORTÉS (1522)

The earliest printed reference to sodomy among the Mexican Indians appeared in the *Letters* by Cortés, the conqueror of Mexico. Hernan Cortés (1485–1547), born in Medellín, was one of the few Conquistadors who received an early education. He studied Latin for two years at Salamanca before reaching Santo Domingo in 1504, and afterwards he worked as a clerk in Cuba. In 1519 Cortés led the expedition to the conquest of New Spain, which he accomplished as one of the great feats of history. Whatever his faults Cortés was the founder of the new colonial society, established Western religious, agricultural and economic values in America, and the best example of Spanish administration. It is proper to record that the hospital created by him at Mexico City in 1521 is still flourishing. Sodomy was mentioned by Cortés in the first account written from Veracruz the 10th July 1519.

Cartas 1960 edition, Primera Relación, p. 18

"Because furthermore on what we have given account to your majesties of the children, men and women they [the Indians] kill and offer in their sacrifices, we have learnt and been informed for sure that they are all sodomites and use that abominable sin [sodomy] . . ."

Actually this account, though inspired by Cortés, was written by the town council elected at Veracruz. To this must be added the testimony of Díaz del Castillo (1632) that Cortés and his preacher Padre Olmedo continually addressed the Indians against the practice of sodomy wherever they went in Mexico, and stopped human sacrifices and anthropophagy.

TOMÁS ORTIZ (1525)

A testimony of considerable weight in the issue of rationality of the American Indian which has been overshadowed by subsequent controversies was that prepared by Fr. Tomás Ortiz (*c.* 1470–1538). He was like Las Casas, a friar of the Dominican Order, and also Protector of the Indians. After several years as missionary and first bishop of Santa Marta in Tierra Firme he was asked in 1525 by the bishop of Osma, Fr. García de Loaysa, President of the Council of the Indies, to give a report on the Caribs of the northern coast of South America. Very few documents can be found where the American Indians were depicted in more vile terms. Bishop Ortiz's report so impressed the Council of the Indies, that the Spanish Emperor Charles V resolved that the Carib Indians be declared slaves, not just on account of their idolatry, but also because of the unnatural vices of anthropophagy and sodomy besides their clearly irrational behaviour. Bishop Ortiz declined to return to Santa Marta because several of his friars had been eaten by the Caribs, but continued his missionary work in New Spain, where he died. His report appeared transcribed by Herrera (1601) and was also quoted by Simón (1627). The three basic aberrant elements of behaviour were described by Ortiz: anthropophagy, unnatural sexual practices, and use of inebriating drugs. Their attitude to death is also mentioned.

1601 edition, Herrera's Vol. III, p. 312; Decade III, Book VIII, Chapter X

P. 312, Chapter X. "The Caribs are declared slaves . . . 1525 . . .
[Fray Tomás Ortiz] said the following concerning the men of Tierra
Firme who were Caribs: they ate human flesh, were sodomites more
than any other race, and that no policy existed among them; they went
naked and had no shame; they were like donkeys, dumb, crazy and
without sense and they did not care about killing themselves or killing
others; they did not keep their work unless it was for their own advantage; they were unreliable; they did not know what was good advice;
most ungrateful and always wanting new things; they bragged of being
drunkards and had wines made from diverse fruits, roots and grains.
They got drunk with smokes and with certain herbs which took them
away from their senses. They were beastly in their vices. The youth
did not show to the old, nor children to parents any obedience or
courtesy. They were not fitted for education or punishment. They were
traitors, cruel and vindictive, very enemies of religion and never forgave. They were lazy, thieves, liars, of low and mean judgement; they
did not keep faith or order; the husbands were not loyal to their wives
nor the wives to their husbands. They were wizards, soothsayers and
necromancers. They were cowards like hares, dirty little pigs, ate lice,
spiders and raw worms wherever they found them. They did not have
the making or skills of men, and when they forgot the things pertaining
to our Faith they were learning they said that those were things for
Castile, not for them, and that they did not want to change their
customs or gods. They did not have beards and pulled out any hair
that grew. With the sick they did not use any pity, and even if they
were neighbours or relatives they deserted them at the time of death, or
took them to the hills to die, with just some bread and water. As they grew
up they became worse: up to ten or twelve years of age, they seemed
to come up with some manners and virtue, but from then on they
became like beastly animals. To end, he said that God never made
people more inclined to vices and bestialities, without any sample to
kindness or policy, and what could be expected from them, men with
such evil aims and manners; and that he dealt with them and had
known them through experience."

GONZALO FERNANDEZ DE OVIEDO (1526)

The statements of Fernandez de Oviedo, published in Spanish in the
first official history of America—which in fact started a hot controversy
on the alleged sodomy of the Indians—brought the aberrant nature of the
American Indians into the open. Gonzalo Fernandez de Oviedo y Valdés
(1478–1557) was born in Madrid, and as a page at the Court with the
Duke of Villahermosa received a fine education. His years in Italy during
the Spanish campaigns against Francis I of France, and as a civil servant
in Valencia and Aragón, were excellent training ground for his appoint-

ment as Supervisor of gold smelting with the expedition of Pedrarias Davila to South America in 1514. The chronicles of America by Fernandez de Oviedo show a man of balanced judgement, and a keen observation of the Caribbean islands and the northern part of South America where he lived. There is considerable confusion about his works, and the *Natural Historia de las Indias* (1526), or *Suma*, must not be confused with the *Historia General de las Indias* (1535), which is a totally different work. The *General History of the Indies*, first published in 1535, was reprinted in 1547, but unfortunately these two early editions only contain the *First Part*, with the 1st to the 19th book of the *General History*: the *Second Part*, or Book XX, appeared as a separate volume (1557). The whole work, which is made up of 50 books, was first published from the original manuscript by J. Amador de los Rios (1851). Detailed descriptions of the inclination of the American Indian towards suicide, homicide, eating of human flesh, homosexual practices, unnatural intercourse between sexes, incest and use of drugs were all present in the *Suma* (1526) and enlarged in the *General History* (1535). As Fernandez de Oviedo's works were the earliest in vernacular, the aberrant nature of the American Indians rapidly gained acceptance throughout Europe.

1526 edition, folio 7, Chapter V

"... Notice this manner of the Indians killing themselves of their own accord.

"... But the [Yuca] with juice that kills grows in the islands where there happened to be a chief or headman of the Indians and many others with him who of their own will killed themselves many together; the headman first by advice of the devil told to those who wanted to kill themselves with him the reasons he thought convenient to attract them to that diabolic end, then they drank from the water or juice of the yuca and suddenly all died without remedy .."

1526 edition, folio 15, Chapter X

"Chapter X. Of the Indians of Tierra Firme and of their customs, and rites and ceremonies.

"How the Indians kill themselves when the chief dies, of their own will; and the reason they are moved to it.

"... When some chief or principal lord dies all most close to him, servants and women of his household who have served him daily, kill themselves because they believe, and thus the Tuyra [devil] has given them to understand, that he who kills himself when his lord dies, goes to heaven and there he serves him to eat or to drink and remains there for ever exercising the same office that he had here while he lived in the house of such a lord ..."

1526 edition, folio 9 verso, Chapter IX

"Chapter IX. Of the things of Tierra Firme

"The Indians eat human flesh and are sodomites and shoot arrows poisoned with herbs ... and these [Indians] who use arrows live from the said Gulf of Uraba or Point called Caribana Westwards, and it is also a coast with cliffs and they eat human flesh, and they are abominable sodomites, and cruel and shoot their arrows poisoned with such herb, that it is by a miracle that any wounded man can escape ..."

1526 edition, folio 44 verso, Chapter LXXXI

"Chapter LXXXI. Diverse peculiarities of things.

"... In many parts of Tierra Firme the Indians are sodomites. Very common among the Indians in many parts is the nefarious sin against nature even in public the Indians who are headmen or principal who sin in this way have youths with whom they use this accursed sin, and those consenting youths as soon as they fall into this guilt wear *naguas* [skirts] like women, which are certain short cotton cloths with which the Indian women cover themselves from their waist to the knees and they wear strings of beads and bracelets and the other things used by women as adornment; and they do not exercise in the use of weapons, nor do anything proper to men, but they occupy themselves in the usual chores of the house such as to sweep and wash and other things customary for women; they are hated extremely by the women, but as these are very subjected to their husbands, they do not dare to talk about it except on rare occasions or with the Christians. They call to these passive [sodomites] *Camayoa* in that language of Cave, and thus among them when an Indian wants to offend another or to tell an insult that he is effeminate and good for nothing he calls him Camayoa."

1535 edition, folios 48–50; Book V, Chapter III

"Chapter III. Of the marriages of the Indians, and how many wives they have, and of their vices and lewdness and in what degree do not take wives or known sexually ...

"... The chief Behechio had thirty wives of his own, and not only for the use of copulation which married men usually have with their women, but for other bestial and nefarious sins; because the chief Goacanagarí had certain women with whom he copulated in the manner vipers do it. Look what unheard of abomination, which he could only have learnt from such animals ...

"... However, much worse than snakes were those who did such things, because nature does not provide vipers with another manner of engendering, and they are forced to such action, but the man who initiates that, see how just it is what God gave him, where such things are done and take place.

"Because, if this king or chief Goacanagarí carries that reputation, it is clear that he was not the only in that nefarious and filthy crime; because the common people (and even the whole kingdom) soon try to follow the prince in his virtues or the same vices they use. And due to this, their faults are greater and deserve greater punishment if they invent some sort of sin or crime; and their merit and glory deserve higher excellence and reward when those in government are virtuous, and, giving in their own persons laudable examples of virtue, invite their subjects to be better, following their lead.

"Therefore, what I have said of these people in this island [Hispaniola or Santo Domingo] and those neighbouring, is quite public, and even in Tierra Firme [Northern South America] where many of these Indians men and women were sodomites; and it is known that there are many of them over there. And look to what degree they boast of such a guilt, that, as other people used to wear some gold jewellery or precious stones around the neck so, in some parts of these Indies, they carried as a jewel a man mounted upon another in that diabolic and nefarious act of Sodom, made in gold relief. I saw one of these jewels of the devil twenty pesos gold in weight, hollow, emptied and well carved, found in the port of Santa Marta, in the coast of Tierra Firme in the year 1514, during the expedition sent by the Catholic King under Pedrarias Davila, his Captain General to Castilla del Oro. And as they brought all the pile of gold taken there, and it was collected for smelting in front of me, as Royal Supervisor of gold smelting, I broke it down with a hammer and smashed it under my own hand on a silversmith's anvil at the smelting house in the city of Darien.

"Therefore, see whether those who boast of such jewellery or wear it on their own persons, will not use of such abomination in a country where such ornaments are used or if they must be taken for something unusual among Indians; On the contrary, it is something very much used and common among them. And thus you must know that those among them who act as the consenting one or take the role of a woman in that bestial and excommunicated act, are given the office of woman, and they wear skirts as women . . .

"Turning back to the subject of this abominable sin against nature, very much practised among the Indians in this island [Santo Domingo], hateful to women, more on account of their own interest than due to their own principles, those women in this island were the most deceitful, dishonest and libidinous women seen in these islands or parts."

Fernandez de Oviedo confirmed the views put forward by *Anglerius* when reporting the conquests of Nuñez de Balboa, and he considered that sodomy was prevalent among the upper classes of the Indian population, a sinful practice in the eyes of the Indians punished by the gods, of a contagious nature easily spread among the common people, and that a peculiar type of *bardajes*, homosexuals in women's apparel, were socially accepted. Furthermore Fernandez de Oviedo described clearly the use of jewellery with sodomitic motives, and finally he stated that sodomy was a universal practice among the American Indians.

The detailed account given by Fernandez de Oviedo of the origin and progress of syphilis from the West Indies, and his veiled remark,

"... see how just is what God gave him [the American Indian] where such a thing is done [sodomy] ...",

should be interpreted in the light of prevalent ideas on the cause of diseases in that century. In this context Fernandez de Oviedo seems to believe that syphilis or *Bubas* was caused by sodomy. This is not strange because the same idea continued to appear. The attitude to death and group suicide first described by Fernandez de Oviedo is also extremely important and was subsequently reported by other historians, including Lopez de Gómara (1552) and Benzoni (1565). Fernandez de Oviedo was also the first to describe the snuffing apparatus used in Hispaniola to obtain hallucinations with the *cohoba* snuff powder; he even illustrated the bifurcate tube to insert in the nostrils in the *Suma* (1526 edition, folio xlvii, Book V Chapter II), but he failed to report the *cohoba* drug and instead described tobacco. He also described coca and its stimulant properties.

1959 edition, Vol. I, p. 179; Book VI, Chapter XX

"Of the herb called *yaat* by the Nicaragua Indians and in the Venezuela territory called *hado*, and in Peru called *coca* ...

"... Its effect, the Indians say, is that this herb calms their thirst and fatigue ... Even when does not remove entirely thirst and fatigue, they say it takes away a greater part of it, and the headache and the pain in the legs ..."

ISABEL OF PORTUGAL (1529)

During the absence from Spain of the Emperor Charles V, his wife, Isabel of Portugal (1503–1539), ruled Spain and America with great prudence. One of her most important orders was prompted by reports of extended inebriation among the Mexican Indians immediately after the conquest of Mexico. The order of 1529, published by the Museo Nacional, Mexico (1892), like another of 1545 and subsequent instructions, must be studied with great care owing to the complex problem developed during the Colonial period by the abuse of alcoholic drinks among the American natives. Contrary to Indian sources maintaining that there was no problem of inebriation in pre-Columbian times, chroniclers and Conquistadors indeed reported extensive alcoholism among the Indians.

1892 edition, p. 37

"The Queen,
    To our President and Judges of our Court and Royal Chancery of New Spain, and to you the Reverend in Christ Padre Fray Juan de Zumarraga, our bishop, I am informed that the native Indians of that

New Spain make certain wine called *Pulque,* where they say that when they have their feasts and most of the year they put a root, they sow for the purpose of putting it in the said wine, to strengthen it and give it a better taste, with which they get drunk; and being drunk they make their ceremonies and sacrifices as they use to do in the old times, and as they get furious they come to blows and get killed. And besides this, that drunkenness is followed by many vices of the flesh and nefarious practices; of which Our lord God is ill served, and to remedy this it should be convenient, not to plant that root; and if it were planted for something else, not to put it in the said wine. And we were begged to order this provision, or as it pleased my mercy. I order you on this and charge you that as soon as you see the above mentioned, you will provide as you think best, taking into account that the penalties you establish be not pecuniary, and you send us account of what you have provided about it. And until this account arrives, is seen, and it is provided as it seems most convenient, be observed what in this matter you order and command. Done in Toledo twenty-fourth day of the month of August of one thousand five hundred and twenty nine years."

HERNANDO PIZARRO (1533)

The Conquistadors were very much interested in the religious and sexual behaviour of the Indians and did not fail to observe the similarities between the nuns in Spain and the chastity by religious vows in Peru, which were reported at an early date by one of the Pizarros. Hernando Pizarro (1502–1578), born in Trujillo, Spain, went to the conquest of Peru after his brother Francisco in 1529 obtained the letters patent for this enterprise. Hernando played an important role there and took part in the capture of Atahualpa, transporting the fifth of his treasure due to the Emperor Charles V. He later defended Cuzco against the assaults of Manco Inca, and defeated Almagro in the battle of Salinas; it was he who ordered Almagro's execution. Because of this action Hernando Pizarro suffered a long imprisonment in Spain and died in Medina del Campo in 1578. In 1533 Pizarro wrote an interesting account of the conquest of Peru addressed to the Audiencia Real of Santo Domingo which was only published in 1920. This describes the nunneries of Peru, with virgins dedicated to the Sun cult and other young women selected by the Inca ruler for his own use or for the marriage of his headmen. Emphasis is given to the penalties suffered by those who broke the chastity vows of the virgins.

1920 edition, p. 175

"... In all these towns there are houses of women kept away: they have a watch kept at their doors and keep chastity. If any Indian has intercourse with any of them both die for it. These houses are in some cases for the sacrifices to the Sun. ... There is another kind of house of

women in each of the main towns, also kept away, gathered among the
headmen of the region and when the ruler of the country visits them,
they take out the best girls to him; and after they take out some, they
put back others in equal number. They are also in charge of preparing
chicha for the warriors passing by. They offer us Indian girls from these
houses... When we arrived at the plains, which are near the coast,
there is another kind of people more ignorant, not so well educated,
but with a large population. They also have houses with women and all
the rest as the villages of the highlands."

FRANCISCO DE VITORIA (1537)

The most fundamental contribution to proving the rational nature of the
American Indian was due to the prince of Spanish theologians, Francisco
de Vitoria (1492–1546). Recent data published by Urdanoz (1960) indicates
that he was born in Burgos almost ten years later than had been accepted
and that his name should be Francisco de Arcaya y Compludo, because
his father had adopted Vitoria instead of his patronymic, as many Basques
did when moving into Castile. Vitoria entered the Dominican Order in
1505, almost as a child, at the College of San Pablo in Burgos, and studied
Latin and Humanities there until 1510; then he went to the Dominican
College of Saint Jacques at the University of Paris. He completed three
years' study of Humanities and in 1513 began studies of theology under
P. Crockaert; from 1516, for six years, Vitoria taught this subject at Saint
Jacques, receiving the degree of Licentiate in Theology at Paris in 1522.
Therefore, before returning to Spain in 1523 as Professor of Theology at
San Gregorio in Valladolid, Vitoria had worked in Paris during the excit-
ing moments of the Lutheran Reformation and the new humanism. In
1526 he was elected to the Chair of Theology at the University of Salamanca, a position he occupied for twenty years with great distinction,
until his death after a long and painful rheumatic ailment. While in
Salamanca, Vitoria was a fellow of the Convent of St. Esteban where he
came in daily contact with the American missionaries of his Order. From
there, in 1510, the first three Dominicans went to Santo Domingo, one
of them the celebrated Fr. Antonio de Montesinos who started preaching
against the abuses suffered by the Indians. From there too went Fr.
Bernardino de Minaya who returned to Rome to request from the Pope
rational rights for the Indians, and studying at the convent was Fr.
Vicente de Valverde, one of Vitoria's pupils who was present with Pizarro
during the capture of Atahualpa and was killed and eaten by the Indians
in 1542. Vitoria is the acknowledged founder of International Law,
establishing its basic principles at Salamanca in 1539 when giving the
lectures *De indis prior* and *De indis posterior seu de iure belli*. There,
with crystal clear reasons based on natural law, Vitoria proved that the
Pope and the Spanish Emperor had no dominion over the American
Indians. He also examined the nature of war, the relations among nations,

and other fundamental ideas in world commerce, to which should be added his theses on migration and exile which are seldom mentioned. H. Grotius's *De iure belli ac pacis* (1625) and *Mare liberum* (1602), like Gentili's *De iure belli* (1612), Pufendorf's *De iure naturae et gentium* (1672) or Textor's *Synopsis Juris gentium* (1680), are based on, but do not alter, Vitoria's original ideas.

1960 edition, p. 641

p. 641: "Of the Indians recently discovered.

p. 642: "The present dissertation will contain three parts. The first will investigate on what rights have the barbarians come under the dominion of the Spaniards. The second what jurisdiction have the Spanish kings upon them in secular and civil matters. The third what the kings or the church can do about them in spiritual and religious matters.

p. 649: "I say that it does not belong to the lawyers to judge this subject, or at least not to them alone. Because as those barbarians are not subject, as I will shortly say, to civil law, their affairs cannot be examined by human laws, but by those divine, where the lawyers are not expert enough to define by themselves such questions . . .

p. 650 [4]: "I will ask first, to proceed in order, if those barbarians before the arrival of the Spaniards, were true owners publicly and privately . . . and it could be believed that this were not the case. Because serfs have no dominion on things . . . and Aristotle succinctly shows that some are by nature serfs, and it is better for them to serve than to command. They are those who do not have enough reason to rule even themselves, and their mind is only adequate to do what they are ordered, and their virtue is more in their body than in their mind. Indeed, if there are any like that, no better than these barbarians who seem to be not very far removed from animal brutes, completely unable to govern, it is better without doubt for them to be ruled than to rule themselves . . .

p. 651 [5]: "Against this stands the fact that they were publicly and privately in peaceful possession of their property then, absolutely (unless proved to the contrary) they must be considered as true owners and cannot be deprived of possession in such circumstances.

p. 653 [6]: "Mortal sin does not impede secular dominion and true dominion.

p. 666: "Conclusion: that the sin of infidelity nor other mortal sins impede the barbarians from being true owners and masters, both publicly and privately, and the Christians cannot occupy their property on these grounds . . .

p. 660: "But there still remains the doubt as to whether they are not owners because they are idiots or of unsound mind.
"Propositions
"First. Irrational creatures cannot have dominion . . . because dominion is right . . . irrational creatures cannot have right, it follows that they cannot have dominion.

"Second. Children prior to reaching the age of reason can be owners.

"Third. Those with unsound mind can be owners, because they can suffer injury, therefore they have the right.

"Fourth. Neither dementia impede the barbarians from being true owners.

p. 665: "I have yet to reply to contrary arguments, where it was proposed that these barbarians were serfs by nature, because they were not capable of governing even themselves; to this I answer that it is not indeed in Aristotle's mind that those with little judgement be by nature serfs and do not have dominion of themselves nor of their things. This is the civil and legitimate servitude that does not make anybody serf by nature.

p. 666: "Definitive Conclusion: That before the arrival of the Spaniards, they were true owners, publicly and privately.

p. 664: "It is proved: Because actually they are not of unsound mind, but they exercise in their own way the use of reason. This is manifested, because they have established their things according to a certain order. They have indeed, cities which require policy, and they have instituted marriages, magistrates, lords, laws, artisans, markets; all of which demands the use of reason. Beside they also have a kind of religion and do not fall in error about things evident to others, which indicates the use of reason ... So I believe that, though they appear to us so stupid and dumb this is due in great part to their bad and barbarous education, because even among us, rustics not dissimilar from animals are not uncommon.

It remains, therefore, firmly from all said, that the barbarians were, without any doubt, true owners publicly and privately ... And it would be a serious thing to deny to these, who never offended us in the least, what we do not deny to Saracens and Jews ...

p. 666: "Of the legitimate titles by which the New World barbarians could come within the jurisdiction of the Spaniards.

p. 669: "1. The (Spanish) Emperor is not the ruler of the whole world ...

p. 682: "6. The Pope has no secular power whatsoever upon the barbarous Indians ...

p. 697: "Fifth Title. The sins of those barbarians ... They say there are sins which are not against natural law, but against the divine positive law, and no war can be made against them on those grounds. There are others however which are against nature such as the eating of human flesh, sexual intercourse with the mother or the sisters or between men, and because of this, war can be waged against them to force them to desist from this. The reason of one and the other thing is that on sins against the positive law it cannot be shown clearly to them that they act wrongly; but in those against natural law they can be shown they offend God and therefore they can be forced not to offend him ever more."

1960 edition, p. 1039

"Lecture on Temperance. Fragment.

"If the Christian princes with their authority and right can wage war on the Barbarians, on account of their sacrilegious custom of eating human flesh or offering human victims in their sacrifices, as happens with those in the province of Yucatan; and in the case where they cannot make it with their authority, can they make it by order and commission from the Holy See....

p. 1040: "... nobody can force or punish another, unless he has jurisdiction over him; as no jurisdiction extends to this matter, therefore nobody has the right to do it.

"These doctors say in the second place that these infidels who commit sins against nature can be forced and obstructed such as the cases of being idolators, sodomites or impudents. The reason being that these indeed can be convinced with complete evidence that they are offending God...

p. 1041: "First Conclusion: The infidel princes can force their subjects to forsake their rites or other similar...

p. 1042: "Second Conclusion: The aforesaid is not only true in respect to sins against nature or against the natural law, but also can be referred to all sins against divine law including that revealed, because in this matter there is no difference among sins.

p. 1047: "Third Conclusion: The Christian princes have no more power over these infidels with the authority of the Pope than without it.

p. 1050: "Fourth Conclusion: The Christian princes cannot wage war on the infidels on account of sins against nature rather than on account of other sins which are not against nature, this is to say, because of the sin of sodomy rather than on account of the sin of fornication... The conclusion is proved because the faithful do not have better dominion over the infidels, than the infidels over the Christians. On the same ground it should follow that the king of the French could make war on the Italians because they commit sins against nature...

"Fifth Conclusion: The Christian princes can wage war on the barbarians because they feed on human flesh and sacrifice men...

p. 1052: "Sixth Conclusion: If war is made on the barbarians on this motive only, if this is ended it is not lawful to prolong it any longer nor to occupy on this ground their properties or their land...

p. 1052: "Seventh Conclusion: Beside this may be other reasons for making war on the barbarians: this is that they refuse to receive the preachers of the faith, when after receiving them they murder them, and other causes of a just way.

p. 1053: Eighth Conclusion: Whatever the motive on which the war against the barbarians is based, it is never lawful to exceed in it more than when it is waged against Christians...

"Ninth Conclusion: Whatever the just motive for the Christian prince to wage war against another heathen, he can induce the infidels without scandal to accept the Christian faith, and suppress their rites, whether they are against nature, or otherwise illicit in any way.

p. 1054: "Tenth Conclusion: No matter how legitimate be the sovereignty obtained by a Christian prince over the heathen, he cannot oppress them more than his Christian subjects, imposing higher taxes, or taking away their freedom or with any other similar oppressions.

p. 1054: "Eleventh Conclusion: Such princes obtaining sovereignty upon them must make laws convenient to their government . . .

p. 1055: "Twelfth Conclusion: If it is convenient to the barbarians to coin their own money, the king does wrongly by not allowing this or by forbidding it.

"Thirteenth Conclusion: It is not enough for the prince to issue good laws for the barbarians, but he is under obligation to place ministers to keep them.

Vitoria, it should be noticed, shared the prejudice of his contemporaries about sodomy being frequent among Italians during the 16th century; this is also apparent in the work of most Renaissance Spanish writers, as a sequel of ancient Roman behaviour. He also accepted the existence in pre-Columbian America of institutionalized human sacrifices, anthropophagy, incest, sodomy and other aberrations against nature, and against the natural and the divine law. But even there he refused to acknowledge any jurisdiction of the Emperor or the Pope over the American Indians or to justify the Conquest even on account of unnatural sins, or irrational behaviour. Vitoria accepted the authority of the native rulers to correct crimes against nature, and the intervention of Christian princes to save human lives and stop anthropophagy, but he also set a clear limit to their actions, denying the Spaniards the right to occupy the natives' land once those crimes had been controlled.

TORIBIO MOTOLINIA (1541)

His real name was Toribio Paredes (c. 1490–1569), which became Fr. Toribio de Benavente, from his native town, when he entered the Franciscan Order in Spain. He adopted Motolinia as a last name, meaning "humble" in Nahuatl language, after arriving in Mexico in 1524. Motolinia soon learnt the Mexican language and he even published a Christian doctrine in Nahuatl and Spanish about 1554. He travelled through the southern areas of Mexico, became rector of the Franciscan order there and keeper of the convents of Puebla, Tlaxcala, Texcoco and Mexico successively. For many years Motolinia was very much interested in the social conditions of the Indians, writing to Charles V about it, and gathering information in documents which have been published under the title of *Memoriales* (1907). *The Historia de los Indios de la Nueva España*, dated 1541, at the Franciscan convent of Tehuacan, has usually been considered as the work of Motolinia; however, it has been pointed out (Guerra, 1968) that it so closely follows the outline later followed by Sahagún in a similar work, that it seems more likely to be a draft of Sahagún's *Historia de las Cosas de la Nueva España*. Lord Kingsborough first published Motolinia's *History* anonymously (1848) as the work of a Franciscan friar, which is the only authorship given on the original MS.; both Motolinia and Sahagún were Franciscans. The *History* attributed to Motolinia is sound and unbiased, and collected at a time when the Mexican customs were still little affected by European influences. Motolinia's report or ritual anthropophagy, hallucinogenic drugs, inebriation and other subjects must be accepted as true representatives of the pre-Columbian Aztec behaviour, which was also found, as he pointed out, among the Tlaxcaltecs and other Mexican groups. In respect of anthropophagy it will only be necessary to quote Motolinia and Sahagún for the civilizations of Middle America; likewise Cieza de León will suffice for South America.

1848 edition, Vol. IX [X], p. 17

"Chapter II. . . . This land was a transfer of hell, to see the inhabitants at night shouting, some calling the devil, others drunk, others singing and dancing . . . In the frequent drinking parties they had, it is unbelievable the amount of wine they used, and what each one of them put inside their bodies. . . . Usually they started to drink after vespers, and hurry up so to drink in groups of ten or fifteen, that those serving wine never stop; with little food, early at night they begin to lose the senses, and whether falling down or singing or shouting, they called the devil. And it was a great pity to see men created at the image of God to turn into something worse than animal brutes; and what was worst, was that they did not end in that sin only, but they committed many others and wounded and hurt each other and it happened to kill themselves, even being good friends or close relations. They [the Mexicans] had another method of getting drunk which made them more cruel; this was by means of some small mushrooms that grow in these lands as they do in Castile, but those of this country are such that, eaten raw (and because they are sour, honey is taken with or after them) the consumers would shortly afterwards see a thousand visions, particularly snakes; and as they lost their senses it would seem to them that their legs and body were filled with maggots which ate them alive, and in this state, half mad, they would go out of doors begging someone to kill them, and in this condition of bestial intoxication . . . it sometimes happened that they choked, and also they became very cruel to other people; these mushrooms are called, in their language, *teunanacatlh*, which means flesh of god, or of the devil whom they worshipped; and in this way, through this bitter foodstuff, their cruel god gave them communion."

1969 edition, pp. 32–33

"Chapter 6. Of the festivity called Panquezaliztli, and of the sacrifices and homicides committed in it, and how they took out the hearts and offered them, and afterwards they ate those sacrificed ... with that cruel knife, as the chest was so tense, they opened the wretched one with great strength and took quickly the heart out ... Sometimes the old priest ate the hearts, others they buried it, and afterwards took the body and pushed it down the steps rolling; and reaching the ground, if they were war prisoners the one who captured it, took it away with his friends and relatives, cooked that human flesh with other foods, and had a feast another day to eat it ..."

1969 edition, pp. 34–37

"Chapter 7. Of the very great cruelties done the day of the god of fire and the god of water ... that day in the morning they took some slaves and war prisoners and brought them tied down hand and foot and threw them into a great fire prepared for this cruelty, and did not let them burn entirely, not for pity, but to make the torment worse ... They committed the same day another greater cruelty never heard of, and it was that they tied down six prisoners of war in those six sticks prepared the day before the festivities; around them there were over two thousand boys and men with bows and arrows and as soon as the assistants came down of tying up the captives, they shot to them arrows like rain; and with the arrows in and half dead, they ran up to untie them down, let them fall from the height ... and gave them a third death sacrificing them, taking out their hearts, dragging them away like sheep to be eaten by the chiefs and headmen ..."

1969 edition, pp. 44–47

"Chapter 10. Of the very great festivity they had in Tlaxcala of many ceremonies and sacrifices ... Afterwards began the sacrifices and killing of the war prisoners to honour that great idol; ... In that temple of that great idol called Camaxtli in the neighbourhood of Ocotecules, they killed four hundred and five, and in another about half a league, a hill further up they killed about fifty or sixty; and in the other twenty-eight parts of this province, in each village according to their resources; therefore the number of those sacrificed that day were eight hundred just in the city and province of Tlaxcala; afterwards they took away each one of the dead they brought alive to be sacrificed, leaving some portion of human flesh for the priests, and then all started to eat chili with that human flesh, they had not eaten for almost half a year."

ALVAR NUÑEZ CABEZA DE VACA (1542)

He was born in Jerez de las Frontera (*c.* 1490–1557), the son of Francisco Vera and Teresa Cabeza de Vaca, and adopted his mother's patronimic because of her noble origin. Between 1511 and 1526 Cabeza de Vaca participated in the wars of Italy and Navarra and in 1527 he joined the expedition to Florida led by Pánfilo de Narvaez as Treasurer. He survived the disaster met by this adventure, and in the company of two other Spaniards and a Negro slave reached Mexico City in 1536, after having crossed America from Florida to California. In all those years among the Indians Cabeza de Vaca and his companions were respected for their empirical practice of medicine. After returning to Spain he wrote a *Relacion ... de lo acaecido en las Indias* (1542), being shortly afterwards appointed Governor of Rio de la Plata. Cabeza de Vaca travelled to Asuncion in Paraguay from the coast of Brazil, but ruled that territory only from 1542 until 1544, when he was sent back captive to Spain, accused by Domingo de Irala of mismanaging the colony, and was condemned to exile in Africa for eight years. After being pardoned he returned to Seville as Judge of the High Court and there died in office. The *Narrative of the expeditions and shipwrecks of Cabeza de Vaca* is one of the great books of the American Conquest, giving data on Indian customs among the tribes of Texas and the North American South-West and also about the Guaraníes of South America. Cabeza de Vaca's account is plain and honest, because he was a man who, despite suffering captivity and abuse from the Indians, kept his respect for them, never returned the abuse and helped the natives in disease and need. Besides institutionalized sodomy he recorded anthropophagy. The fact that the *Commentaries of Cabeza de Vaca* (1555), the second part of his account, were written by his secretary Pedro Hernandez do not diminish their value. It must be pointed out that the generally praised translation into English (1851) by Thomas Buckingham Smith, which has been followed and edited after its first appearance, is incorrect in certain respects. For instance, the original Spanish word used by Cabeza de Vaca (1542 ed. signature f4 verso) *amarionados*, i.e. *amariconados*, meaning "effeminates", has been translated by T. B. Smith and others as "emasculate" which is not correct. Cabeza de Vaca was describing the institutionalized *bardajes* or men practising sodomy among North American tribes, a custom which has persisted until the present day.

1542 edition, signature c₇, verso

[Chapter XIV. How the four Christians departed]
   "... and five Christians who were in a ranch on the coast, came to such extremity that they ate each other, until only one was left, who being alone had no one else to eat ..."

1542 edition, signature d₇

[Chapter XVIII. Of the account given by Esquivel]
   "... Thus in obedience to their custom they take life, destroying even their male children on account of dreams. They cast away their daughters at birth, and cause them to be eaten by dogs ..."

1542 edition, signature f₄

[Chapter XXVI. Of the nations and languages]

". . . In the time I was thus among these people I witnessed a diabolic practice, that is I saw a man married to another man and these are some effeminate men, impotents who go habited like women and perform their duties, and use the bow and carry very heavy loads, and among these we saw many of them effeminate as I say, and they are more corpulent than other men and taller; they bear very heavy burdens . . ."

1555 edition, folio 62, Chapter VI

"Chapter VI. Of how the governor and his party began to walk inland. . . . These are a people of a race called Guaraníes . . . who eat human flesh, not only of their Indian enemies with whom they are at war, but of Christians as well, and even among themselves they eat each other . . ."

1555 edition, folio 67, Chapter X

"Chapter X. Of the feat the Indians have of horses. . . . In this Iguatú . . . the people who live there are of the Guaraní race; they eat human flesh . . ."

1555 edition, folio 73, Chapter XVI

"Chapter XVI. Of how they kill the enemies they capture and eat them up . . . This race of Guaraníes is a people whose language is understood by all the other races of this province and eat human flesh of other enemy tribes when they are in war one against another; and if that is the case if they are captured in war, they bring them to their villages and have a good time and pleasure with them dancing and singing; all this lasts until the captive is fat, because as soon as he is captured they force him to get fat and give him everything he wants to eat and even their own wives and daughters to enjoy them in his pleasures, and of fattening nobody else cares but the wives of the Indians, the most principal of them; who lay down with him . . ."

1555 edition, folio 135, Chapter LXXXII

"Chapter LXXXII. How the rebels gave the Indians licence to eat human flesh. The officers and Domingo de Irala to obtain the help of the Indian natives of that country, they gave them licence to kill and eat their Indian enemies . . ."

BARTOLOMÉ DE LAS CASAS (1542)

The derogatory attitude of Fernandez de Oviedo against the natives in the *Natural Historia de las Indias* (1526), and above all the accusation of extended sodomy among them published in the *General Historia de las*

Indias (1535), received virulent attacks from Bishop las Casas, who was probably instrumental in the delay of publication suffered by the second and third part of Fernandez de Oviedo's *General Historia*. Moreover, it can be accepted that the works by Fernandez de Oviedo led Bishop las Casas to write his own works in favour of the American Indians. Bartolomé de las Casas (1474–1566), known as the Apostle of the Indians, was born in Seville and studied in Salamanca, sailing to Cuba in 1502 with his father and uncle. Las Casas became a priest around 1510, though after this date he still participated in the American Conquest and received land and Indians for his services but he failed as a colonist. In 1514 he went through a profound religious crisis and devoted the rest of his life to strive in favour of the American Indians. He went to Venezuela, Santo Domingo and Nicaragua and after entering the Dominican Order he was appointed Bishop of Chiapas; he never went to Peru, although in 1543 las Casas was offered the see of Cuzco; this is why his information on the Peruvian Indians comes from secondary sources. Las Casas wrote in 1542 a *Brevisima relación de la destrucción de las Indias* presented to Charles V, in which he dismissed the charges of irrational behaviour and unnatural vices of the American Indians, particularly sodomy, and which was published in 1552, accusing in turn the Spanish colonizers of great cruelties. The reaction in Spain and abroad to las Casas' *Brief account* was such that the Bishop decided to keep two major works, the *Apologética Historia de las Indias* and the *Historia de las Indias*, unpublished until after his death. In 1547 las Casas returned permanently to Spain, and took up residence at the convent of San Gregorio in Valladolid, where he kept rewriting his *History of the Indies* until his death in Madrid at the age of 92 years. This book was not printed until 1875, and the *Apologetic History* suffered a similar fate, remaining unpublished until 1909. In both works las Casas violently attacked Fernandez de Oviedo and tried to refute the ground for irrationality attached to the American Indian. He referred to the rationality issue which was defined by Papal Bull in 1537, and glossed Cicero:

Historia de las Indias, 1951 edition, p. 396; Book II, Chapter LVIII

"All the nations of the world are men, and for each one of them there is but one definition; all have understanding and free will, all have five exterior senses and their four interior senses and they are moved by the objects of these; all take satisfaction in goodness and feel pleasure with delicious and happy things, and all reject and abhor evil and are upset by hard things and by things which hurt them, etc. All this says [Marcus] Tullius [Cicero] in book I *De legibus.* . . ."

The account of las Casas on hallucinogenic drugs, although it appeared in similar versions both by Pané and Anglerius, was probably obtained from first-hand observations, because he was a resident of San Domingo and had opportunities to see the snuffing of *cohoba* powder.

Apologética Historia, 1909 edition, Vol. I, pp. 444–446

Chapter CLXVI

"Of the religion professed by the Indians of the Hispaniola island.

p. 445: "in this island . . . it is believed that the priests they called *behicos* talk to the devil, and also the lords or kings. . . This was made in this manner: They have ready certain powders of certain herbs very dry and well ground, the colour of cinnamon or ground picietl, it was sort of brownish; they placed them upon a round plate, not flat, but somehow concave or deep, made of wood, as beautiful, polished and pretty, as if it were made of gold or silver; it was almost black and shone like jet. They had an instrument of the same wood and material and with the same polish and beauty; the form of that instrument was in size like a small flute, all hollow like a flute, two thirds of it opened into two hollow branches, in the same way as we open the two middle fingers away from the thumb, when we extend the hand. Those two branches placed in both nostrils and the end of the flute, let us say, in the powder on the plate, they sniffed by inhaling, and absorbing received into the nose the amount of powder they wanted to have, and as soon as they received them they became out of their minds, or almost as if they had drunk strong wine, and were drunk or almost drunk. These powders and these ceremonies or acts were called *cohoba* . . . and they talked . . . in confusion I do not know what things or words . . . in this way they prophesied and made divination; from there they heard or learned what good, adversity or evil were to come . . ."

The question of unnatural vices of the Indians was the issue most violently denied by las Casas, and first mentioned in his memorandum to the Emperor in 1542, which was published with his tracts at Seville in 1552. He accepted the existence of sodomy among the Maya and traced the practice to a priest, probably the Toltec-Aztec tradition of Tezcatlipoca, in the *Apologetic history*, and finally he resumed discussion of the problem of American sodomy in the *History of the Indies*.

Brevisima relación, 1552 edition, signature b₅, verso

"Account about the freedom requested by the begging Indian Reason 6.

". . . The Spaniards have defamed the Indians with the greatest crimes as human beings of this world ugly and evil, without any reason that their own personal interests to deprive them of their manhood if one could ever imagine to say that, for instance . . . they have defamed them a thousand times and accused them of being infected with sodomy; but this charge is a great falsehood and wickedness, because in all the large islands: Hispaniola, Cuba, San Juan [Porto Rico] and Jamaica, and seventy isles Lucayas, where there were villages full of people, there was never memory of such vice, as we can testify having carried out researches from the beginning. Neither was found such vice in Peru or Yucatan and the same in all these parts, with the exception of some places where it is said there are some, . . ."

Apologética Historia, 1909 edition, p. 627, Chapter CCXXXIX

". . . Concerning the abominable sin [sodomy] what must be truly said is that it was never found among those people [Maya-Cakchikel of Vera-Paz], on the contrary, it was always held [among them] as a great and nefarious sin until a demon appeared under the disguise of an Indian, named Cu, and in another language Chin, and in others Cavil and Maran, who induced them to commit it, as he himself executed it with another demon; from there it happened that some of them did not consider it sinful, saying that if that demon or god had committed it [sodomy] he had persuaded them that it was not a sin. Due to this fact some parents provided their youngsters with a boy to use him for a woman, and if someone else got at him he was ordered to pay for him in the same way as they did in respect of women, when some raped his neighbour's wife. With all this corruption, if somebody forced some boy against his will, he was punished similarly to those who raped a woman, and what is more, all the old men and women reprimanded and reproached the youngsters who consented among themselves to those evil deeds, which were a great sin, advising them to abstain from it, because, those who consented to or committed such actions would die. Finally, there were always some among them who grumbled, reproached and abominated it [sodomy]."

Historia de las Indias, 1951 edition, Vol. II, p. 517; Book III, Chapter XXIII

". . . As we said in our Apologetic History the people of these four islands, Española [Santo Domingo], Cuba, San Juan [Porto Rico] and Jamaica, and those of the Lucayos, did not eat human flesh, nor did they use the sin against nature [sodomy], or theft and other evil habits. On the first nobody has ever been in doubt until today, about the second, none of those who dealt with and knew these pople did, except [G. Fernandez de] Oviedo, who pretended to write the history of things he never saw or knew, or witnessed anyone of these, accused them of the abominable vice [sodomy] saying they were all sodomites, as easily and imprudently, as if he were saying that their colour was a bit dark or more brownish than those of Spain. What I say here is true because in many years in this island [Cuba] I saw and knew the people there and dealt with the Spaniards and with the friars and the Spaniard who came with the First Admiral [Columbus] the first time they arrived, and with my own father, who then came with him, and I never heard, or suspected of those in Spain who are our own; on the contrary, I heard sometimes the Spaniards themselves, who oppressed and killed them [the Indians] to say 'oh, how blessed were these people if they were Christians' knowing the natural kindness they had and their lack of vices; and afterwards, searching on purpose into it and asking those persons who might know or suspect something about it, if it existed, I was told that no memory or suspicion ever existed [of sodomy]. And among several people there was an old woman, Indian chief or lady, who had been married to a Spaniard, one of the first in the island [of Cuba], while I was taking her confession, I look into this and asked her whether before the arrival of the Spaniards in the island had been among the men any habit or blemish of this vice [sodomy], and she replied to me: 'No father, because if it existed among the Indians, the women would eat them in bites, and no man could remain alive'. . . .

(p. 518 ". . . In the isle of Cuba when we went, we only found one Indian who wore *naguas* [skirts] which is women's dress, covering from the waist to the knee, and from that we suspected there was something there, but we did not investigate it, and it could be that for some reason that man and others, if by chance such existed, were engaged in women's offices, and wore that dress, not for that nefarious aim [sodomy], but in the manner referred to by Hippocrates and Galen: (for these describe) certain Scythians, who develop certain illness due to horse riding, and to cure themselves bleed certain veins: as a result of this they end in being men unsuitable for women, and as soon as they learn this fault in themselves, they immediately change their dress and devote, offer and accept themselves to women's jobs, not for an evil purpose; and it could happen there or in other parts of the Indies [America] where they could be found, or due to other causes, according to their rites and customs, and not with the purpose of those depravities [sodomy]. To assert, as [Fernandez de] Oviedo does, that all of them were sodomites, those of that and this island, I believe that in writing it, he is now sorry, wherever he is now, and pray God this sorrow may bear fruit in his conscience [G. Fernandez de Oviedo died in 1557]. He falsely accused those in these islands and many others in these Indies [America] with the infamy of great sins and of being beasts, because he never opened his mouth, while dealing with the Indians except to speak evil of them and these infamies have flown almost all over the world, when days ago he rashly published his false history [*General Historia de las Indias*, 1535] which is accepted by everybody, as he did not deserve because of his many great lies told about these people; but people only consider those printed things, whatever they may be, as long as they are interesting new things that fit in with what they need to protect their own interests, and because it is an old habit to believe more easily what it is evil than good. Because if the history by [Fernandez de] Oviedo were to carry written on the title page that the author had been a conqueror, robber and killer of the Indians and had thrown many of them into the mines, where they died, and was thus their cruel enemy, as it will be told and he himself confesses, at least his history might have little credit and authority among prudent and sensible Christians."

Las Casas returned again and again to attack Fernandez de Oviedo and defend the American Indians accused of generalized sodomy:

Historia de las Indias, 1951 edition, Vol. III, p. 321: Book III, Chapter CXLII

"... And because I have already said twice that [Fernandez de] Oviedo was the main enemy of the Indians, and above in [Book III] chapter 23 I dealt about this matter it seems proper to mention some false accusations ... stating those infamous and terrible habits [of sodomy] ..."

Historia de las Indias, 1951 edition, Vol. III, p. 326; Book III, Chapter CXLIV

"... We must answer every one of the faults mentioned by [Fernandez de] Oviedo against the Indians ... as for where he says that they were sodomites, it is already truly stated in [Book III] chapter 23 that he wickedly and falsely accused them of that nefarious crime ..."

To support his statements las Casas quoted twice in the *Apologetic History* certain laws alleged to be in use among the Mexican Indians, where the penalties for those administering narcotic drugs or practising sexual aberrations were severely punished.

Apologética Historia, 1909 edition, p. 536

"... Some of these laws above mentioned are not entirely authentic, because they were taken from an unauthorised small Indian book; but those which follow are all held authentic and true; in them four main crimes are forbidden and punished: the first witchcraft, the second highway robbery and theft, the third sensual offences, and the third [fourth] war"

Apologética Historia, 1909 edition, p. 562

"[Concerning witchcraft]

"It was law that those practising witchcraft and enchantments to bring a curse upon the city, be sacrificed by having their chest opened. There was another law that a witch who put to sleep with enchantments those in a house to be sure of robbing them should be hanged. It was the law to hang those killing with potions. It was the law to hang those who in the highways in order to do evil, pretended to be messengers of kings of chieftains"

"Pertaining to lust.

"They hanged those forcing their mothers, and if the mother was willing, gave her the same punishment; and this sin was held among them horrible and abominable. They hanged those brothers who sinned with their sisters. They hanged those who sinned with their step-daughters, and also the woman if she had not been forced. They had the death penalty for those who did the same with their stepmother.

They stoned both adulterers. No woman or man was punished of adultery if her husband was the only one to accuse them, but it had to be witnessed and confessed, and if the adulterers were important people they were strangled in prison. They had the death penalty for those who killed their wives merely on suspicion or on circumstantial evidence, even if she was found with someone, because it was for the judges to punish. In some parts they punished the husband who had any intercourse with his wife after she had betrayed him. The law did not have any punishment for those who approached another man's concubine, unless she had been with the other a long time and they were considered married by their neighbours. They hanged those who committed the abominable sin, and also those who dressed like women. They hanged the physician or witch who gave potions to expel the children from the womb and did the same with pregnant women who took something for that purpose. Any priest or high priest found with a woman was sent away into exile, deprived of his property, and punished very severely. And if they were found guilty of the nefarious sin, in some places they were burnt, in others strangled or killed in some other way.

"Pertaining to thieves

"They made a slave of the thief if he had not spent the stolen goods, and if he had spent them, if it was valuable, he was killed. Those who robbed something from the market were by law publicly beaten to death outright with clubs there in the same market. They hanged those who stole a certain amount of corn cobs, or pulled out the maize, excepting the first line next to the road, because from this one travellers had licence to take some cobs for the road. It was law rigorously kept, that if somebody sold some lost child for slaves, the seller was made a slave himself and his property was divided into parts: one was for the child, and the other for the buyer, and if the child had been sold by many, everyone of them were made slaves . . ."

One of the most interesting contributions by las Casas is his reports of the confessions used by the Totonacs and the Cachikels to relieve their guilt and as a preliminary ritual in the treatment of disease.

Apologética Historia, 1909 edition, p. 464; Chapter CLXXVI

"[The Totones or Totonacas] They had a notable ceremony and work or religious act, in which they meant or manifested the faith or opinion they had of the great God and of the other gods, and this was a vocal confession; they made it in this way: Each one went to a corner of his house and they put their hands in the manner of someone who is very worried, sometimes twisting them, other intertwining their fingers one with the other, crying, and those unable to shed tears, moaning or grieving; others went to mountains, others to springs, others to rivers, others to temples, where each one by himself confessed his faults, mistakes and sins to their gods, with such sorrow and repentance that to watch them was a thing worth seeing. I was certified by the friars of Saint Dominic, true apostles of the Chiapas bishopric that the people in that area confessed to the true God of everything they considered sinful, and among other things they accused themselves of worshipping the idols, and gave to God as a reason the fear they had of the demon, and the fact that their parents had accustomed them to it. This confession was done twice a year at certain times, and during the course of those exercises, which had to be more than one, several, they never laughed or accepted any pleasure but everything was sadness, sorrow and bitterness; it was called in polite Mexican language *Maiolcuita*."

Apologética Historia, 1909 edition, p. 470; Chapter CLXXIX

"When it happened that travelling they faced a danger, they immediately made acts of repentance and sorrow for their sins; they told their sins, and called themselves sinners, hurting themselves in the chest and rubbing their faces, lamenting and calling themselves unhappy ones . . ."

Apologética Historia, 1909 edition, p. 471; Chapter CLXXIX

". . . to obtain health and peace and good crops they took great care . . . if some one fell ill the first thing they did was to make some sacrifices or send to the sorcerer some quails or other fowls of such and such a colour according to the illness, as laid down by their beliefs, to be offered by the priest. If he was a lord, he always had a physician with him; other people did not, but the wife soon took—if the husband was ill—or he if she was ill, a cloth or something valuable, and went with it to the physician and told him: Sir, your child is ill; he begs you much to visit him; and without waiting for a reply, they placed the present in front of him. The physician got free quickly and accompanied the messenger, and visited the patient, and if it was a light complaint, applied some herbs and other things he used for remedies; but if the illness was acute and dangerous, he told the patient: You have committed a sin; and he harassed and afflicted the patient repeating this, that he was forced to confess what perhaps he had done many years before, and this was held as the best medicine; to throw the sin out of the soul for the health of the body. From this it comes that now after being converted it is a marvellous thing the devotion and faith they have in the Holy Sacraments, especially that of Confession, and it is incredible to those who have not seen it how much they bother asking for it, and until they obtain the confession how great is their perseverance and diligence. Therefore once they confessed their sin, the physician cast lots to see what sacrifice was the best for the offering and the patients were so obedient that no order or sacrifice was left unfulfilled, even if they had to dispose of all their assets . . ."

Apologética Historia, 1909 edition, pp. 626–629; Chapter CCXXXIX

"Of the sins and offences forbidden and punished in the provinces of Vera Paz.

"The laws belonging to the people of the said province of the Vera Paz . . . referred according to our ten divine Commandments . . . In respect to the fourth they kept it as closely as we do, because the parents taught, and induced them with great diligence, to honour, obey and serve their parents . . . Concerning the fifth which forbids to kill, to injure or vex anybody, they kept it as we do . . . In referring to the sixth Commandment the people of this land had so much notice that when they said, sin without qualification, they meant the sin of the flesh, mainly fornication, though they use the term for other sins of different nature, but *antonomatice*, that is by excellence, by sin they understood, as we said, that of the flesh . . .

". . . Among other customs these [the Maya] had good and bad, they used two, one good, or which at least in principle had a good aspect, and the other bad, but the bad one perverted or destroyed the good one. The good one was that as soon as each one of them fell ill he soon confessed his sins telling them to the physician in charge of his cure, or to the priest or sorcerer who counted the days in their superstitions, as we said above, or the young men confessed to their parents, or the wife to the husband, or the husband to the wife, or to any of their relatives, and this was a good habit, or at least it had the beginning or appearance and shade of goodness. The bad or irrational was that as soon as the woman in that confession said that a man had sinned with her, she was accused in front of the lord, and without witnesses or any proof the man who had been her accomplice was punished even if he denied it, and this error carried so much weight that they hanged him for what the woman said in confession. This took place when our friars were in that land (it happened to me which I saw and I punished those implicated in it), although not precisely in the village where it happened; the wife of a headman, being seriously ill and close to death, confessed that she had committed sin with a certain young man, who was hanged. Indeed this was a custom unjust and irrational . . ."

Before assessing las Casas' testimony it must be kept in mind that his *Brief Account of the Destruction of the Indies* in 1552, with its prompt translation into most European languages, contributed more than any other text to depict in cruel and sombre shades the Spanish Conquest of America. In point of fact it was las Casas' book which started the so called "black legend" of Spain. Becerra's bibliography of las Casas (1949) and the basic studies by Hanke (1949) and Gimenez Fernandez (1953) show the lengthy controversy provoked by his work and writings. Las Casas set out to exalt the virtues of the Indians rather than to offer an unbiased study of them, a thing he was the first to acknowledge. Since the letter written by Fr. Toribio Motolinia to Charles V in 1555 we know that las Casas was unreliable in his accounts, that he was inclined to extreme exaggeration in Indian matters, and that he was considered a troublemaker among his religious colleagues, as well as by the Conquistadors; but his struggle for the Indians indeed changed the outlook in American history. However, las Casas as a historian was not honest, and in his desire to help the natives distorted many facts which until now have been accepted as correct. One case in point was the depopulation of the Antilles and the American continent after the Spanish arrival. He alleged this to be due to the cruelty of the Conquistadors who killed every Indian, when the true fact is that the natives died in most cases as a result of infectious diseases, smallpox in particular, imported from Europe, because they lacked the acquired immunity of the Spaniards. The extinction of North American Indians on a much larger scale took place after the arrival of British pilgrims in 1620, introducing smallpox and measles; among the Hottentots in 1713 owing to smallpox brought by the Dutch; the Eskimos in Greenland in 1733, also by smallpox from the Danes; and this has occurred every time two populations with different immunities exchange infectious diseases. Las Casas had just cause for complaint against the Conquistadors, but he did not disclose this, but for a short reference in his *Brief relation . . .* (1552) to the trend towards suicide among the natives. Serrano y Sanz (1907) has examined las Casas' psychological doctrines, although more interesting from our point of view is the analysis by Menendez Pidal (1963) showing las Casas' mental imbalance as disclosed by his life and works. The important fact, however, is that both the *Apologetic* and the *History of the Indies* proved Fernandez de Oviedo's points. Las Casas confirmed, while dealing with the Maya, the religious connotations of sodomy; the existence of youngsters provided by the parents for their teenage boys to use in sodomitic practice until they reached the time of marriage; the penalties similar to those in cases of rape if someone other than the owner used those boys for sodomy; and also the existence among the Siboneys in Cuba of institutionalized *bardajes,* men dressed like women and performing women's duties.

CODEX QUAUHTINCHAN (1545)

The *Toltec-Chichimec History,* also known as *Annals of Quauhtinchan,* now Cuauhtinchan, a village near Puebla in Mexico, was written 26 years after the Spanish Conquest; it is in the Nahautl and Chocho–Popolaca language with pictographic illustrations of Indian manufacture, on 50 leaves of European paper. L. Boturini (1746) first described this Codex, which was edited by K. Th. Preuss and E. Mengin (1937) and more recently by H. Berlin and Silvia Rendon (1947). The manuscript describes the migration of the Nonualc-Chichimecs from Tula, the ancient Toltec capital, and their struggles with the Toltec–Chichimecs. The latter after fighting the Olmec-Xicalanca settled in Cholula. They founded Quauhtinchan, and this Codex contains a calendar of 428 years mentioning events from the year

A.D. 1116; the curious thing about this *Annals of Quauhtinchan* is that most of the records are just a list of years or very brief points about rulers, wars, or natural phenomena. However, the events leading to the initial flight from Tollan or Tula by the Toltec–Chichimecs, as a result of Uémac's lewdness, are told in great detail, leaving no doubt of his debauchery. *Codex Quauhtinchan* confirms many events of this nature told by Sahagún, Alva Ixtlilxochitl, and Veytia, which are the sources to give an understanding of the sexual problem of the Toltecs before their fall.

1947 edition, p. 68

"11. Here are the nations allied to the Toltecs at the great Tollan . . .

12. In the year 1 Tecpatl [=A.D. 1116] they arrived in Tollan, coming from the hill of Colhuaca, the Toltec–Chichimec . . .

13. The Toltec–Chichimecs with their colonists were still happy for one year.

14. In the year 2 Calli [=A.D. 1117] they get annoyed, they quarrel and they go to face the one called Uémac.

15. The Toltecs had just seen the child and immediately the Toltecs have taken him, they educated and raised him with care.

16. Was it by chance the offering, the present to the god Tezcatlipoca, his arts and mood which brought destruction and decay to the Toltec–Chichimecs and Nonualca–Chichimecs, and made the Toltecs to face their colonists the Nonualca?

17. When he was a young man Uémac ordered his house to be watched by the Nonualcas.

18. And when the Nonualcas said to him: 'It is all right our prince, we will do what you wish.' Afterwards the Nonualcas kept the house of Uémac.

[p. 69] 19. And he soon asked for women and told the Nonualcas: 'You procure me a woman, I order you that she be big in the hips, four palms.'

20. The Nonulacas answered him: 'It is all right, we will go and search for her with the hips four palms broad.'

21. And then they gave him the woman of four palms, but even then he was not pleased. 'She does not have the measure yet,' he told the Nonualcas. 'Her hips are not big enough, as I want them. Her hips do not reach four palms, I want them very big.'

22. Now the Nonualcas got very annoyed and left. And afterwards they were mad because of this, the Nonualcas took and fixed obsidian knives in their sticks.

23. Full of rage the Nonualcas said: 'Who is cheating us? Who opens and works the soil for the Toltecs? Surely, we will go to war, we will take care of the one who asks things from us.'

24. Then the Nonualcas get ready eagerly their shields, their obsidian swords, and arrows. Then the colonists wage war on the Toltecs. They kill each other.

25. The Nonualcas are annoyed. They make the Toltecs suffer, the colonist of Uémac. Icxiconatl and Quetzalteneyac say: "Why has to come the ruin and the destruction of the Toltecs? Was it I who started this, was it I who asked the woman to be involved in the quarrel? We will make war only to kill Uémac who was responsible for this quarrel."

26. Then said the Nonualca Xelhuan, Ueuetzin, Quauhtzin, Citlal-macuetzin: 'Do not get angry, my noble Lord. Have I done anything? Let Uémac be dead.'

27. And when Uémac learnt the agreement of Toltecs and Nonualcas, Uémac soon fled. The Nonualcas went in his pursuit throwing arrows and shouting the cry of the coyote.

28. During the pursuit he went into the cave of Cencallco and after he went inside, they caught him from the top, they took him out and there on the summit of the cave he was shot with arrows and killed."

JUAN GINÉS DE SEPÚLVEDA (1547)

The ideas held by the greater part of the colonists concerning the American Indians were expounded in Spain by Juan Ginés de Sepúlveda (1490–1573). Born in Pozoblanco, Cordoba, he first studied Humanites in Cordoba and then Philosophy at the University of Alcalá de Henares. In 1515 Sepúlveda moved to the University of Bologna where he wrote a life of Cardinal Albornoz (1521) and several tracts on Aristotelian problems (1527); afterwards he became engaged in a revision of the New Testament (1533) under Cardinal Caietanus. Whatever his critics have written against him concerning his promotion under Charles V, or the financial backing received from the Conquistadors, the fact remains that Sepúlveda was the finest Latin writer in Spain of his time and a historian of merit, as is shown by his works on Charles V and Philip II and the *Deeds of the Spaniards in the New World*. He was the chronicler and chaplain to Charles V, but this position did not help much during the bitter controversies about America. Sepúlveda had written on war supporting the stand of the Spanish Emperor against the Turks and the Protestant princes, he knew very well the facts of the American Conquest and colonization, due to his friendship among others with Hernán Cortés; it was natural that Sepúlveda, in his beautiful literary style, made known the ethical and legal reasons supporting the rights of the Spanish conquistadors to subjugate the American continent. Sepúlveda in 1547 wrote a dialogue between himself as Democrates and a Lutheran named Leopold, entitled *Democrates alter* or a *Treatise on the rightful causes of the war against the Indians*, which because of the rabid opposition of las Casas was not allowed to be printed in Spain. Several years later his friends in Rome published a summary under the title *Apologia pro libro de justis belli causes* (1550) which was prohibited and seized in Spain, but led to the theological controversies with las Casas at Valladolid in 1550; after these Sepúlveda retired and died years later in his native town. Hanke (1959), Lipschutz (1967) and other historians focus their arguments against Sepúlveda on his mention of the Aristotelian idea—resurrected in our time in respect of race prejudice—that the Indians were born to servitude, and that this justified their conquest. However this point, previously refuted by Vitoria in 1539, was only one of the arguments used by Sepúlveda, and from the biological and psychiatric point of view other arguments presented both by Vitoria and Sepúlveda were indeed sound and have been neglected by previous writers. The degree of distortion apparent in the psychological image of the American Indian in the eyes of the Spanish theologians, concerning not just religion, but human life and sexual practices become clear in Sepúlveda's *Democrates alter*, first published in a complete bilingual text by Menendez y Pelayo (1892).

1892 edition, pp. 260–261

"Democrates alter. Dialogue on the just motives for war.

pp. 260–261. Preface: "Whether it is just or unjust for war to be waged by the Kings of Spain and our nationals to subject and still try to subject to their dominion those barbarous people who live in Western and Southern lands who in Spanish language are usually called Indians . . . Democrates and Leopold.

pp. 272–273: "D. Common and civil life is only based in the precepts of the Decalogue and in the other natural laws . . .

pp. 274–275: "D. The written divine law does not differ in any way from natural law, because rejection of evil and election of good are divinely printed in the rational soul (St. Cyprian).

pp. 276–77: "D. Philosophers call natural law that having the same value everywhere, without depending on whether it is agreeable or not.

pp. 288–289. "D. There are other reasons of just war less clear and less frequent, but nevertheless not less just or less founded in the natural and divine law; and one of them is to subject with arms, if it is not possible by other means, those who by natural condition must obey others and reject their sovereignty . . .

pp. 304–305. "D. You should know the customs and nature of both peoples; the Spaniards rule over these barbarians of the New World and neighbouring islands, because in judgement, skill, virtues and humanity the natives are so inferior to the Spaniards, like children to adults, women to men, and there exists between them such difference as that of ferocious and cruel people to the most clement people, of those prodigiously intemperant to those conservative and temperate, and I dare to say as from monkeys to men . . .

pp. 306–307. "D. And what can I say about the temperance, both in gluttony and lust, when there is no nation in Europe comparable to Spain in frugality and sobriety? . . .

pp. 308–309. "D. . . . even their own nationals in their vices and sins do not go usually against the laws of nature . . .

"... Compare now these qualities of prudence, ingenuity, temperance, humanity and religion with those possessed by these little men where you will not even find remnants of humanity, who do not possess any science, do not know writing, do not preserve any monument of their history, but certain obscure and vague reminiscences of some things recorded in some paintings and do not have written laws, but barbarous institutions and customs. If we refer to virtues, what temperance or gentleness are you going to expect from men given to all sort of intemperance and nefarious lewdness who eat human flesh?

pp. 312–313. "D. . . . And concerning the way of life of those living in New Spain and the province of Mexico who I have already said are considered the most civilized of them, and they brag of their public institutions, because they have cities built according to plans, and non-hereditary kings, elected by popular vote, and carry commerce among themselves in the way of civilized people. But see how mistaken they are and how I differ from such an opinion, seeing on the contrary in these very institutions a proof of their rudeness, barbarous and inborn servitude of these men. Because to have houses and some rational way of living and some kind of commerce, it is a thing that natural need itself demands, and only serves to prove that they are not bears or monkeys, and they do not lack entirely reason. But on the other hand they have established in such a way their republic, that nobody individually possesses anything, not even a house, or a piece of land which he can dispose of or to leave in his testament to his heirs, because everything is in the hands of their lords . . .

pp. 314–315. "D. . . . the nature and customs of these little men . . . their impious religion and of the nefarious sacrifices in reverence to the demon in place of God, to whom they offered human hearts as the best offering . . .

The second reason that justifies war against the barbarians is that their sins, impiety and intercourse are so nefarious and displeasing to God that, offended mainly by them, He destroyed by the universal deluge all mortals with exception of Noah and a few innocents.

pp. 316–317. "D. . . . they are explained in this manner by a very ancient writer named Beroso. 'They were anthropophagi, promoted abortion, they had sexual intercourse with their mothers, daughters and sisters and with men and beasts'. . . and due to the sin of nefarious intercourse fell from heaven fire and brimstone and destroyed Sodom and Gomorrah . . .

pp. 318–319. "D. . . to these barbarians contaminated by nefarious intercourse and with the impious cult of the gods, it is not only lawful to subject them to our dominion . . . but they can be punished with even more severe war . . ."

pp. 348–349: "L. . . . The reasons upon which you (Democrates) found the justice of the war waged by the Spaniards on the barbarians: the first is their being barbarous, uncivilized and unhuman men by nature serfs. . . . the second . . . to banish nefarious intercourse and the amazing crime of devouring human flesh, crimes which offend nature . . . the third to free from serious offences very many innocent mortals whom the barbarians immolated every year. The fourth to propagate the Christian religion wherever the occasion presents . . ."

CODEX MENDOZA (1548)

The Codex Mendoza was made by native scribes *tlacuilos* at the request of the Viceroy of Mexico, Antonio de Mendoza (1491–1552) in order to offer the Spanish Emperor Charles V a description of the life of Mexican Indians before their conquest. It is written on 72 leaves of European paper with illustrations in colour after the pre-Columbian pictographic technique and explanatory text in Spanish. It was sent to Spain in 1549, but the ship carrying the Codex fell into the hands of French corsairs and thus the codex passed in 1553 to the ownership of A. Thevet, the French royal cosmographer. Richard Hakluyt bought it in 1584 while he was chaplain to the English ambassador in Paris and it finally ended up at the Bodleian Library, Oxford. Some illustrations of the Mendoza Codex were used by S. Purchas (1625) and A. Kircher (1652), and they were reproduced in colour by the ill-fated Lord Kingsborough (1831). During this century the codex has been published in facsimile by F. Del Paso y Troncoso (1925) and J. Cooper Clark (1930). The first 18 plates of the Codex Mendoza depict the founding and progress of Tenochtitlan or Mexico City, showing the expanding influence of the Aztecs year by year. There follow 39 plates of taxation records of the areas subject to the Mexicans, and finally a description of the life of the Mexicans, their education, artisans, wars, laws, marriage and many interesting aspects of their customs and behaviour.

1938 edition, folio 58, verso

"The explanation of the four sections of drawings on the next page is the instruction the Mexicans gave their children, so that they should always be suitably employed in some useful occupation . . .

"In the second section, at the age of eight, in case of disobedience, parents threaten their children with *maguey* spikes so that they weep for fear . . .

In the third section, at the age of nine, when a son is disobedient, the father ties him hand and foot and thrusts *maguey* spikes into his shoulders and body; the mother pricks her daughter's wrist with a *maguey* spike . . .

"In the fourth section, at the age of ten, children who are disobedient and will not work are beaten with a stick.

folio 59 verso: "The explanation of the following page is that children of the age of eleven, who disregard verbal reproof, are compelled to inhale *axi* smoke, a cruel torment, to make them give up idleness, and to employ their time usefully instead . . .

"In the second section, at the age of twelve, if the children would not listen to their parents, the father took his son and laid him, naked and bound, on damp ground keeping him there a whole day, in order to reform him . . .

folio 61 verso: "In the third section are shown the punishments chief priests inflict on subordinates who do wrong, or are easeless in their duties [they are depicted pricking maguey spikes into the subordinates]

folio 62 verso: "The second section shows how youths are punished according to the laws of the State of Mexico [the young men are shown receiving blows, being pricked with maguey *spikes*, and having their hair cut]

folio 70 verso: "The drawings on the first section of the following page represent the punishments, as prescribed by the laws of the Mexican state, for certain offences; they were inexorably carried out.

"In the second section although intoxication was forbidden upon pain of death, as already mentioned above, to men and women alike, yet those who had reached the age of seventy years, provided they had children and grandchildren, were exempt from this prohibition. . . ."

CODEX BADIANUS (1552)

The Badianus Codex was the work of Martín de la Cruz (fl. 1552), an Indian physician, who was a student at the Franciscan Convent of Tlatelolco, outside Mexico City. This codex has been wrongly attributed to Juan Badiano, the Mexican scribe and Latin teacher at Tlaltelolco who in 1552 prepared the Latin version of the medical information given in Nahuatl by de la Cruz under the title *Libellus de medicinalibus Indorum herbis*. The original of this manuscript, with beautiful pictographic reproductions of Mexican medicinal herbs, was unearthed in the Vatican library by Clark (1929) and Thorndike (1929); a later 17th-century copy, probably by Cassiano dal Pozzo, exists at the Royal Library, Windsor. Gates (1932) published an English translation, soon afterwards superseded by the facsimile edition and study by Emmart (1940), and a Spanish version with ethnobotanical analysis (Guerra 1952). León Pinelo (1629) described four other illuminated manuscripts in the library of Philip II which are not extant. The Codex Badianus represents the ideas on therapeutics of the Aztecs and therefore contains the treatments, from head to toes, of many ailments including mental diseases, where medicinal plants are mostly used in combination with certain procedures which are reminiscent of pre-Columbian incantations. Among many interesting items it describes the treatment for the diseases caused by the exercise of political power, anxiety, and fear.

1940 edition, folio 39, verso 46, pp. 276–277

"Chapter VIII. Trees and flowers for the fatigue of those administering the government and holding public office. The bark of the quetzalylin tree, of the flowers eloxochitl, yzquixochitl, of the almond with its fruit, which is tlapalcacauatl, the flowers cacaloxochitl, huacalxochitl, mecaxochitl, hueynacaztli, and all good-smelling summer flowers, the leaves of the trees aylin, oyametl, ocotl, axocotl, hecapahtli, tlacoyzquixochitl, quauhyyauhtli, tomazquitl, auatl, tepeylin, ayauhquahuitl, and tepapaquiltquahuitl, flowering summer herbs with their stems, which you are to gather early in the morning, before the winds arise, are to be macerated in clear spring water, each by itself in a new pot or vessel, and this for one day and one night; then to them is to be added huitzquahuitl, a wood of reddish sap, to stain them, likewise the blood of wild animals, namely tlatlauhqui ocelotl, cuetlachtli, miztli, ocotochtli, yztac ocelotl, tlaco ocelotl, is to be sought, so that the body may be anointed with it together with the above mentioned juices. In the second place, precious stones, quetzalytztli, eztetl, tlahcalhuatzin, tethuitl, and white clay, and little pebbles which are encountered in the stomachs of the small birds huexocauauhtli, huactli and apopohtli, should be thrown into water, in which they should be left for one night that their healthful juice may be drawn out, with which the body should be frequently washed. Thirdly, it should be saturated with both the brain and bile of the animals tlatauhqui ocelotl, yzatac ocelotl, cuetlachtli, miztli, ocotochtli, coyotl, and then with the brain, bile and crushed bladder of the yztacepatl. Indeed, these medicaments bestow the bodily strength of a gladiator, drive weariness far away, and, finally, drive out fear and fortify the human heart. In addition a leading man or anyone else, who wishes to obtain this rebuilding of the body, should eat the meat of a white rabbit or of a white fox whelp, either roasted or boiled."

1940 edition, folio 51, verso, pp. 304–315

"Chapter X. Of the falling or comitial sickness, remedy for fear or faint-heartedness, mental stupor, for one afflicted by a whirlwind or bad wind, warts, fetid odour of the infirm, odour of armpits, phthiriasis, and phthiriasis of the head, one crossing a river or lake, a traveller. Comitial disease.

"For a recently-developed epilepsy will prevail the stones found in the intestines of the hawk, of the small birds huactli and the rooster, the root quetzalatzonyatl, a stag's horn, whitish incense, white incense, a hair of a corpse, the burned flesh of a mole shut up in a jar, which then are to be well ground in hot water. The epileptic is to drink the liquor so that he will vomit, and before this it will not be useless for him to drink the juice of the shrub called tlahtlacotic; the root is to be ground up.

"Observe the time, when the epilepsy is about to come, for at that very moment the epileptic is to be set upright and his ribs and sides are to be pricked. When coming to himself, he should drink dog's bile, and at the same time his head is to be moistened with a poultice made of leaves of quetzalatzanyatl and tetzitzilin and the herb or shrub acocohxithuitl ground in water. He is to eat the brain of a fox and a weasel, cooked. He is then to be fumigated or perfumed with the good odour of a mouse nest buried on a bed of coals, of whitish incense and of feathers of the bird cozcaquauhtli.

"Cure for one who has been affected by a whirlwind or bad air is to be treated. Let one who has been affected by a whirlwind drink the wholesome juice of the herb quauhyayaual, acxoyatl, branches of pine and laurel, ground in water. The juice is to be boiled. Let him drink the decoction; for if drunk it drives out the bad air invading the inside. Secondly, he is to drink the juice of stones ground in water, a red crystal, a white pearl, whitish earth, and leaves of the herb tlatlan-quaye, which you are to boil together with incense. Anoint him with the carefully prepared liquid of the cones of cypress and cedar, and of the leaves of the quauhyyauhtli tree, as well as the leaves of the herb xiuhecapahtli, crushed in water with incense. . . .

"Remedy for fear or faint-heartedness. A timid person should take for a drink a potion made of the herb tonatiuhyxiuh which imitates the gleam of gold, the herb tlanextiaixihuitl, tetlahuitl and whitish earth, which then are to be moistened in stream or river water, to which you add the flowers cacaloxochitl, cacauaxochitl and tzacouhxochitl. Anoint him with an ointment which you should make of the blood of a fox, a fox whelp, the blood and excrement of the worm acuecueyalotl, laurel, the excrement of a swallow triturated in water and sea-spume. But one who has been frightened by a lightning-bolt or merely by a flash of lightning is to be anointed with the sap of the tree that was struck, the crushed leaves and all the herbs that grow not far from it. Further, the water with which the ointment is to be cleared should have an acid taste.

"For mental stupor. He whose mind is in this condition should drink the juice of the tlahtlacotic root crushed in warm water so that he will vomit. A few days later both the bark and roots of the flowers yolloxochitl and cacauaxochitl are to be crushed in water; he is to drink the juice before lunch, so that the evil humour lodged in his breast may be rooted out. Thirdly, grind in water the stones of the stomach of the birds xiuhquecholtototl and tlapaltotl, tetlahuitl, the precious stones tlahcaluatzin, eztetl, and a pearl. Then divide the liquor; he is to drink part, and immediately you are to pour part over his head. When this has been done, he is to carry in his hands the stone found in the stomach of the huactli, likewise the gall bladder of the night owl, for by carrying these things and by drinking this potion he will regain his intelligence and be restored to soundness of mind. His forehead, moreover, is to be anointed with the brain of a stag and the feathers of a dove, crushed and put in water, and human hair. On his neck he shall carry the stone found in the stomach of the swallow."

FRANCISCO LÓPEZ DE GÓMARA (1552)

Francisco López de Gómara (1511–1566) studied in Alcalá de Henares and afterwards enjoyed a scholarly reputation in Rome. In 1540 he became chaplain to Hernán Cortés and shared not only his confidences, but the reports of other great explorers and conquistadors such as Andrés de Tapia, Gonzalo de Umbría, Sebastian Cabot and Pedro Ruíz de Villegas. This compensates for the fact that he never visited the New World. Much of the criticism against the *Historia general de las Indias* (1552) by López de Gómara was in fact aimed at Cortés' reputation, but it is wise to keep in mind that owing to the free style of the *History of the Indies* and the *Conquest of Mexico* his books were prohibited from circulation in the November of the very year they were printed. There is no interdependence between the accounts of Cortés and the chronicles of López de Gómara and the reports of sodomy by the latter cover areas other than Mexico. On the other hand, the disagreement in the accounts of general events in the *Conquest of Mexico*, between López de Gómara and Díaz del Castillo, do not alter the basic facts, and in matters of sodomy the one confirms the other. According to López de Gómara sodomy spread over all Indian cultures, and the *History of the Indies* shows in the dedication that the materials he had gathered for the book made sodomy and anthropophagy the main blemishes of the American Indians.

1552 edition, title page verso

"To Don Carlos.

"... the men of the Indies ... were great sinners of idolatry, sacrifices of living men, they ate human flesh, talked to the devil, sodomy, multitude of wives and others likewise."

After this introduction López de Gómara describes the customs of every American area then known using the information provided by their explorers.

1552 edition, folio 16 verso

"Customs of the Española island [Santo Domingo]

"They have intercourse very easily with women and even like ravens and vipers. Apart from that they are the greatest sodomites, lazy, ungrateful, unreliable and mean ..."

folio 24 verso: "River of Palmas.

"... the men marry other men who are impotent or castrated and go around like women, perform their duties and are used as such and who cannot carry or use the bow ..."

folio 25: "Panuco

"... they are likewise the greatest *putos* [sodomites] and they have brothels of men publicly where they resort at night thousands of them or more or less according to the village ..."

folio 26 verso: "Isle of Cuba

"... for the slightest reason they [the men] leave their wives and they [the women] for no reason leave the men. But during the delights of their weddings they [the women] dispose of their bodies as they please or because the husbands are sodomites. The woman goes naked, inviting and easily stimulating the men, and excessive use of that heinous sin [sodomy] makes them [the women] evil."

folio 28: "Yucatan

"... few are accustomed to sodomy ..."

folios 38 verso:

"Customs of those in Darien

"... They have public brothels of women and in many places even of men who dress and serve like females without feeling it infamous. On the contrary they take excuse of that to avoid going to war."

folio 40:

"Santa Marta

"... They are great sodomites and take great pride in it. In the necklaces they wear around the neck they put as a jewel the god Priapus and two men one above the other from behind carved in gold. One piece of these weighed thirty castilians. In Zamba named by the Indians Nao, and in Gavia the sodomites wear long hair and cover their pubic parts like women, but the others have tonsures like friars and this is why they are called the crowned ones ..."

folio 41:

"Venezuela.

"... There are many sodomites who only differ from being entirely women but to have teats and the inability to bear children."

folio 111:

"Customs of Nicaragua.

"... There are public whores [costing] ten cocoa beans, which are like hazel nuts, and where they have them [prostitutes] they stone the sodomites ..."

In the text of the *Conquest of Mexico* (1552) references to sodomy are also present.

1552 edition, folio 127

"Customs of the men [of Mexico]

"... they are very much inclined to lewdness both with other men as well as women without shame or concern ..."

López de Gómara in closing his work appraises the accomplishments of the Spaniards with the following sentence:

1552 edition, folio 136 verso

"How the Indians benefit from the Conquest . . .

"There is no longer sodomy, hateful sin . . ."

López de Gómara offered sound information on the depopulation of America resulting from the American Indians' contracting European diseases to which they lacked immunity, imported by the Spaniards. He also reported the spreading of suicides; information ill-used later on by Benzoni (1565). The account by López de Gómara about the *cohoba* snuff to produce hallucinations and medical diagnosis, seems to be taken from Martyr d'Anghiera (1511), and likewise his description of inebriation.

1522 edition, folio XVI

". . . When they have to make divination and answer questions they eat a herb called *Cohoba* ground or complete, or take the smoke of it through the nose. In this way they loose their senses and see a thousand visions. After the fury and the virtue of the herb ceases they recover and tell what he has seen and heard in council with gods. And he says what the god wants. However he replies to please the inquirer, or in such a way that will not be caught by his words. That is the style used by the father of lies. To cure people they also take that herb *cohoba*, which cannot be found in Europe . . ."

folio XVII:

". . . They dance many together and very much in these *Areitos* and some times the whole day and its night. They end all drunk of certain wine of that place [Hispaniola] which they get while they are in the dance . . ."

". . . the most harmful thing [for the Indians] was to come to the village with the Spaniards because they got small-pox, a disease new to them and kill infinite numbers . . ."

". . . and all of them died or killed themselves. Because of fifteen times over one hundred thousand people who used to have this island [Hispaniola] alone, there are now not even five hundred. Some died of hunger, others of travails and many of small-pox. Some killed themselves with yuca's sap, and others with poisonous herbs. Others hanged themselves from trees. The women did likewise as their husbands and hanged next to them. And they expelled their children by certain arts and potions to avoid having children who were going to serve the foreigners . . ."

folio LXVII:

". . . [The Incas] whatever the occasion they do not miss the opportunity to get well drunk when they have a feast. Many times they sacrifice their own children . . ."

MANUEL DA NÓBREGA (1552)

This Portuguese missionary (1517–1570) studied humanities at the University of Salamanca and graduated in Canon law at Coimbra in 1541. By then he was a priest and entered the company of Jesus in 1544. P. da Nóbrega went to Brazil in 1549 and at first he was engaged in missionary work at Bahia where he wrote his early letters describing the customs of the Tupinamba Indians and other Brazilian tribes, showing his interest and love for the natives. In 1553 he accompanied governor Tomé de Sousa on the visit to Cape S. Vicente and remained the Provincial of the Jesuits in Brazil until 1559. It was P. da Nóbrega who advised the Portuguese governor to launch the military campaign against the French Huguenot settlers at Rio de Janeiro under de Villegagnon. He was with P. José Anchieta S.J. pioneer in the religious colonization of Brazil by the Portuguese. P. da Nóbrega's letters were published jointly with some by other Jesuits in Brazil and Asia, translated into Italian at Venice (1558 and 1559) under the title *Diversi Avisi*, and give details of the sexual practices and anthropophagy among the Brazilian Indians.

1558 edition, folios 32–37

[letter from P. Manuel da Nóbrega to Doctor Navarro S. Salvador (Bahia) 10th August 1549]

"... [The Indians] guide themselves in everything by their inclinations and sensual appetite ... they have many wives and only for the time they are pleased with them ... They wage war one nation against another ... if it happens they capture prisoner some of their enemies in war, they keep him for some time and gave him their daughters as wives ... afterwards they slaughter him with a great feast and gather their friends ... and if he left children they also eat them ... this is the most abominable thing to be found. If they kill anyone in war they take him cut in pieces, they smoke it and afterwards they eat him with the same solemnity .."

1558 edition, folios 38–41

[letter from P. Manuel da Nóbrega to the Provincial of the Company of Jesus in Coimbra, 1549]

"... When they capture someone in the war they carry him with great feast with a rope by the neck, and give him as a wife the daughter of the headman, or anyone he wishes. And they fatten him like a pig before eating him ... dead they cut quickly his thumb because he used it to shoot arrows and the rest was cut in pieces for eating roasted or boiled ..."

1558 edition, folios 48–50

[letter from a Jesuit from Pernambuco]

"... The heathen ... eat the enemies and human flesh, and have many women as wives ..."

1558 edition, folios 52–55

[letter from a Jesuit from S. Salvador]

"... Of this vice of eating one another they cannot abstain. And it is so common among them, that once while I travelled talking to one or two who were being fattened, if they wanted to be rescued, they replied that they did not want to be purchased because it was convenient to their honour to go through that death . . ."

1558 edition, folios 239–242

[letter from P. Pedro Correa, who was eaten by the Indians, dated at S. Vicente 8th June 1554]

"... a feast was arranged according to the Brazilian custom of slaughtering many prisoners which he tried to avoid . . ."

1558 edition, folios 242–245

[letter from a Jesuit at S. Vicente about the death of P. Pedro Correa dated 15th March 1555]

"... The customs are already very different ... they no longer kill or eat their enemies or drink as before ... The Indians had imprisoned a Christian to eat him . . ."

1556 edition, folios 246–248

[letter from P. Ambrosio Perez at Bahía de S. Salvador dated 15th June 1555]

"... It is so difficult to take them [the Indians] from their wars, of eating one another . . ."

PEDRO CIEZA DE LEÓN (1553)

The problem of Pre-Columbian sodomy was not restricted to the Antilles or Middle America, but was more deeply rooted in the Inca empire. The first to give a balanced report on this matter was the Andalusian chronicler Pedro de Cieza de León (1520–1554) who went to America when only 15 years old. He played an important role in the conquest and colonization of Tierra Firme and Peru, and after suffering some misadventures because of his loyalty to the Conquistador Robledo, he began to write at Popayan in 1541 his *Historia del Perú*, concluded at Lima in 1551. Cieza's *History of Peru* published at Seville (1553) shortly after he retired to Spain, is only the first part of his work and contains 121 chapters; the early death of the author prevented the publication of the rest which, though incomplete, has been printed in recent years. Despite this deficiency, Cieza's book is the most authoritative and coherent study of the Incas in the 16th century. The references to sodomy in the works of Cieza de León are numerous and unbiased. Furthermore he makes plain the extent of anthropophagy in Tierra Firme in a manner never before described, and relates the prevalence of incest and the Indian indifference to death.

1553 edition, folio 34, Chapter XXVII

"...As for the abominable sin I have not heard that these [in Cali] or any of those described above used it. On the contrary if some Indian under the advice of the devil commits this sin he is thought by them very low and they call him a woman. They marry the nieces and some lords to their sisters as the rest of them."

1553 edition, folios 62 verso–63, Chapter XLIX

"Of how these Indians care little to have their wives virgins; and how they used the nefarious sin of sodomy.

"... Because these [Indians of Puerto Viejo] were evil doers and vicious, despite the fact that among them there were women in abundance and some of them beautiful, most of them used (so I have been assured) publicly and openly the nefarious sin of sodomy, on which they greatly prided themselves. It is true that in years past, Captain Pacheco, and Captain Olmos, who are now in Spain, gave punishment to those who committed the above mentioned sin, warning them how our all powerful God is displeased. And they put fear into them in such a way, that now this sin is used little or not at all ..."

1553 edition. folio 64, Chapter L

"[The Indians of Manta] ... were not even as bad in the use of the nefarious sin [sodomy],"

1553 edition, folio 66, Chapter LII

"... As there is in Peru a story of some giants who landed on the coast at the point of Santa Elena in the vicinity of the city of Puerto Viejo ... as they had no women of their own and the Indian women of the neighbourhood were too small for them, or else because the vice was habitual to them and inspired by the devil, they practised the unspeakable and horrible sin of sodomy committing it openly and in public without fear of God or personal shame. The natives say that our Lord God, unwilling to conceal so wicked a sin sent them a punishment suited to the beastliness of the crime, and when all the giants were together engaged in this accursed sodomy, there came a fearful fire from heaven to the accompaniment of a great noise, in the midst of which a shining angel appeared holding a sharp, bright sword with which he slew them all at a single stroke ..."

1553 edition, folios 80–81, Chapter LXIV

"How the devil made the Indians of these regions believe that it was pleasing to the gods for them to have Indians as temple assistants so that the chieftains could have carnal knowledge of them committing the nefarious sin of sodomy.

"In the first part of this history I have described many customs and usages of these Indians, both those which I gathered for myself when I was travelling among them and those which I have heard from certain friars and persons of standing who, it is my belief, under no circumstances would deviate from the truth of what they knew and have learnt. . . .

This was, that certain tribes in the vicinity of Puerto Viejo and the island of Puna indulged in the abominable sin [sodomy]. I believe this was so, for the Inca lords were free from this, and the other native chieftains too . . . It is held to be certain that in the shrines and temples where conversation was held with [the devil] he let it be known that it was to his service for certain youths to be attached to the temples from childhood, so that at the time of sacrifices and solemn feasts, the chieftains and other men of rank could indulge in the cursed sin of sodomy. And so that all who read this may know how this diabolical ceremony still persisted among them, I shall set down an account of it which was given to me in the City of Kings [Lima] by Father Domingo de Santo Tomás which I have in my possession and runs as follows:

" 'It is true that as a general thing among the mountaineers and the Yungas the devil has introduced this vice [sodomy] under a kind of cloak of sanctity, and in each important temple or house of worship they have a man or two, or more, depending on the idol, who go dressed in women's attire from the time they are children, and speak like them, and in manner, dress, and everything else imitate women. With these, almost like a rite and ceremony, on feast [days] and holidays, they have carnal, foul intercourse, especially the chiefs and headmen. I know his because I have punished two, one of them of the Indians of the highlands, who was in a temple, which they call *huaca*, for this purpose, in the province of the Conchucos, near the city of Huánuco, the other in the province of Chinca, where the Indians are subjects of his Majesty. And when I spoke to them of the evil they were doing, and upbraided them for the repulsiveness of the sin, they answered me that it was not their fault because from childhood they have been put there by the caciques to serve them in this cursed and abominable vice, and to act as priests and guard the temples of their idols. So what I deduced from this was that the devil held such sway in this land that, not satisfied with making them fall into so great sin, he made them believe that this vice was a kind of holiness and religion, to hold more power over them.'

"Fray Domingo gave me this in his own handwriting and everyone knows how zealous he is of the truth. And I also recall that Diego de Gálvez, who is now secretary to his Majesty in the Court of Spain, told me that when he and Peralonso Carrasco, one of the old conquistadors who resides in the city of Cuzco, were coming from the province of the Colla, they saw one or two of these Indians who had been put in the temples as Fray Domingo relates."

1553 edition, folio 100 verso, Chapter LXXXIII

"Of the lake of Bombon [Purnpu] of Chinchaycocha which is presumed to be the source of the great La Plata river.

". . . They are free of the sin of sodomy; so much so that they have an old witty proverb which is to the effect that in olden times there must have been in the province of Huaylas some given to this grave sin. This was considered so foul by the neighbouring Indians that to shame and insult them they used, referring to this, a phrase that has not disappeared 'Asta Huaylas' which in our language means 'May the men of Huaylas run after you'.

1553 edition, folios 117, Chapter CI

"How these Indians observed their ceremonies and anniversary celebrations, and what their temples were once like.

". . . It is believed of them [the Incas] that they abhorred the abominable sin [sodomy], although it is said that certain of the rustics who guarded the llama-herds indulged in it secretly, and those whom they kept in the temple . . ."

1553 edition, folio 129, Chapter CXVII

"Because some people say awful things of the Indians . . . and they are so evil that they not only use the abominable sin but, furthermore, they eat one another. And because I have written in my history something about it . . . I wish to make it clear that it is not my intention that this should refer to all of them, but, that in one province they eat human flesh, and sacrifice the blood of men, in others they abhor this sin. And it is the same as regard the sin against nature [sodomy]; in some places it is considered very distasteful, and not only do they not use it, but they dislike it; such are their customs."

1880 edition, pp. 98–101; Part II, Chapter XXV

"Of how the Incas were free of the abominable sin [sodomy] and of the other vices displayed by other princes of the world.

"In this kingdom of Peru, it is notorious among all the natives that in certain villages in the vicinity of Puerto Viejo the abominable sin of sodomy was practised, and also in other lands there were no doubt evildoers, just as in the rest of the world. I must point out a great virtue of these Incas, for being such absolute rulers who had to account to nobody for what they did, and with no one to whom to render an account, though they spent their nights and days in taking their pleasure with women and in other pastimes, yet never was it said of any of them that they were guilty of the aforesaid sin, on the contrary they despised those who used it, looking down on them as vile and contemptible for glorying in such a filth. Not only did they themselves not indulge in this, but they did not even allow anyone whom they knew to practise it to enter their homes or palaces. Aside from this, it seems to me that I heard it said that if it came to their knowledge that anyone had committed this sin, he was so severely punished that he was pointed out and known to all. There is no doubt of this, but rather it is to be fully credited that this vice was to be found in none of them, neither among the Orejones nor among many other nations. And most of those who have written about the Indians, accusing them in general of this sin and stating that they were all sodomites, have exaggerated, and should retract what they have said, for with this they have condemned so many nations and peoples who are far freer of this than I can state. For, apart from Puerto Viejo, sinners of this kind were not to be found in all Peru, except as happens in every place, and that there was one, or six or eight, or ten, and these secretly practised this vice. As for those who served as priests in the temples, with whom it is known that on feast days the headman had carnal knowledge, they did not think they were doing wrong or committing a sin, but did this as a sacrifice prompted by the devil. It might even be that the Incas were unaware that such thing was done in the temples; and even though they overlooked certain things, it was so that they would not be disliked, and they may have felt that it was enough for them to order that the sun and their other gods be worshipped everywhere, without taking measures to forbid ancient religions and customs the loss of which is like death itself to those born in them."

Cieza de León emerges from his chronicles as a fair and balanced author, for he presented the Incas free from sodomy, though he left no doubt of its existence as institutionalized in ceremonial religious practices in the highlands and used also among the highlanders. On the other hand he certainly confirmed that in the coastal areas neighbouring Puerto Viejo, now Ecuador, and further north, sodomy was common practice. Cieza de León is also the best witness of the true nature of anthropophagy in South America, in every gruesome detail, the extent of incest, and the real picture of inebriation in pre-Columbian Peru.

1553 edition, folio 12 verso, Chapter XI

"Of the Cacique Nutibara, and of his territory: and of other caciques subject to the city of Antioquia.

"... He had many wives. Near to the door of his house, and the same was done at the house of his captains, there were many heads of his enemies whom he had eaten which were kept there as trophies. All the natives of this country eat human flesh."

1553 edition, folios 13 verso, Chapter XII

"Of the customs of these Indians. ..."

"... These Indians [of Antioquia] ... they eat all those that are captured, and place their heads before the doors of their houses. ... the caciques of the valley of Nore collected all the women they could find from the land of their enemies, took them home, and used them as if they had been their own. If any children were born, they were reared with much care until they reached the age of twelve or thirteen, and, being then plump and healthy, these caciques ate them with much appetite, not considering that they were their own flesh and blood. In this way they had many women solely to bring forth children, which were afterwards to be eaten; and this is the greatest of all sins that these people commit. I saw myself what occurred between one of these chiefs and the licentiate Juan de Vadillo, who is now in Spain, and if he is asked respecting what I now write, he will say that it is true. It is that, when I and my comrades entered these valleys, a chief named Nabonuco came to us peacefully, and brought with him three women. When night came on, two of them laid down on a mat, and the other across it to serve as a pillow. The Indian then made his bed on the bodies of these women, and took another pretty woman by the hand. When the licentiate Juan de Vadillo saw this proceeding, he asked the Indian chief why he had brought that other woman whom he held by the hand. The chief replied, in a gentle voice, looking him in the face, that he was going to eat her. On hearing this, Vadillo was astonished, and said: 'What! are you going to eat your own wife?' The chief, raising his voice, replied, 'Yes, truly; and I will also eat the child she bears me.' This happened in the Valley of Nore. ... Owing to these wars, when we discovered the valleys we found so many human heads at the doors of the chiefs' houses, that it seemed as if each one had been a butcher's shop. ..."

1553 edition, folio 17, Chapter XV

"Of the customs of the Indians of this land, and of the forests that must be traversed in order to reach the town of Anzerma.

"The Lords or Caciques and their captains have very large houses, and near the doors there are stout canes that grow in these parts, on the top of which are placed many heads of their enemies ... To others they give most terrible deaths, cutting off their limbs, eating them, and placing their heads on the top of canes ..."

1553 edition, folio 22, Chapter XIX

"The sacrifices offered up by these Indians, and what great butchers they are in the matter of eating human flesh ... On the top of the platform they fastened the Indians whom they took in war by the shoulders, and cut out their hearts, which they offered to their gods or to the devil, in whose honour they made these sacrifices. Presently, without any long delay, they eat those whom they had thus killed ... Up to this time there are no clergymen or friars in any of these provinces, for the

Indians are so evil disposed, and such butchers, that many of them have eaten the knights who possessed *encomiendas* amongst them ... The Indians are so fond of eating human flesh, that they have been seen to take women on the point of bringing forth, quickly open their bellies with knives of stone or cane, and take out the child; then, having made a great fire, they roast and eat it, together with the mother, and all is done with such rapidity that it is a thing to marvel at ..."

1553 edition, folio 23, Chapter XX

"Of the Province of Paucura, and of the manners and customs of the natives ... Among the houses of the chiefs they have stout canes planted in a circle so as to form a cage, from which those who are put in cannot possibly escape. The captives are taken in war and are put into this cage and very well fed, and when they are fat, they are taken out on days of festivity, killed with great cruelty and eaten. I saw several of these cages, or prisons, in the province of Arma. It is worthy to note, that when they wish to kill any of these unfortunates, with the intention of eating them, they make them kneel down and bow their heads, and then give them a blow on the back of the neck with such effect that they never speak again. I have seen what I describe, and the victim never speaks, even to ask for mercy; nay, some even laugh when they are killed, which is a marvellous thing, but it proceeds more from bestiality than from courage. The heads of those who are eaten are stuck on the points of the canes."

1553 edition, folio 24, Chapter XXI

"Of the Indians of Pozo, and how valiant they are, and how dreaded by the neighbouring tribes ... One Rodrigo Alonso, I, and two other Christians, being in the province of Paucura, went in chase of certain Indians, and on entering a village there came out the freshest and prettiest Indian girl I have ever seen in all these provinces. When we saw her we called her, but as soon as she heard us, she shrieked as if she had seen the devil, and ran towards the Indians of Pozo, thinking it better to be killed and eaten by them than to fall in our hands. And so it was that one of those Indians, who were our allies, before we could prevent him, gave her a cruel blow on her head, while another came up and beheaded her with a stone knife. The girl when they approached her, knelt down and awaited her doom, which they gave her. They then drank her blood, and ate her heart and entrails raw, carrying off the head and limbs to eat on the following night. I saw two other Indians, who killed those of Paucura, and the victims laughed pleasantly, just as if they had not been the men who were to die. In fine, all the Indians of these parts have the custom of eating human flesh ... In this place the adelantado Don Sebastian de Belalcazar and his captain and lieutenant-general Francisco Hernandez Girón captured the marshal Don Jorge Robledo, and cut off his head, besides putting others to death. And that they might not have to carry the bodies of the marshal and the others to Arma, the Indians ate them. Nevertheless they burnt a house over the remains of the bodies."

1553 edition, folio 25, Chapter XXII

"Of the province of Picara, and of the chiefs of it . . . Nor is human flesh distasteful to these Indians, any more then to those of Pozo, for when we first entered their country with the Captain Don Jorge Robledo, more than four thousand of these natives of Picara marched with us, and killed and ate as many as three hundred hostile Indians . . ."

1553 edition, folio 26, Chapter XXIII

"Of the provinces of Carrapa, and of what there is to be said concerning it . . . These people are very rich in gold, for they had very large pieces, and beautiful vases, out of which they drank their wine made of maize. Those who drink this liquor soon lose their senses, yet the Indians are so vicious that they will sometimes drink an *arroba* [about 10 litres] at one sitting, not at one draught, but by taking many pulls. Their bellies being full of this beverage, it provokes vomiting, and they throw up as much as they like. Many of them hold the cup out of which to drink in one hand, and in the other the penis to urinate. They are not great eaters, but all the Indians we met with are generally addicted to excessive drinking . . ."

1553 edition, folio 30, Chapter XXVI

"Which touches upon the provinces in this great and beautiful valley, up to the city of Cali . . . When the Spaniards abandoned the first site, the hill tribes came down in great numbers, and, falling upon the unfortunates who were sick and dying of hunger, soon killed and ate all those who survived. These are the reasons why the people of this valley are so reduced that scarcely any are left . . . In the skirts of the mountains there are many villages of Indians of different nations and customs, who are very barbarous, and who all eat human flesh, which they hold to be very delicious . . . Near the doors of their houses they keep, from motives of pride, many feet of the Indians they have killed, and many hands. They preserved the insides, that they may lose nothing, and hang them up in rows like sausages in great quantities, and the heads and the entire quarters are also kept . . . Outside the house they have many heads placed in rows, entire legs, arms, and other parts of the bodies, in such abundance as to be hardly credible. If I had not myself seen what I write, and did not know that there are now many people in Spain who have also seen it, I would not venture to state that these men are such butchers of other men for the sole purpose of eating them; but we know for certain that these Gorrones are great butchers in the matter of eating human flesh . . ."

1553 edition, folio 33, Chapter XXVIII

"Of the villages and Indians' chiefs who are within the jurisdiction of this city of Cali ... In the centre of his village there was a great and lofty round wooden house, ... there was a long board stretching from one end of the house to the other, on which many human bodies were placed in rows, being those of men who had been defeated and taken in war. They were all cut open and this is done with stone knives, after which they eat the flesh, stuff the skins with ashes, ... Not content with natural food, they turned their bellies into the tombs of their neighbours ..."

1553 edition, folio 38, Chapter XXXII

"This city of Popayan ... They are warlike, and as great butchers as those of the provinces of Arma, Pozo and Antioquia. ... The natives were the cause of the loss of thousands of lives, eating each others' bodies, and sending their souls to hell. ... All the Indians eat human flesh."

1553 edition, folio 46, Chapter XXXVIII

"In which it is stated who were the Inca kings, and how they ruled over Peru. ... in ancient times ... these early tribes were bestial, and that many ate human flesh, others taking their mothers and daughters for their wives. Besides all this, they committed other greater sins ..."

1553 edition, folio 52, Chapter XLI

"Concerning the villages beyond Quito as far as the royal palaces of Tumebamba, and of some customs of the natives ... After they have eaten their maize, with meat or fish, they pass all the rest of the day in drinking chicha, or wine made from maize, always holding the cup in their hand. They are very careful and orderly in their festive songs, the men and women holding hands, and going round to the sound of a drum. They recount former events in their songs and ditties, but they always go on drinking until they are very drunk. And as they are without judgement, some of them take the women they please and carry them to some house to use them in their lust without considering wrong; because they do not realize the virtue of morals, neither care to be honest, nor care for anything in the world."

1553 edition, folio 67, Chapter XLVIII

"How these Indians were conquered by Huayna Ccapac, and how they conversed with the devil, sacrificed to him, and buried women alive with the bodies of their chiefs ... When they [the Puerto Viejo Indians] took any of their neighbours prisoners, with whom they had war or enmity, they assembled (as they themselves declare) and, after having got drunk with their wine, and also having made the prisoner drunk, the chief priest killed him with lancets of stone or copper. They then cut off his head, and offered it, with the body, to the accursed devil, the enemy of human nature ... They mourned for their chiefs when they died, and put the bodies in tombs, together with some women alive, and all their most precious effects. . . ."

1553 edition, folio 71, Chapter LVI

"How the city of Santiago de Guayaquil was founded and settled, of some Indian villages which are subject to it, and concerning other things until its boundary is passed ... It is said by some of them that when they sowed their fields, they sacrificed human blood and the hearts of men to him whom they reverenced as god; ... When the chiefs were sick, to appease the wrath of their gods, and pray for health, they made other sacrifices of a superstitious nature, killing men (as I was told), and believing that human blood was a grateful offering ... when any of the chiefs died, ... The body was buried with live women ... "

1553 edition, folio 77 verso, Chapter LXI

"How these Yuncas were very superstitious, and how they were divided into nations and lineages ... When the lord ate, a great course of people assembled, and drank their beverage made from maize or from roots. . . . They spent many days and nights at their banquets and drinking bouts; and certainly it is marvellous the quantity of chicha that these Indians drink, indeed the glass is scarcely ever out of their hands. . . ."

1553 edition, folio 78, Chapter LXII

"How the Indians of these valleys and of other parts of the country believe that souls leave the bodies and do not die; and why they desired their wives to be buried with them ... when the chief dies, they bury with him his treasure; and his wives, youths, and persons with whom he had much friendship when alive, are also buried ... "

1553 edition, folio 79, Chapter LXIII

"How they buried their dead, and how they mourned for them, at the performance of their obsequies. . . . In these valleys the custom is very general of burying ... many women and the most confidential servants possessed by the chief when alive ... "

1553 edition, folio 111, Chapter XCV

"Of the forest of the Andes, of their great thickness, and the huge snakes which are bred in them, and of the evil customs of the Indians who live in the interior of these mountains. . . . There are certain female monkeys very large moving among the trees, with whom by temptation of the devil ... they [the Indians] have intercourse like if they were women. . . . I do not assert or deny it, because there are many men with understanding and reason, who know there is a God, heaven and hell, and leaving their wives had dirtied themselves with mules, bitches, mares and other beasts . . . Francisco de Almendras who was resident of the village of La Plata caught an Indian woman and a dog committing this sin [of bestiality] and ordered the Indian woman to be burnt . . ."

1553 edition, folio 10, Chapter VIII

"In which other customs of the Indians subject to the city of Uraba are described. . . The sons inherit their fathers' property, if they are born of the principal wife, and they marry the daughters of their sisters. Their chiefs have many wives . . ."

1553 edition, folio 18 verso, Chapter XVI

"Of the customs of the Caciques and Indians in the neighbourhood of the town of Anzerma, of the founding of that town, and who its founder was. . . These Indians . . . are even greater butchers and eaters of human flesh. . . They marry their nieces, and sometimes their sisters. . ."

AGUSTIN DE ZÁRATE (1555)

The account of Agustín de Zárate (1514–c. 1560) in matters prior to the Spanish conquest of Peru has a certain interest in strengthening the general belief about sodomy, but he never achieves the exactness of Cieza de León. Zárate was born in Valladolid, Spain, and worked for over 15 years as secretary to the Royal Council of Castile. In 1545 Charles V appointed him Inspector of the Treasury in Peru with the new Viceroy Blasco Nuñez Vela. Upon arrival, however, Zárate changed his allegiance and went over to the side of Gonzalo Pizarro, in rebellion against the king; this resulted in his subsequent imprisonment in Spain from 1546 to 1553. Zárate's *Historia del descubrimento y conquista del Perú*, published in Antwerp 1555, seems to be based upon notes by Rodrigo Lozano for the pre-Hispanic period, though later events were witnessed by Zárate himself.

1555 edition, Book 1, folio 5

folio 5. Chapter IV: "Of the people living below the Equinoctial line and other outstanding things there.
"... the people who live below the line, and in the environs of it have the looks of the Jews, they talk gutturally like the Moors, they are inclined to the nefarious sin, and due to this ill-treat their wives and do not care for them . . ."
folio 6 verso. Chapter V: "Of the springs of bitumen in the Saint Helena point and the giants that were there.
folio 7: "It is thought among the Spaniards to be true . . . that this people [the giants] were much inclined to the vice against nature, the divine

justice removed them from the earth sending an angel to this purpose as it happened in Sodom and in other places . . ."

folio 7 verso. Chapter VI: "Of the people and things beyond the Equinoctial line towards the South by the sea coast."

folio 8: "[In Puma] . . . the lord . . . all the servants of his house and keepers of his women had their noses and genitalia cut off . . ."

DAMIÁN DE LA BANDERA (1557)

The seclusion of women with chastity vows under the Incas was, according to Bandera, of three types: *Ucllas* or perpetual virgins dedicated to the cult of the sun in the temples; *Mamaconas*, those kept for the service or marriage to the Inca ruler; and *Acras* or selected ones who were eventually given by the Inca in marriage to his captains and headmen. Damián de la Bandera (*c.* 1520–*c.* 1583) was in 1557 corregidor of the Huamanga and wrote an early account to Viceroy Mendoza about the laws and customs of the Indians, mentioning the penalties for those who had relations with the virgins, and the sodomites. Bandera became very interested in ancient Peru and prepared further reports in 1582 on these matters for Viceroy Enriquez.

1920 edition, p. 68

p. 68: " . . . Should an Indian lie with a woman belonging to the Inca, or the sun, or the *huacas*, he and she die without excuse. . . ."

p. 79: " . . . The Inca punish with great severity the nefarious sin [sodomy] and also any Indian who performed any human sacrifice, or killed any other Indian to the *huacas* and furthermore those who took the neighbour's wife . . ."

CODEX CHIMALPOPOCA (1558)

The Codex Chimalpopoca received that name in 1850 after F. Galicia Chimalpopoca who prepared its translation from the Nahuatl into Spanish for Brasseur de Bourbourg. It is also known as the *Annals of Cuauhtitlan*, after Cuauhtitlan, a village north of Mexico City equidistant between it and Tula, the ancient Tollan, centre of the Toltec civilization. It is the earliest manuscript on this subject, and it seems to have been written between 1558 and 1570 by pupils of Fr. Bernardino de Sahagún. P. Feliciano Velazquez (1945) in his annotated translation indicates that the *Annals of Cuauhtitlan* are followed by the legend of the Suns, chapters previously translated by F. del Paso y Troncoso (1892–1903). There are three separate sections in the M.S.: (1) in Nahuatl, credited to Alonso Vexerano or Bejarano, a learned Indian of Cuauhtitlan and teacher at the college of Santa Cruz of Tlaltelolco, Mexico; (2) in Spanish, by Pedro Ponce; and (3) in Nahuatl believed to be written by Martin Jacobita, the Indian rector of the Tlaltelolco College. Both Indians were teachers of F.

de Alva Ixtlilxochitl who eventually owned the MS; afterwards the codex went to Sigüenza y Góngora, the library of the Jesuits, where Veytia had a chance to study it, after the description given by Boturini in 1746, and finally it came to the Museo Nacional, Mexico, and was published in 1892. The Codex Chimalpopoca recalls the existence of giants on Mexican soil in ancient times, the development and fall of the Toltec civilization, details of the fight between good and evil represented by Quetzalcoatl and Tezcatlipoca, and also gives for the first time an account of the corrupt sexual debauchery which led to the total destruction of the Toltecs. The story of Huemac, the homosexual excesses of Tezcatlipoca the high priest, afterwards accepted as the most powerful god by the Aztecs, are told in the *Annals of Cuauhtitlan* in plain language, and were confirmed in other works by Sahagún, Ixtlilxochitl, and Veytia, who, however, used a more euphemistic literary style. The story of how Tezcatlipoca, with the help of two other priests or demons, intoxicated Quetzalcoatl, his elder sister Quetzalpetlatl and his pages, is told at length. The writing is highly symbolic and obscure at times, involving the giving of his body by a youth, and ambiguous sentences about sexual intercourse, sodomy and incest committed by Quetzalcoatl in his drunkenness which led to his leaving Tollan in shame. The sodomitic experience of Huemac also induced by Tezcatlipoca is clearly described, and the *Annals of Cuauhtitlan* narrates the years of pestilence and famine following the sexual excesses that led to the fall of the Toltec civilization.

1945 edition, p. 8

[Departure of Quetzalcoatl from Tollan]
"When he [Quetzalcoatl] did not obey them in respect of human sacrifices, the demons reached an agreement. Those called Tezcatlipoca, Ihuimecatl and Toltecatl said: 'He must leave his town so we can live there'. And they added 'Let us make *Pulque*; we will give it to drink to make loose his judgement and be unable to make penitence.' Afterwards Tezcatlipoca spoke: 'I say we must go to give him his body'. . . .

"First went Tezcatlipoca, he took a double mirror made of jeime and wrapped it; and when he arrived where Quetzalcoatl was he told his pages who took care of him: 'Go and tell the priest: a youth has arrived to show and give you your body'. . . ."

p. 12: "[Quauhtli king of Tollan] . . . was substituted by Huemac, who was minister of Quetzalcoatl, to whom demon women went to ridicule and he had intercourse with them; they were the devil Yaotl [enemy] and the one called Tezcatlipoca, who had lived in Tzapotlan and came from there to ridicule Huemac when they changed themselves into women and he had intercourse with them, in that moment he ceased to be minister of Quetzalcoatl. . . . [Then follows an account of the pestilences, famine and social unrest which afflicted the Toltecs]."

p. 14. 1 Tecpatl: "In this year the Toltecs were destroyed, it happened during the time of Huemac."

p. 15. 7 Tochtli: "In this year Huemac committed suicide in Cincalco de Chapoltepec."

CRISTOBAL DE CASTRO (1558)

One of the most interesting early reports about the Peruvian Indians under Viceroy Mendoza was prepared by Fray Cristobal de Castro (fl. 1558) vicar of Saint Dominic's monastery in Chincha, and Diego de Ortega who in 1558 was the Corregidor of the Chincha Valley, then holding about 20,000 Indian inhabitants. Like Bandera, he described the laws and customs under the Incas and gave a record of the penalties suffered by those who broke the laws; it is interesting to notice that, as in the case of sodomy offences, the punishments not only applied to both offenders, but to their families as well. Then they were flung down a precipice, although after the Spanish conquest the accounts also mention the Spanish penalty of burning at the stake.

1936 edition, p. 242

"... the sins and crimes they [the Indians] committed were mainly of women who were secluded for the Inca or *agra* to have intercourse ... anyone who had intercourse with a woman *agra* died for it, himself and his family."

JUAN DE SAN PEDRO (1559)

In 1550 twelve Augustinian friars sailed from Seville to Peru; two of them tried to reach the area of Huarochiri and two others Guamachuco. The names of these missionaries were Juan de San Pedro, Juan del Canto, Antonio Lozano and Juan Ramirez. They are usually considered to be the authors of a report to Philip II *Relacion de la religión y ritos del Perú* written in 1559, first published among the *Documentos inéditos* ... (1884) and reprinted with notes (1918). Internal evidence seems to indicate that this report was prepared by Fr. Juan de San Pedro (1513–1594) shortly before he sailed back to Spain. He was born in Spain, but after entering the Augustinian order went to Peru in 1550 and spent several months at the Lima convent learning the Quechua language. Fr. Juan de San Pedro was missionary in Guamachuco and elected in 1557 Provincial of the Order, a position he also held in 1567 and from 1587 until his death. He visited Spain in 1559, but returned to Peru in 1563, went to Trujillo, and afterwards was Rector of Our Lady of Guadalupe and Chuquisaca. The report on Peruvian religion was based on first-hand observations and accounts provided by the Augustinian's *Yanacona*, Marcos a native servant, referring to rituals of the Incas and their use of confession in disease.

1918 edition, p. 43

"... It is a frightful thing that these Indians also had vocal confession and they confessed, which was found out in this way: A Padre was travelling through a *xalca* or land with plenty of snow, and saw that in the snow there was an Indian seated, and called his *yanaconas* and servants and asked them to bring that Indian, and he began to persuade him to say what he was doing in that mountain or *xalca*, as it is called in the language of Peru, covered by snow and so cold, and [the Padre] said that some idol or *guaca* existed there, in view of the way he was there to worship or *mochar*, attracting him with menaces, he [the Indian] said that he would declare why he was there, and it was due to penitence ordered by the *alco*, who is the wizard; and he asked him [the Indian] why he made that penitence, and he replied that it was after confession; then he said who was the *alco* or priest, and he [the Augustinian] asked for him, an old Indian, and from that many were discovered. And the manner of his confession was that they said their *ochas*, which in their language means their guilt, and they confessed if they had stolen anything or quarrelled, if they had not served well their lord or headman, if they had not showed respect to the Zupai or demon and to the *guaca* or idol, to fulfil that ordered by the devil..."

1918 edition, p. 44

"... and I was warned that the wizards also forced them to confess that they had attended the [Christian] doctrine of the *Padres* willingly. So, after they [the Indians] said they had said everything, all their sins and *ochas* they took a *coy* [guinea pig] killed it and looked at the entrails and if it was healthy and good they said to him: "Go child of God because your sins have been forgiven", but if the entrails were damaged, had some lesion or not, they called him son of the devil, bad and perverted, and said that he had not confessed well his sins and gave him severe penitences so that many died, and after finishing the penitence they returned and said what they thought best and that was forgotten and repeated the process with the *coy* until they found the entrails good. And this was done even more in other parts, Cuzco and Collas, than in Guamachuco, and held this as a very truly account..."

JUAN POLO DE ONDEGARDO (*c.* 1559)

Juan Polo de Ondegardo (*c.* 1515–1574) was born in Valladolid, Spain, and after studying law, he went in 1543 to Peru under commission by the Conquistador Hernando Pizarro. After the Civil Wars of Peru he prepared the *Mining Regulations* and between 1558 and 1561 has was appointed Corregidor of Cuzco. Polo took an active part against the rebellion of Hernandez Girón and also in the exploration of the area between Peru and Rio de la Plata. While in Cuzco he became very interested in Peruvian antiquities and studied their mummies and archaeological remains.

From 1559 he began to write accounts such as *Relación del linage de los Incas, Errores y supersticiones de los Indios, Instrucción contra las ceremonias y ritos que usan los Indios* and several others. The one on *Errors and superstitions of the Incas* was published in the *Confessionary for Priests of Indians* at Lima in 1585 and influenced the decision of the third Church Council at Lima. He died in La Plata. Several historians, such as Acosta (1590) and perhaps Zárate (1555), used in their works the information on Peruvian antiquities gathered by Polo de Ondegardo. He reported the use of vocal confession, provided a clear idea of the meaning of disease among the Inca, and the value of confession in their religious interpretation of disease.

1916 edition, pp. 12–15

"Chapter V. Of the Confession and Penitence they did for their sins.

"1. They held the belief that all diseases were due to sins they had committed and to remedy it they used sacrifices; and besides this they confessed vocally, and almost in all the provinces they had confessors deputed for this; higher and lower, and sins reserved for the high one; and they received penitences sometimes severe, especially if the man who committed sin was poor and had nothing to give the confessor. And this office of confession was also held by women. This practice of confessors wizards called by them (*Ychuri vel ichuri*) was and is more universal in the provinces of Collasuyo. They believe it is a very great sin to hide any sin during the confession. And the *Ychuris* or confessors find out by lots or by looking into the entrails of some animal if some sins have been concealed, and punish them by striking them in the back with a certain stone, until they say all, and perform the penitence and make the sacrifice. This confession is also used when their children, or wife, or husband, or their headman is ill, or when they are under considerable stress: And when the Inga was ill all the provinces, particularly the Collas, made confession.

"2. The confessors were bound to secrecy; but with certain limitations. The sins they mainly accused themselves of were: The first to kill one another other than in war. Item to take the neighbour's wife. Item to give herbs or witchcraft to do evil. Item to rob. And considered it a very severe sin to neglect the care of the worship of their *huacas*, and not to keep their festivities, and to speak evil of the Inga, and not to obey him. They did not accuse themselves of sins and internal actions. And according to some priests' accounts, after the Christians arrived in the land they accused themselves to their *Ychuris* or confessors also of their thoughts. The Inga did not confess his sins to any man but to the sun, so that it could tell Viracocha to forgive him.

"3. After confession the Inga had a certain wash to complete cleansing from his faults and it was in this fashion: standing in the middle of a stream he said these words. I have said my sins to the sun, you river receive them and take them to the sea where they can never be found. These washings were used by the others who confessed with a ritual very similar to that used by the Moors called by them *el guado* and by the Indians *opacuna*. And when it happened that a man lost his children they took it for a great sin, saying that the son died before the father because of the latter's sins. And to those when they had confessed and done the washings called *opacuna* (as it has been said) they had to be beaten with certain nettles by a monstrous Indian such as hunchbacks or those deformed by birth.

"4. If the wizards or soothsayers by their lots or auguries affirmed that a patient was to die, they did not hesitate to kill their own children even if they did not have another. And with this they believed they obtained their health saying they offered their child in sacrifice in place of themselves. And after the arrival of the Christians to this land this cruelty has been found in some parts."

1916 edition, pp. 26–30

"Chapter X. Of witchcraft.

". . . and as soon as someone feels ill he runs to those wizards to undo the damage they suspect has been done by some wrong of their own, and with gestures and several superstitions they prepare this [potion], and many times they kill the patients with what they give them for cure . . ."

1916 edition, pp. 37–42

"Chapter XIV. Of the sacrifices and things they sacrificed.

p. 41: ". . . and the [wizards] one and the other sometimes (with all possible dissimulation) listen to the sins of the sick man asking by exquisite means, to avoid giving away that they are *Ychuris* (the ancient confessors) and at the time they listen to them or after they have heard them (if not all of them, at least part of them, which they think are those that seem sufficient to mitigate the illness) they make their ceremonies saying fictitious words, give their penitences, and with equivocal words they give them to understand they should not forsake their ancient rites, which are good for the remedy of their illnesses . . ."

1916 edition, pp. 189–203

"Instruction against the ceremonies and rites used by the Indians according to the time of their infidelity.

"Chapter III. Of wizards and witchcrafts.

p. 195: "1. The usual thing is to resort to wizards to be cured of their illnesses calling them to their homes or by going to them . . .

"3. They also go to confess their sins with them and fulfil the penitences given no matter their severity, to worship and sacrifice to the *huacas*, to fast, to give silver or clothing, to do penance . . .

"6. In some places they suffer a dancing disease called *Taqui onco* or *Cora onco*; to cure it they call the wizards or they go to them and they do a thousand superstitions and witchcrafts where there is idolatry, and they confess with the wizards and other various ceremonies . . ."

1916 edition, pp. 197–201

'Chapter V. Of auguries and superstitions.

p. 199: "8. They also use in various parts, both in the plains and in the highlands, whether they are ill or healthy, to go and wash in rivers and springs with certain ceremonies under the belief that they wash the soul of its sins, and that the waters carry them away, and they take a grass, kind of feather-grass, which they call (*Ychu*) and spit on it and make other ceremonies telling their sins, there in front of their wizard with a thousand ceremonies and they believe that in this way they are purified and cleansed of sins or of their diseases . . ."

FRANCISCO CERVANTES DE SALAZAR (1562)

Francisco Cervantes de Salazar (*c.* 1520–1575), considered to be the father of Mexican humanism, was born in Toledo and studied Canon Law in Salamanca, being a pupil and friend of the philosopher Luis Vives. After a short period in Flanders, and as secretary to García de Loaisa at the Council of the Indies, Cervantes de Salazar became professor of Rhetoric at the University of Osuna, but in 1550 left this Chair to take up the same appointment in 1553 at the University of Mexico. In his official capacity as historian of Mexico he wrote a *Crónica de Nueva España* (*c.* 1562), which was first published and edited by F. del Paso y Troncoso in 1914. What Cervantes de Salazar said there about the Mexican Indians is the harshest report ever written, describing their violent life, continuous inebriation and sodomy.

1914 edition, p. 33; Chapter XV, Book I

"Of the manner the Indians have to settle.

". . . they could be visited [by the missionaries] and avoided the idolatric worship, sodomies, drunkenness, rapes, adulteries, and homicides which every day are committed due to their [settlements] being so far away . . ."

Chapter XVI: "Of the character and inclinations of the Indians in general. . . . they committed frequently the sin of sodomy, which among the other sins, because of its hideousness is called [the sin] against nature . . ."

HERNANDO DE SANTILLAN (1563)

Hernando de Santillan (*c.* 1520–1576) was born in Seville and arrived at Lima in 1550 as lawyer of the Court. He played important administrative roles during the Civil Wars of Peru and was commissioned to draft a system of taxation for the Indians of Peru. As a result, Santillan prepared in 1563 a *Relación del Origen, descendencia política y gobierno de los Incas* first published by Jimenez de la Espada (1879). Against the background of customary Inca law, Santillan mentioned in passing the existence of confession, but of a superstitious nature.

1879 edition, p. 33

". . . Some people say they used confession among themselves and that those were confessors to this aim: in this there are variances, because there are no news that the Incas confessed, and if this matter was in the law they also had to keep it;

". . . What I have heard from somebody which seems reasonable is that these people [Inca] had so many superstitions and omens . . . someone suspicious of some Indian man or woman, got up and said to the *curaca* [priest] and wizard: 'This Indian has *hocha*' (that means sin) . . . and took the Indian woman or man to the confessors and there they confessed themselves."

GEROLAMO BENZONI (1565)

Some Spanish historians give little credit to the work of Gerolamo Benzoni (1519–1570) and even doubt that he ever visited the New World. He was born in Milan into a humble family, but Benzoni managed to travel through France, Germany and Spain, and in 1541 left Seville to accompany the Conquistadors for the next 14 years in Central and South America. He first arrived in Cubagua, went to Margarita Island, the coast of Paria and joined the expeditions to Peru in 1550; went back to Panama, in 1554 visited Guatemala and returned finally to Seville from Cuba in 1556. Benzoni published in 1565 *La historia del Mondo Nuovo* reprinted in Venice in 1572 in the original Italian, but afterwards translated into Latin and other languages. It is clear that Benzoni used earlier Spanish authors, particularly Martire d'Anghiera, Fernandez de Oviedo, las Casas and López de Gómara, and selected the passages which were damaging to the Spaniards. Apparently Benzoni's family had been ruined during the Spanish wars in Italy, and certain prejudice against them becomes manifest in his text; nevertheless there are many useful references in his work. Despite the Papal Bull on the rationality of the Indians, Benzoni still considered the American Indians to be irrational brutes; he confirmed the extent of anthropophagy, human sacrifices, homicide in funeral rituals, habitual inebriation, incest and the spread of suicide during the Spanish conquest.

1565 edition, folios 51–52

"... the courage of the Romans was tested in the fight against warlike and most ferocious barbarous nations of the Orient, while the Spaniards have surrender and subject irrational animals, true occidental beasts ...

"There were many [Indians] who in despair went to hang themselves into the woods, not before killing their children saying that it was better for them to die than to live such a miserable life, serving so cruel thieves and ferocious tyrants. The women interrupted their pregnancies with certain herbs, and to avoid give birth to their children and afterwards they followed their husbands and hang themselves. Some of them threw themselves from high mountains into their abysses, others into the sea, others into the rivers, some let themselves die of hunger; one committed suicide with his obsidian knife, another crossed his chest and sides with wooden spears; in the end two million Indians there were in this island [Hispaniola] adding those who committed suicide to those who died of travails; and those victims of the Spaniards, at the present time can only be found about one hundred and fifty ..."

folio 774: "... [In Cartagena the Indians] eat their enemies, have devoured many Spaniards and would do the same with the rest if they could ..."

folio 76: "... Then the natives [of Santa Marta] finding themselves oppressed from everywhere by strange people, unable to support so much sorrow and offences, went to the woods to hang themselves, cursing and renouncing to the name of Christians, both men and women; those who did not have instrument to do it, because most of them went naked, help each other and hanged themselves by the hair from the branches of the trees, and afterwards let themselves fall with most sad lamentations, shrieks and cries and so then went dying."

folio 104: "The customs of these people [of Nicaragua] are almost similar to the Mexicans: they eat human flesh ..."

folio 163: "Another day I went to Peclansemeque [near Puerto Viejo] and finding the Indians of this village drinking I wanted to stay and see how they used to get drunk ..."

folio 168: "In this great province of Quito, like in others of Peru ... the temples ... had many virgins called *Mamaconas* who did the spinning and weaving just for the gods; they sacrificed men and children, but they did not eat human flesh ... When a lord dies, they prepare a large grave and place next to him much gold and silver pieces, with some of their most beloved wives and servants; clothes, maize and wine, so they can eat and drink until they reach the other world. This manner of funeral is used in many parts of the Indies ...

folio 169: "when they travel [in Peru] ... they put in the mouth a herb called *Coca*; they take it as sustenance when they have to walk a whole day without food or drink; this herb is there main merchandise ... The only amusement of these people, like the rest in these lands, is to drink, and when they are drunk each one of them takes the woman they like best and let loose their lust; they do not respect their mothers or sisters; and the rulers and people of the Court marry to their sisters . . ."

PEDRO DE CASTAÑEDA (1565)

Pedro de Castañeda (c. 1515–c. 1570) a soldier native to Najera, who was one of the earliest colonists of Culiacán, Sinaloa, left an *Account of the Expedition to Cibola in 1540* which contains very interesting data on the customs among the Indians of the south-west of North America. Castañeda in 1540 joined the expedition led by Francisco Vasquez de Coronado (1510–1554) in search of the famous golden cities of Cíbola and Quivira. Although no treasures came out of it, the Coronado expedition reached the Grand Cañon, Colorado, and many remote areas expanding considerably the geographical knowledge of the continent. Castañeda's *Relación* is known from a 1596 copy at the Archivo de Indias, Seville, translated into English by G. P. Winship (1896) and reprinted by F. W. Hodge (1953). The information provided by Castañeda about anthropophagy, marriage customs, divorce, prostitution and sodomy among the Sinaloa Indians is accurate, straightforward and interesting.

1953 edition, pp. 344–346; Part II, Chapter I

"Chapter I. Of the Province of Culiacan and of its habits and customs . . . the Tahus . . . do not eat human flesh nor sacrifice it . . . among them there are men dressed like women who marry other men and serve as their wives. At a great festival they consecrate the women who wish to live unmarried, with much singing and dancing, at which all the chiefs of the locality gather and dance naked, and after all have danced with her they put her in a hut that has been decorated for this event and the chiefs adorn her with cloths and bracelets of fine turquoises, and then the chiefs go in one by one to lie with her, and all the others who wish follow them. From this time on these women cannot refuse anyone who pays them a certain amount agreed on for this. Even if they take husbands, this does not exempt them from obliging anyone who pays them . . . The custom is for the husbands to buy the women whom they marry of their fathers and relatives at a high price, and then to take them to a chief who is considered to be a priest, to deflower them and see if she is a virgin . . . At these times they all get drunk . . .

" . . . The Pacaxes . . . are more barbarous. Some of them who live near the mountains eat human flesh. They are great sodomites, and have many wives, even when these are sisters . . .

" . . . the Acaxes . . . go hunting for men just as they hunt animals. They all eat human flesh, and he who has the most human bones and skulls hung up around his house is most feared and respected."

1953 edition, pp. 346–349; Part II, Chapter 2

"Chapter 2. Of the Province of Petlatlan and all the inhabited country as far as Chinchilticalli . . . There is much sodomy among them . . . the valley of Suya . . . the people . . . are great sodomites. They drink wine made of the pitahaya, which is the fruit of a great thistle which opens like the pomegranate. The wine makes them stupid . . ."

CODEX MAGLIABECCHI (*c.* 1565)

This pictographic Mexican Codex at the Biblioteca Nazionale Centrale, Florence, was named after its donor Antonio Magliabecchi (1633–1716). It was first identified by H. Harrisse (1885) and afterwards studied and published in facsimile by Zelia Nuttall (1903). Several copies seem to have been made of it in Mexico during the 18th century. It is painted in 80 leaves—originally 92—of Italian paper in the second half of the 16th century with title and manuscript explanatory notes in Spanish: *Libro de la vida que los Indios antiguamente hazian y supersticiones y malos ritos que tenian y guardavan.* The first part of this Codex shows a series of motives used by the Mexican Indians in their ceremonial cloths. Although those appearing in the Codex Magliabecchi had limited psychiatric meaning, it is important to remember that the pattern in similar cloths or "mantas" still manufactured today by the Huichol Indians of Mexico show profound sexual symbolism, retained from pre-Columbian times. It follows the pictographic representation of the 20 Mexican days, the 52 years' cycle, feasts, gods, rites and sacrifices. Some of the feasts to Tezcatlipoca and Quetzalcoatl have a special psychological meaning. As regards sexual practices, the important feasts were those of Pillavanaliztli (sexual and drinking initiation of the children) and the description of *temazcalli* or steam bath houses. It should be noted that in the section on medical diagnosis one reading of the maize grain meant death, another recovery, and the third that the illness was due to sodomitic practices. The plates of ritual anthropophagy, penitence and self-mutilation and the rebus writing depicting *ololuihqui, teonacatlatl, toloachtl*—drugs used to produce hallucinogenic effects—are also extremely important. It has been suggested that this Codex was prepared for Cervantes de Salazar.

1903 edition, folio 1

folio 1 (1): "Book of the life of the ancient Indians and superstitions and evil rites they had and kept.

folio 20 (32) verso: "This is the feast called by the Indians *Toxcal* . . . the demon they celebrated in it was called *Tezcatepocatl* . . .

folio 21 (33) verso: "This is the feast called *Eçalcoaliztli* . . . the demon honoured in it was *Queçalcoatl* . . . in this feast the Indians made sacrifices in their sexual organs they called *motepuliço*, that means sexual organ sacrificed; some of them say they did this so that their god should be pleased and give them procreation . . .

folio 28 (40) verso: "This feast is called by the Indians *Huepactli* . . . and in the same day they celebrated other feast called *pilavana* meaning drunkenness of the children because there the boys danced with the girls and gave each other to drink until they were drunk and committed with each other their ugly things and fornications. These Indians were already a little bit grown up about nine to ten years old, this knavery was not done everywhere but among the *Tlalhuicas* . . .

folio 64 (76) verso: "This is a figure of the baths of the Indians which they call *temazcale* where they have an idol at the door who was advocate in their diseases and when some sick person went to the baths they offered incense which they call *copale* to this idol. And they dyed their bodies in black in reverence to the idol they called *Tezcatepocatl* who is one of their greater gods. They used in these baths other nefarious knaveries for example many Indian men and women bathed naked and committed inside many obscenities and sins in this bath.

folio 65 (77) verso: "This is a manner of diabolic medicine the Indian physicians had. And it is that when somebody fell ill they call the physician woman or man. And afterwards that physician to see what end was the illness going to have, placed in front of him an idol and facing him the patient. That idol was called *Queçalcoatl* meaning feathered serpent and he on a *petate* [carpet] with a white cotton cloth on the top. He took in the hand twenty grains of maize which is from where they make bread and threw them on the cloth like dice and if the grains left a vacuum in the middle, a sort of field, with the grains around, it was a sign that he was going to be buried there, meaning that he should die of that illness. If one grain fell on the top of another it meant that his illness was due to being a sodomite, and if the grains of maize withdrew half to one side, half to the other side in such a way that a straight line could be made in the middle without touching any grain it was a sign that the disease was going away from the patient and that he would be cured.

folio 66 (78) verso: "This is another figure showing the manner the Indians had to make penitence. They placed on high a seated idol whom they call *Mictlantecutli* meaning lord of the dead and in front of him they sacrificed their ears, others their tongues, others the calves of the legs, by passing through their ears and their tongues very sharp thorns and made penitence in that way.

folio 71 (83) recto: [This picture is a rebus for *coatlxihuitl* or green vine like a serpent, which is the hallucinogenic drug *ololiuhqui*.]

folio 72 (84) recto: [This picture represents *toloachtl*, another hallucinogenic drug, and the two Indians have glyphs coming out of their mouths to indicate that they are talking under its influence.]

folio 73 (85): "This bundle is from a root which they used to prepare the wine called *opactly*. "This [woman] served the wine to the rest until she made them drunk."

folio 74 (86): [Figure depicting *pulque*.]

folio 75 (87): [Sacrifices to Tezcatlipoca.]
folio 78 (90): [Figure depicting an Indian eating hallucinogenic mushrooms with Mictlantecutli behind.]

BERNARDINO DE SAHAGÚN (c. 1565)

The information on ancient Mexico provided by Bernardino de Sahagún (1499–1590) is indisputably the most reliable source from that area. His family name was Ribeiro but he adopted, as usual, the name of his native village when entering the Franciscan Order, after his studies at the University of Salamanca. In 1529 Sahagún went to Mexico, just eight years after the Conquest, and devoted the rest of his long life to writing an exhaustive anthropological study of the Aztecs. He mastered their Nahuatl language and one of the versions of the *Historia general de las cosas de Nueva España* is in this Mexican language. The first version was written at Tepepulco between 1558 and 1560. After Sahagún was transferred to Tatlelolco he wrote a second version in Spanish between 1560 and 1565. Finally Sahagún moved to Tenochtitlan or Mexico City where he produced another extensive version in Nahuatl between 1565 and 1568. However, some of the texts studied in this work were written in 1571; it has already been pointed out (Guerra, 1966), that an anonymous draft written in 1541 at Tehuacan and published by Kingsborough (1848), which has been attributed to Motolinia, could be the original first draft by Sahagún. The first book of Sahagún is devoted to the Mexican gods, which are the key for an understanding of the spiritual and religious life of ancient Mexico, and it is complemented by the third book dealing with the history of those gods. Intimately related is the second book pertaining to the calendar and festivities, and the fourth and the fifth on judicial astrology and auguries. Other books in Sahagún's *General History of the things of New Spain* are devoted to natural history, science, medicine and the conquest of Mexico. In the book on the Mexican gods, Sahagún describes the technique of confession to Tlazolteotl, and the background of homosexuality behind the cult to the most powerful and capricious of the Aztec gods, Tezcatlipoca.

1938 edition, Book I, Chapter III

Vol. I, p. 16. Chapter III: "It deals with the god called Tezcatlipoca, who is generally considered a god among the natives of this New Spain; he is another Jupiter.

"The god called Tezcatlipoca was considered a true god and invisible, he was everywhere, in heaven, on earth and in hell; and they believed that when he was on earth, he provoked wars, animosities and disagreements, from which resulted much suffering and insecurities. They said that he incited one against the other to have wars and because of this he was called Necoc Yaotl, meaning he who sowed disagreements between parties; and they said he was the only one knowledgeable about ruling the world, and only he gave prosperities and wealth, and only he took them away when he pleased: he gave riches, prosperities, and fame, and strength and power, and dignities and honour, and took them away when he pleased; they feared and worshipped him because of this, as it was in his hand to lift and to drop them, after the reverence they offered him.

1938 edition, Vol. I, pp. 24–29; Book I, Chapter XII

Chapter XII: "Which deals with the goddess of lustful things who was called Tlazolteotl, another Venus.

This goddess had three names: one was called Tlazolteotl, that means the goddess of lust; the second name was Ixcuina, they call her by this name because they say there were four sisters . . . The third name of this goddess is Tlaelquani, that means eater of filth, because according to what lustful women and men said they confessed their sins to these goddesses, no matter how obscene and dirty they were, they forgave them.

"They also said that this goddess, or goddesses, had the power to provoke lust and to inspire fleshly acts and to protect obscene love; and after the sins were committed they said they had the power to forgive them, and to clean them by forgiveness if they confessed them to their sorcerers who were the soothsayers who kept the books of prophecies and fortunes of those born, and the witchcraft and horoscopes, and the traditions from the ancients which were handed down to them. So as soon as the penitent decided to confess he went in search of one of those mentioned, in front of whom he used to confess and said to him: 'Sir, I wish to reach god all powerful, the protector of all whose name is *Yoalli-Ehecatl*, that is, Tezcatlipoca; I wish to tell my sins in secret.' On hearing this the seer told him: 'Welcome my son, what you are saying is for your good and benefit.' After saying this, he looked into the book of prophecies called *tonalamatl* in order to find out which day was the most convenient for that act; after seeing the convenient day he said: 'such day you will come, because then rules a good sign, in order that this be done fruitfully.' In the day ordered to come, the penitent bought a new mat and white incense called *copalli*, and wood for the fire to burn the *copalli*; and if the penitent was an important person or in a position of dignity, the seer went to his house to confess him, or perchance the penitent, though an important person, went to the soothsayer's house; in arriving, he swept very well the place where he placed the new mat, so that the confessor could rest on it, and afterwards he lit the fire and the soothsayer cast the *copalli* into the fire, and spoke to the fire saying: 'You, lord father and mother of the gods, the oldest god, learn that this your subject, this your servant has come here and he comes with great pain, and this is because he knows that he has erred, he has fallen, stepped, and come across some filth of sins and certain serious crimes deserving death, and because of this he arrives heavy-hearted and tired. Our lord most compassionate, as you are the protector and defender of all, receive into penitence, hear the anxiety of this your servant and subject.' On finishing this prayer the soothsayer turned to the penitent and talked to him in this way: 'My son, you have come to the presence of the god helper and protector of all; you came to make public your internal stench and corruption; you come to open the secrets of your heart, take care not to fall into a precipice, not to fall into an abyss lying in the presence of our lord. Undress yourself, throw out all your shame in the presence of our lord, which is called *Yoalli-Ehécatl*, that is *Tezcatlipoca*. It is true that you are in front of him, though you are not worthy to see him, nor can he talk to you, because he is invisible and cannot be touched; beware therefore how you come, what heart you bring, do not hesitate to publish your secrets in his presence; tell your life, present your actions in the same way as you did your excesses and offences; pour forth your evils in his presence, tell with sorrow to god our lord, who is the helper of all and has his arms open and is ready to embrace you and to take you on his back; beware not to leave out anything because of shame, beware not to leave anything because of wickedness.' This understood, the penitent took an oath to tell the truth in the manner that they swear, touching the ground with the hand and licking what stuck to it; and afterwards he cast *copalli* into the fire, which was another token of telling the truth, and then he sat in front of the soothsayer, and because he considered him to be the image and vicar of god began to talk in this manner: 'Oh our lord, who receives and protects us all, listen to my stench and corruption; in your presence I become naked and throw out all my base actions, how many I have committed; they are not indeed hidden, my evil deeds, because everything is manifest and clear to you!' After this was said, he then began to tell his sins, in the same order that they were committed, entirely clearly and tranquilly, in the same way as a song is recited very slowly and well pronounced, as if he were following a straight road, without deviating to one side or another. At the end of telling everything he had done, he began again to talk to the soothsayer in this way: ..."

1938 edition, Book III, Chapter II

Vol. I, p. 265. Chapter II: "Of the esteem in which the god called Titlacáuan or Tezctliapoca was held.

"The god called Titlacáuan they said was the creator of heaven and earth and was all powerful ...

p. 266: "And they even said more, that this god called Titlacáuan gave to those living poverty and misery and incurable and contagious diseases such as leprosy and buboes, and gout and scabies and dropsy; he sent these diseases when he was angry with those who did not keep or broke a vow and penitence requiring fasting, or if they slept with their wives or wives with husband during the fasting period. And the said sick people were very sad and grieved, came begging and saying to him: Oh God, whose name is Titlacáuan grant me the mercy of removing and taking away this disease that kills me, and I will do nothing but will mend my ways; if I were cured from this disease, I make a vow to serve you and earn my living, and if I gain something from my work I will not eat it up or spend in anything, but to honour you and will give a feast and banquet to dance in this humble home! And the sick person annoyed because he could not get cured, reproached him in anger and said: Oh Titlacáuan *puto* [sodomite], you make mockery of me! Why do you not kill me? And some such sick persons got well and others died . . ."

1938 edition, Book IV, Chapter IX

Vol. 1, p. 320. Chapter IX: "Of the sixth sign called *Ce Miquiztli*, and of its prosperous fortune. They said that this was Tezcatlipoca's sign in reverence of whom they specially made many offerings and sacrifices, and made feast and gave presents to the slaves, each one to their own at home."

p. 321: "and they said that if anybody wrangled with the slaves in those days, he got poverty, disease and unhappiness himself, and deserved to be a slave, because he ill-treated the much loved son of Tezcatlipoca, because they said Tezcatlipoca was not the faithful friend of anybody, but that he looked for the opportunities to take away what he had given; and some of them when they lost their state in despair wrangled with Tezcatlipoca and said to him: 'You, Tezcatlipoca, you are a *puto* [sodomite] and have made mockery of me and cheated me . . ."

1938 edition, Book III, Chapter V

Vol. 1, p. 270. Chapter V: "Of another fraud done by that necromancer called Titlacáuan.

"The said Titlacáuan did another fraud, by transforming himself to look like a foreign Indian, they call *tobeyo*, his whole body naked as those of his race used to go; he was selling green pepper and sat down in the market in front of the palace. And Huemac, who was the lord of the Toltecs in secular matters . . . had a very beautiful daughter . . . and the said daughter of the lord Huemac looked towards the *tianguez* [market] and saw the said *tobeyo* naked and his genital organ, and after seeing it the said daughter earnestly desired the genital organ of that *tobeyo*, and began to be very ill due to the desire of what she saw; all her body was swollen, and the said lord Huemac . . . asked the women attending his daughter, what is wrong with my daughter? . . . And the women replied Our Lord, this illness is due to the occasion when the Indian *tobeyo* was around naked and your daughter saw and looked at the genital organ of that *tobeyo* and she is love sick . . . and when he was brought before the lord Huemac . . . he said to him, you are desired by my daughter, you must cure her . . . go and get inside to see my daughter, there inside where she is kept; and the said *tobeyo* did as told, and slept with the said daughter of the lord Huemac and soon she was cured and well . . ."

When describing the medicinal plants used by the Aztecs, Sahagún left a good description of all drugs used by them to affect mental behaviour and produce hallucinations and even madness.

1939 edition, Vol. III, p. 118

Book X, Chapter XXIX: "They also had a wide knowledge of herbs and roots and of their properties and virtues: they themselves discovered and were the first to use the root which they called *peyotl*; it was eaten and those who drank it, drank it instead of wine; this they did with the roots they called *nanácatl*, evil mushrooms which also intoxicate as does wine. And after they had eaten and drunk they foregathered on the plain and danced and sang for joy all through the night and day; this on the first day. The following day they all wept a great deal and they said that they cleaned and washed their faces and eyes with their tears . . ."

1939 edition, Vol. III, pp. 229–231

Book XI, Chapter VII: "In which all the herbs are dealt with.
    "1. Of certain herbs which produce madness.
"There is a herb called *coatl xoxouhqui* which produces a seed called *oluliuhqui*; this seed intoxicates and drives men mad. Ill-wishers give it as a drink to those whom they wish to harm, and those who eat it have visions and see dreadful apparitions. Witch doctors give it to their enemies to be eaten with their food and taken with their drink. This herb is medicinal and its seed, when ground and applied, is good for gout.
"There is another herb, like a prickly pear, which is called *peyotl*; it is white and is found in the north. Those who eat or drink it suffer from frightful visions or uncontrollable laughter; the intoxication lasts for two or three days and then disappears. It is similar to a food of the Chichimecs, which nourishes them, gives them strength and courage in battle, takes away thirst and hunger and, they say, protects them from danger.
"Another herb is called *tlápatl* and is like a bunch of hair. It has small heads, without thorns, which resemble lemons; its skin is green, its leaves wide and its flowers white; the seed is black and noisome. It takes away the appetite of those who eat it and causes permanent intoxication and madness. The seed is good for gout when it is applied to the painful spot. Its smell is harmful as well as its seed.
"There are other plants call *tzitzintlápatl*, so called because of its thorn heads. It has similar properties to the above-mentioned *tlápatl*.
"There is another herb called *mixitl*; it is small and vine-like, green

and with seeds. It is good for gout when ground and placed on the afflicted area. It is not edible or drinkable as it causes vomiting, constricts the throat and tongue, engendering thirst and cracks the tongue; if it is eaten its taste is not unpleasant but its effect is to rob the body of its strength. And if the eyes are open when it is eaten they cannot thereafter be shut, and if they are closed they cannot be opened. If he who eats it is standing upright he cannot bend down and he loses the power of speech. Wine is an antidote for this herb.

"In these lands there are some little mushrooms called *teonanácatl* which grow under hay-fields; they are round and the stem is slender and circular. They have an unpleasant taste, damage the throat and intoxicate. They are an effective remedy against fevers and gout; not more than two or three should be eaten at a time. Those who eat them see visions and suffer from heartburn. Those who eat many of them become lascivious.

"Another poisonous plant is the *tochtepete* whose leaves are small like those of the Peruvian tree and whose roots are white. If anyone eats or drinks it he dies because it destroys the intestines; and if the herb is put in *pulque* or water—even if it is later removed, the poison remains—he who drinks it dies. It is said that witch-doctors cast spells with this herb.

"There is another herb called *atlepatli* which grows by running water and in marshes. It is deadly poison and any creature that eats it or drinks it will die. If it is applied to the skin it causes red hot blisters. Due to its effectiveness against leprosy it is called *xiotl*.

"There is a herb called *aquiztli* whose branches are long and slender; it resembles a bunch of hair or bushes and it causes the face and body of he who urinates or spits on it to swell; if it touches the skin it brings up blisters. It is good for smallpox, if drunk its juice will bring out the spots.

"There is another herb called *tenxoxoli*; its leaves are like those of the red mace; its root causes vomiting and blood vomit.

"Another herb is known as *quinichpatli* and is similar to a bush. It is deadly poison and when mixed with their food it kills rats. If it is applied to gangrenous wounds it eats away the rottenness leaving healthy skin . . ."

If the *History of the Mexican Indians* attributed to Motolinia (1541) has already given an idea of the extent of homicides and anthropophagy among the Aztecs, the Tlaxcaltecs, and other Mexican nations, it is the undisputed, reliable and systematic work of Sahagún which gives an itemized account of the calendar of human sacrifices taking place among the Aztecs throughout the year. Sahagún in fact gives two renderings of the festivities and sacrifices; the first, a brief account, appears in Chapters I–XIX of Book II, and the second, giving great detail of the religious rituals, occupies Chapters XX–XXVIII. Only excerpts from the brief version are quoted here, since this provides a convenient summary.

1938 edition, Vol. I, p. 84; Book II, Chapter I

"Chapter I. Of the calendar of the feasts of fixed date, the first of which is the one that follows: Atlcahualo or Quauitleóa.... In this month they slew many children: they sacrificed them in many places upon the mountain tops, tearing from them their hearts in honour of the gods of water, so that these might give them water or rain.... When they took the children to be slain, if they wept and shed many tears ... they took it as an omen that they would have much rain that year. Also in this month they slew many captives ... [pp. 119–122] ... Great numbers of children were killed every year in these places; and after being killed they cooked and ate them ... All the captives ... were tied upon a stone ... and went to fight with them .. they tear their hearts ... made up in portions they were divided to be eaten after cooked."

1938 edition, Vol. I, p. 85; Book II, Chapter II

"Chapter II. Tlacaxipehualiztli... In the first day of this month they made a feast in honour of the god called Totec, and by another name called Xipe when they slew and flayed many slaves and captives.... After having torn their hearts and poured the blood into a bowl ... they carried him to their neighbourhood where he was dismembered and divided in order to be eaten. Before dismembering the captives they flayed them ... They slew other captives, battling with them. [pp. 123–128] ... They cooked that flesh with maize and gave each one a piece of the flesh in a bowl or plate, with its broth and cooked maize, and they called that meal tlacatlaolli; after eating they went to get drunk ..."

1938 edition, Vol. I, pp. 87–88; Book II, Chapter III

"Chapter III. Tozoztontli. The third month was called tozoztontli; in the first day of this month they made a feast to the god called Tlaloc, who is the god of rain. In this feast they killed many children in the mountains ..."

1938 edition, Vol. I, pp. 89–90; Book II, Chapter IV

"Chapter IV. Uey tozoztli. To the fourth month ... according to the accounts of some people the children they killed were gathered in the first month, buying them from their mothers, and they kept slaying them during successive festivities until the rains really started ..."

1938 edition, Vol. I, pp. 90–91; Book II, Chapter V

"Chapter V. To the fifth month ... On the first day of this month they celebrated a great feast in honour of the god called Titlacauan, and for another name Tezcatlipoca ... In his honour they slew in this feast a chosen youth who might have no blemishes in his body, who was reared in all luxuries during a year, and trained in the playing of music, singing and speaking ... he had long hair down to the waist. When they slew the youth in the feast reared to that purpose, soon they produced another who was to die after one year. He walked around the village finely arrayed with flowers in his hand, ... twenty days before this feast came, they gave this young man four comely young women reared for this purpose, with whom for all the twenty days he had carnal intercourse ... Five days before he was to die, they celebrated feast and banquets for him ... they tore out his heart ... they cut the head off ...."

1938 edition, Vol. I, pp. 92–93; Book II, Chapter VI

"Chapter VI. Etzalqualiztli. To the sixth month ... On this same month they slew many captives and other slaves, arrayed with the ornaments of these gods called Tlaloques, in whose honour they slew them in their own *cu*."

1938 edition, Vol. I, pp. 93–94; Book II, Chapter VII

"Chapter VII. Tecuilhuitontli. To the seventh month ... among them went the woman who was the likeness of this goddess and who was to die arrayed in rich ornaments ... Thus dancing they took many captives from the temple of Tlaloc, and with them the woman who was to die, who was the image of the goddess Uixtocihuatl. There they slew first the captives and then her. Many other ceremonies were performed during this feast and there was also great drunkenness. All of which is set forth at length in the account of this feast ...."

1938 edition, Vol. I, pp. 94–96; Book II, Chapter VIII

"Chapter VIII. Uey tecuilhuitl. To the eighth month ... To honour this goddess they slew a woman on the tenth day of this month, arrayed with ornaments they depicted the same goddess. ... As soon as all thus dancing arrived at the temple where that woman was to die, ... one of them took her upon his back, shoulder against shoulder; and being like that, they struck off her head and then tore out her heart and offered it to the sun. ... [p. 166] Some were sentenced to death for drinking pulque ... they were slain in front of the people ...."

1938 edition, Vol. I, pp. 96–97; Book II, Chapter IX

"Chapter IX. Tlaxochimaco. To the ninth month ... [p. 168] Into this dance came women, prostitutes; and went holding hands, one woman between two men, and a man between two women ... The old men and women drunk wine and fell intoxicated, and quarrelled one with the other shouting ...."

1938 edition, Vol. I, pp. 97–99; Book II, Chapter X

"Chapter X. Xocotl huetzi. To the tenth month ... on this feast they threw into the fire alive many slaves bound hand and foot, and before they had quite died, they took them forth dragging them out of the fire, in order to tear out their hearts before the image of this god ... After the captives had kept vigil ... they cast into their faces some powder which they call *yiauhtli*, that they might lose their sense of feeling and not suffer so greatly their deaths ..."

1938 edition, Vol. I, pp. 99–100; Book II, Chapter XI

"Chapter XI. Ochpaniztli. To the eleventh month ... They danced in silence for the honour of this goddess and they slew a woman, in great silence dressed with the ornaments which they depicted in this goddess, ... that woman should not know she was to die, ... for they held that to be a bad omen. ... One of them took her upon his back, shoulder against shoulder, and swiftly they struck off her head, and then flayed her, and a stout youth put on her skin. ... this one before Huitzilopochtli, tore out the hearts of four captives, and the rest he left for the priest to slay. ..."

1938 edition, Vol. I, pp. 101–102; Book II, Chapter XII

"Chapter XII. Teotleco. To the twelfth month ... On this day they had many captives to burn alive; and a great mound of coals having been piled up, certain young men went dancing about the edge of the fire disguised as monsters. And, thus dancing they proceed casting into the fire these miserable captives in the manner which has already been said ..."

1938 edition, Vol. I, pp. 102–104; Book II, Chapter XIII

"Chapter XIII. Tepeilhuitl. To the thirteenth month ... Upon arrival of the feast in honour of the mountains they slew four women and one man. ... After they had slain them and torn out their hearts ... they cut off their heads and inserted a rod through them, and they carried the bodies to the houses which they call *calpul*, where they divided them in order to be eaten ..."

1938 edition, Vol. I, pp. 104–105; Book II, Chapter XIV

"Chapter XIV. Quecholli. To the fourteenth month ... they slew many slaves in honour of this god ... The hunt ended, they slew captives and slaves on a *cu* they called Tlamatzinco. They bound them hand and foot and carried them up the steps of the *cu*—as one carried a deer by the hind and forelegs to slaughter. They slew them with great ceremony ..."

1938 edition, Vol. I, pp. 105–106; Book II, Chapter XV

"Chapter XV. Panquetzaliztli. To the fifteenth month ... On the ninth day of this month they adorned with great ceremonies those whom they were to slay ... he slew four of those slaves in the ball court which was found in the courtyard which they called Teotlachtli; ... and in certain places he slew in each one a slave. And from that point onward two factions began a mock battle; some died in the skirmishing. After many ceremonies finally they slew captives in the *cu* of Huitzilopochtli, and many other slaves; and having slain one, they sounded musical instruments, and stopping they seized another to slay him, and on killing him they played again, and thus they did to each one until finishing them all . . ."

1938 edition, Vol. I, pp. 107–108; Book II, Chapter XVI

"Chapter XVI. Atemoztli. To the sixteenth month ... they made images of the mountains of *tzoal* ... they opened the chests with a *tzotzopaztli* which is an instrument women used for weaving ... torn the hearts out and cut the heads off, and then divided the whole body among them and eat it . . ."

1938 edition, Vol. I, pp. 108–109; Book II, Chapter XVII

"Chapter XVII. Tititl. To the seventeenth month ... in honour of this goddess they slew a woman and after they had torn out her heart, they cut off her head, they made a dance with it. The one leading carried the head by the hair in the right hand, making the dancing movements ... This woman arrayed in this way with the ornaments described in the story, danced alone, some old men made the rhythm, and dancing she sighed and cried thinking that soon she was going to die ... they tore out her heart and cut her head off . . ."

1938 edition, Vol. I, pp. 109–111; Book II, Chapter XVIII

"Chapter XVIII Izcalli. To the eighteenth month ... every four years in this feast they slew slaves and captives in honour of this god, and perforated the ears of all the children born in those years ... They did not kill anybody in ordinary years but in leap years which were every four years they slew captives and slaves in this feast . . ."

JUAN MATIENZO DE PERALTA. (1566)

The survey of the institutions and the social structure of the Inca rule, written by Matienzo with the purpose of adapting the Spanish colonizing procedures, provide glimpses of the sexual problems and drug addiction in ancient Peru. Juan Matienzo de Peralta (*c.* 1520–1579), born in Spain, worked for 16 years at the Chancery of Valladolid after obtaining his Law degree. In 1560 he went to America as Judge of the Royal Audiencia of Charcas, La Plata, a position which he occupied from 1561 until his death. In 1565 he visited Cuzco to obtain the submission of the Inca Titu Cusi Yupangui and during the years 1572 and 1573 he accompanied the Viceroy Toledo on his journey through Southern Peru. Matienzo published a legal work in Rome (1558) and another appeared posthumously in Mantua (1580), but his most interesting contribution to pre-Columbian legal history, *Gobierno del Peru*, finished in 1567 was printed in 1910. This work shows contempt for the native Indians, their customary law and behaviour, emphasizing their lewdness, drunkenness and coca consumption. As a prevention against the prevalent incest Matienzo suggested the need for parents to sleep separately from their children.

1910 edition, pp. 15–35

p. 15, Chapter 5: "they are vicious about women . . ."

p. 17, Chapter 6: "The headmen, *curacas* . . . we must try that they do not rob their Indians, neither to take away their daughters, nor for them to have many wives or concubines."

p. 19, Chapter 8: "in drunkenness and other vices they are inclined."

p. 35, Chapter 14: "the children must sleep away and not together with the parents."

JERÓNIMO DE ESCOBAR (*c.* 1567)

Among the documents pertaining to the ancient Spanish colonies in America published by the Academia de la Historia, Madrid (1884) there is a Report by Jerónimo de Escobar (fl. 1567) to Philip II, undated, but which internal evidence shows to be written about 1570. Escobar was born in Toledo of noble family and became a member of the Augustinian Order in 1566. He was Solicitor General of the province of Popayan, for many years carried missionary work among the Chibcha Indians and had first-hand knowledge of the customs of these Indians in present-day Colombia. He died in Cadiz shortly after being appointed bishop of Nicaragua. His *Relación* repeats the stories of anthropophagy, incests and sodomies earlier reported by bishop Ortiz and Cieza de León.

1884 edition, pp. 447–480

"[In Pasto the Indians] . . . fall into a thousand vices, they have so-called *taquies*, sort of public dances, where they make the whole village to dance in the square, with large earthen jars of beer [*chicha*] which is the wine they use to get drunk . . . while they are drunk, they kill each other, and they do lewdness unworthy to tell Your Highness, because the father do not respect the chastity of the daughter, neither the brother with the sister, and thus they commit awful incests . . ."

p. 455: "[In Popayan] . . . they have as neighbours near by, Indians very warlike, who caused them harm and eat human flesh and eat those Indians they can get, as they have already eaten many . . ."

p. 464: "[San Sebastian de la Plata] This village is almost destroyed by some Indians nearby, bloodthirsty, also for the past forty years have not laid down their arms; they eat human flesh . . ."

p. 480: "[Santa Fé de Antioquia] ... there were over one hundred thousand Indians; they were very warlike one against the other, they ate human flesh, and they had sort of butchers among them of this flesh; it was great among these Indians to hang in their houses and doors the skulls of their enemy Indians they had eaten ... they raised and fatten with great care their own children and kept them to eat them in feasts and dances, in the same way they fatten pigs, without really need of food, just for vice ..."

BERNAL DÍAZ DEL CASTILLO (1568)

No historian of Mexico enjoys a higher reputation than Bernal Díaz del Castillo (1495–1581). Born in Medina del Campo, he went to America with Pedrarias Davila in 1514, and afterwards he joined the expeditions of Juan de Grijalba and F. Hernandez de Córdoba to the Mexican coast, before accompanying Hernán Cortés in 1519 in his conquest of Mexico; Díaz del Castillo is the most accurate and reliable historian of these events. The *Historia verdadera de la conquista de la Nueva España*, written around 1568 in Guatemala but published much later (1632) contains observations on sodomy among the Maya and the Aztecs. During the first expedition in February 1517 with Hernandez de Córdoba, Díaz del Castillo landed in the Maya area at Cape Catoche, Yucatan, and he left a description of what was found in the houses of the Indians.

1632 edition, folio 2 verso, Chapter II

"Abominable figures of the idols of the Indians
"... had many idols and other evil looking figures in such way that the figures of the Indians looked as if they were committing sodomies one with the other ..."

After joining Cortés in 1519 Díaz del Castillo landed in Veracruz and their expedition first moved northwest into Cempoala, where he writes that the Spaniards requested the Mexican Indians:

1632 edition, folio 34 verso, Chapter LI

"... that they should leave the sacrifice [of human beings] to steal from one another, and the dirt of sodomies ..."

1632 edition, folio 35, Chapter LI

"... that they should be cleaned of sodomies, because they had boys dressed in women's dresses, who were earning their living in that perverted occupation ... and all the chiefs and principal priests replied ... they would try to avoid those customs."

Further on, when Díaz del Castillo described the character and way of life of the Mexican priests, he wrote,

1632 edition, folio 36, Chapter LII

"... those popes were the sons of Indian chiefs and did not have wives, but they had the perverse occupation of sodomies, and fasted certain days ..."

Díaz del Castillo also recorded some of the addresses that Hernán Cortés and his priest the Mercedarian friar Bartolomé de Olmedo gave to the Indians against anthropophagy and sodomy; Cortés said,

1632 edition, folio 42, Chapter LXI

"... and now I furthermore tell you Olintecle and all chiefs here present, to leave your sacrifices, not to eat the flesh of your neighbours, and not to carry on with sodomies, nor those wicked things you are accustomed ..."

And at the first meeting in Mexico City with the Emperor Moctezuma, Hernán Cortés told him,

1632 edition, folio 67, Chapter XC

"... not to tolerate sodomies or thefts ..."

Fray Bartolomé de Olmedo acted in a similar fashion and during those critical days at Cholula preached to the Indians,

1632 edition, folio 61, Chapter LXXXIII

"... not to sacrifice human beings or to eat them, not to steal from one another, and not to carry on those wicked things [sodomy] they are accustomed ..."

Besides confirming the general appraisal of sodomy over the area of the territory under Mexican control, the testimony of Díaz del Castillo is particularly vivid in describing the institutionalized practice of sodomy among the Huaxtec on the coast of the Gulf of Mexico and the widespread use of youngsters and non-castrated *bardajes* as a normal and well-established custom. This confirms the high incidence of sodomy in that vicinity earlier reported by the Conquistador Anónimo in 1519.

TOMÁS LÓPEZ MEDEL (*c.* 1569)

There have until now been considerable misconceptions about the life of Tomás López Medel (*c.* 1521–1582). He was born in Tendilla, Guadalajara the son of Francisco Medel a farmer, and studied at Alcalá de Henares receiving the degree of Bachelor in Canon Law in 1539. López Medel went to Paris and afterwards to the University of Bologna where he became Doctor in Canons. After residence in Seville he was appointed Judge of Guatemala in 1549, visiting Mexico, Chiapas and the Yucatan area between 1551 and 1552. He was an honest and trusted official and in 1557 was promoted to the same position in Santa Fé de Bogota

executing there some difficult commissions. After fifteen years in the
Indies López Medel returned to the University of Alcalá and wrote a
Tratado de los tres elementos . . . de las Indias Occidentales which he
presented to the Pope when in 1570 went to Rome and received Holy
Orders. After becoming a priest he was offered the see of Guatemala but
because of his age and poor health he was instead made in 1574 director
of the Hospital Real de Villafranca de Montes de Oca, Burgos, where he
died. His book, wrongly dated by Tozzer (1941) as written in 1612, contains excellent first-hand information on America, discussing anthropophagy, the sodomy occurring among native priests in pre-Columbian
times, human sacrifices and the confession among the Maya.

1641 edition, pp. 221–229; Part III, Chapter XX

"Concerning the false religion and idolatry of the Occidental Indians
and their abominable and savage custom of eating human flesh and of
hunting and killing one another for this purpose, and concerning their
bloody and horrible sacrifices in which they killed and sacrificed men
to their gods.

". . . In Mexico and Guatemala and Yucatan and in all those provinces
they had . . . sacrifice of men . . . with an extremely sharp flint . . . opened
. . . the side of the heart and tore it out and threw it on high, offering
to their gods . . . And this kind of sacrifice was very usual and ordinary . . . Those compelled were captives . . . whom they kept in prisons
and in cages for this purpose, fattening them . . . were so many in
number, especially in Mexico that each year, it is painful to state, some
Indians affirm more than fifty thousand were killed each year . . . The
sacrificed bodies of those captives . . . their flesh was weighed and sold
publicly for human sustenance as if they were sheep or pigs or other
animals, for it is meat they crave and they ate it with great pleasure.
And in addition to the flesh of these sacrifices, everyone who had slaves
that he had taken in various wars killed the one he wished of them
when he had fancy to do so, and in his way also many died . . .

"The Mexicans and Guatemalans had a great number of priests in
those temples . . . where they practised such abominable lusts and sins
that it is an abominable and disgraceful thing to describe; as those
men had already acquired so many rights, or more properly speaking,
introduced such nefarious and widespread customs in this case among
the people that in order not to offend chaste ears it is necessary to pass
over them in silence . . .

"Among other sacrifice . . . in those provinces of Yucatan was . . . one
or two Indian virgins . . . to Chichen Itzá . . . at a large and deep
cenote . . . they drowned her.

"The Yucatecans had a certain other sacrifice of fire, . . . those priests
. . . passed over all that fire and hot ash, dancing and singing . . . With
regard to the Peruvian Indians . . . there were also in those temples of
theirs . . . a large number of maidens and virgins . . . with a vow of

perpetual virginity and continence . . . punished with terrible penalties those who were found with any one of them and the penalty for the maidens was also death . . .

"The Indians of the New Kingdom (Tierra Firme) had another kind of sacrifice peculiar to them . . . to shoot with arrows some children . . . the custom of eating human flesh . . . among the Panche Indians . . . was so ingrained that they are enough for themselves and those of the New Kingdom.

". . . The lords were buried in certain vaults . . . many male and female slaves . . . and some of their most dearly beloved wives.

"There also existed among the Occidental Indians their kind of oral confession of sins, I mean of those sins that were considered such by those peoples, such as homicide, theft, and adultery, etc. although it was not uniform nor of the same kind in all regions. The Yucatecan Indians had the custom of confessing themselves once in their lives, and this when they felt they were so near death that they could not escape, and they made this confession of theirs in public and before anyone who wished to hear it, telling the whole course of their lives and telling there their public and private guilts, and sometimes many troubles and dissentions arose from this, especially from the confessions of the women with regard to their husbands, if it happened that they escaped and survived their illness, so that in all ways that infernal spirit, either all at once or by degrees, always managed to make trouble among those poor people . . .

"The custom of eating human flesh was so ingrained and accepted among those barbarian peoples that in many parts and regions the nefarious custom of killing men described was not to make a sacrifice and oblation of them to their gods as the Mexican and Guatemalans and many others did it, but purely and solely for this end of satisfying and feeding their appetite for eating human flesh and having it for their sustenance. Some of these people depraved in this respect, when they were unable to hunt and kill other men secretly and by stealth, did it openly and shamelessly and do it, those tainted by this vice going armed and on the point of war to other regions to make their attacks and wage war on them like one who goes to a boar hunt or for other game, and this was even the most usual thing . . .

After this López Medel describes his own observations on anthropophagy in South America, referring to the Tupi Indians of Brazil, the Caribs near the Marañon river, the Panche settled on the shores of the Magdalena river, and those of Popayan, the Pisaos and the Zuazo Indias of Tierra Firme.

FRANCISCO DE TOLEDO (1570)

The reports on ancient Peru collected by the Viceroy Toledo have always been studied by historians with controversial views. Francisco de Toledo (*c.* 1514–1584) was born in Oropesa, Spain, a younger son of the Count of Oropesa and therefore related to high Spanish nobility, including the King, Philip II, who in 1568 appointed Toledo Viceroy of Peru. Toledo arrived at Payta in 1569 and from that port moved southwards by land visiting Trujillo and other towns before reaching Lima. But he did not remain in the capital; on the contrary, from 1570 to 1573, accompanied by learned men like Acosta, Polo de Ondegardo, Matienzo, Sarmiento de Gamboa and others he visited most of Peru. Viceroy Toledo carried out considerable public works and governmental reforms on the *encomienda,* the *mita,* and other systems of personal servitude of the Indians, which lasted even after the Colonial period. His rule according to some historians was marred by the capture and execution of the last Inca King Tupac Amaru in 1572, but they forget that the viceroy could not escape that decision, being faced with growing armed rebellion and the assassination of his peace emissaries. The reports on Peruvian customs gathered by Toledo show his deep interest in them, and sometimes supply information concerning the behaviour and sexual practices of the Indians.

1882 edition, p. 199

[Report transcribed by the clerk Alvaro Ruiz de Navamuel in 1570]

"... Furthermore it is offered as hearsay evidence that in the province of Collas there were some Indians who committed the nefarious sin (sodomy) and in order to execute this sin they dressed like women and used cosmetics. Some witnesses say that they were punished and others that they were not..."

Another anonymous report to Juan de Sarmiento in 1570 describes the most promiscuous sexual behaviour among the Peruvian Indians.

1920 edition, p. 148

"... This is the most ungrateful people, above any other in the world, much inclined to lie and most inclined to lewdness, so much so that brother does not respect sister, nor father daughter, rather the fathers are accustomed to rape them, nor does the son respect his mother, and it happens many times that the son beats the mother to allow his lust, and finally no respect is held in these matters concerning prudery, any more than beasts..."

DIEGO DE LANDA (*c.* 1570)

Some early reports on sexual behaviour in the Maya area were contested by Diego de Landa (1524–*c.* 1579) who although born in Spain, where he entered the Franciscan order, spent most of his life in Yucatan. He arrived among the Maya in 1549 and for over 30 years was devoted to missionary work. Unfortunately, Landa's zeal in the propagation of the Catholic doctrine and eradication of Pagan beliefs led him to burn most of the Maya codices at Maní; this action has been bitterly deplored by some historians who forget that Tlacaélel, the Aztec leader, had done exactly the same thing in Mexico during the fifteenth century, destroying all the codices of the subjugated Indian nations to secure religious and political hegemony among the Nahuatls. On the other hand Landa eventually became Bishop of Yucatan and was deeply interested in the ancient history of the Maya; in about 1570 he wrote a *Relación de las Cosas de Yucatan*, first published by Brasseur de Bourbourg (1864), which constitutes the cornerstone of our knowledge of Mayan antiquity and the understanding of their hieroglyphic writing.

1864 edition, p. 178, Chapter XXX

p. 176, Chapter XXX: "Punishment of the adulterers, murderers, and thieves . . .

p. 178: "and considering that I have seen that in other parts of the Indies they used the nefarious sin [of sodomy] in such houses, in this land [Yucatan] I have not learnt that they did such a thing, and I do not think they did it, because those with the sores of this pestilential misery [sodomy] they say are not friends of women as these here were; for in those places they took the bad public women and made use of them, and the poor [women] who among this people happened to have that office, although they received presents, had so many men coming to them, that they were worn out and died . . ."

1864 edition, p. 150, Chapter XXVI

p. 150, Chapter XXVI:
   ". . . the *chaces* [sorcerers] went afterwards to the children . . . They asked those grown up if they had committed any sin or had any obscene contact, and if they had done it they confessed them and put them apart . . ."

1864 edition, p. 154, Chapter XXVII

p. 154, Chapter XXVII: "Confession among the Yucatecs: fastings and superstitions. Variety of idols. Offices of the priests.
   "The Yucatecs knew by nature when they did evil, and in the belief that because of evil and sin came deaths, diseases and suffering, they have the custom of confession when they felt proper, in this manner: when by illness or something else they were in danger of death, they confessed their sin, and if they neglected it, their closest relations or friends reminded them of it, and then they publicly said their sins, if the priest was there to him, if not to the fathers and the mothers, and wives to husbands and husbands to wives. The sins of which they usually accused themselves were theft, homicide, of the flesh, false testimony, and with this they thought they were safe and many times if they escaped there were quarrels between husband and wife, on account of the unhappy events, or with those who motivated them.
   "The men confessed their weakness [of the flesh] but for those with

their slave [girls] by those who have them, because they said it was lawful to use one's property in the way one pleased. They did not confess the sins of intention, though they considered them bad and in their advices and preaching said they should be avoided. The abstinences they usually made were salt and pepper in their cooking, which they considered severe, and they abstained from their wives to celebrate their festivities."

1864 edition, p. 201, Chapter XXXIII

"... They said also and held it as absolutely certain that those who hanged themselves went to this heaven of theirs; and on this account, there were many persons who on slight occasions of sorrow, troubles or sickness, hanged themselves in order to escape these things and to go and rest in their heaven, where they said that the goddess of the gallows, whom the called Ix Tab, came to fetch them. They had no memory of the resurrection of the body and give no account from whom they learned of this heaven and hell of theirs..."

PEDRO SARMIENTO DE GAMBOA (1572)

The life of this explorer makes one of the most interesting biographies of the 16th century. Pedro Sarmiento (1532–1592) was born in Pontevedra, and his youth was crowded with studies of mathematics, history, navigation and even magic, which later on led him into trouble with the Holy Office. He went to Mexico in 1555 and resided in Puebla, but had to leave for Peru in 1557, prosecuted by the Inquisition. At Lima Sarmiento devoted himself to teaching, but in 1564 again fell into trouble with the Inquisition, and was fortunate in 1567 to leave commissioned as pilot with the expedition of Alvaro de Mendaña which discovered the Solomon Islands. In 1570 Sarmiento was appointed cosmographer of Peru but again ran into trouble with the Inquisition in 1574 because of his interest in magic. The appearance of Francis Drake's ships in South America in 1579 gave Sarmiento an opportunity to sail in his pursuit, and in 1580 the chance to explore the Magellan Straits. Sarmiento was taken prisoner by the British in 1586 and only in 1590 regained his freedom and reached Madrid. He died in Sanlúcar de Barrameda. The *Historia Indica* written by Sarmiento de Gamboa in 1572 has interesting observations on the confessions used by the Indians of Peru.

1920 edition, pp. 150–151

pp. 150–151: "They have likewise in many parts of Peru, mainly in the Andes, their confessors and houses built for confession, but old men say that in ancient times there appeared a man who from descriptions given of him, should be some sort of holy man who instructed them in Christian things and confession, from whom was left the confession they now used bad and superstitious, which was used before the

Christians arrived and even now in hiding in certain round houses that they have for this purpose in the fields; and each family has its own confessor who usually is the headman or principal. They usually are sorcerers to whom they do not dare to refuse anything because they believe that the confessors know everything and that they would die if they left anything [out of the confession]; they confess alone, though married men confess in front of their wives, and the wives in front of their husbands, without concealing anything, and after leaving the place nothing must be said concerning things told in confession. The things they accused themselves of were everything we have in the commandments of the Decalogue, which are not to revere their *guacas* or worshipping places where the devil use to talk to them, not to honour certain festivities they have; and so on with all the commandments of the law [of God]; but for theft, of which they do not accuse themselves, only the *chapoyas*, because they have licence to rob because they are good men of war; now after the arrival of the Christians they accuse themselves of many other things, such as taking willingly their children to be baptized, and going often to doctrine and the Church, and having served diligently the fathers at the doctrine and the Christians, and because of these the confessors give them very great penitences, such that sometimes have left them there at their feet half dead, and I have learnt from fathers who have found them like that, because they struck them with certain large stones in the back, and afterwards they ordered them to make other great penitences of long fasts, walking through the deserts without food or drink . . ."

JUAN LÓPEZ DE VELASCO (1574)

Little is known of the early life of Juan López de Velasco (*c.* 1540– *c.* 1600), who under the patronage of Juan de Ovando at the Council of the Indies wrote a *Geografía y descripción universal de las Indias* in 1574, first published by J. Zaragoza in 1894. López de Velasco was appointed cosmographer and historian of the Royal Council of the Indies from 1571 to 1591, when he was made secretary to King Philip II. His work is concise and to the point, with considerable technical and scientific value; now and again he makes remarks about the areas and the character of their inhabitants which are balanced and relevant to the ancient history of the natives.

1894 edition, p. 30

p. 30: "Of the religion and customs of the Indians
    ". . . in most or almost every one [of the provinces] they destested the nefarious sin.
p. 160: "District of La Florida
    ". . . they detest the nefarious sin and those who commit it are shamed by being forced to dress in women's garments . . .

p. 185: "Audience of Mexico
    ". . . the natives of these provinces . . . are much inclined to vices . . .
p. 401: "Kingdom of Peru
    ". . . the Indians of this province are all different . . . although they
are all alike in being poor, miserable and vicious, and in different ways
worshippers of the devil.
p. 405: "Audience of Quito
    ". . . the people and natives of it are most vicious and beastly in their
idolatry and vices and perverted inclinations of eating human flesh.
p. 445: "Puerto Viejo
    ". . . The Indians [are] . . . worshippers of the devil and vicious in the
nefarious sin. Among the Indians of this province the recollection is still
vivid that in bygone times certain giants arrived in boats made of
reeds . . . and those giants having arrived into this land without women,
the Indians assert that as there were not [women] in the land as they
needed them, they [the giants] were so dissolute in the nefarious sin
that an angel came from Heaven and a great fire which consumed
every one of them . . ."

It is curious to find that López de Velasco, in respect of the sodomitic
giants, was in 1574 quoting the work of Andrea Bacci (1524–1600) who
was made papal archiatro or physician to Pope Sixtus V. Bacci wrote
several books on precious stones and on medical subjects, but his reference to sodomy in America appeared in his book *De Thermus* (1571) when
he was writing about petroleum springs near Tumbez and this was probably taken by him from Cieza de Leon or Zarate.

JERÓNIMO ROMÁN Y ZAMORA (1575)

Jerónimo de Román y Zamora (1536–1597) was born in Logroño and
entered the Augustinian Order after a disorderly youth. Despite the fact
that P. Román never visited America, he was well informed through his
position close to Philip II and as historian of the Augustinian Order, besides being consultant to the Holy Office of the Inquisition. This is the
reason why Román's main work *Republicas del mundo* published at
Medina del Campo, (1575) offers sound information regarding pre-Columbian America including both Mexican and Peruvian areas.

1575 edition, folio 182 verso. Book III, Chapter VIII
    ". . . and in this way they cure them with great diligence. Their medi-
cines were herbs, and other simples they knew and learnt. After apply-
ing the medicines a wizard or sorcerer or those who cast lots to find
out what chances, and sacrifices were needed more agreeable to the
gods to give health to their sick lord. . . . All these matters and others
being done they order the patient to confess all his sins. What these
Indians confessed commonly was the sin of fornication or adultery,

because this was the most serious they had, because it caused damage to parties, or having sinned with an unmarried woman, because if she was his slave it was not considered a serious sin, because he had her at his use and will, like anything purchased, therefore if they confessed and said I have six sins, it was understood they were of the flesh; they also considered it sinful not to celebrate some of their feasts, but they did not confess to have eaten out of place, or too much; but here it was sinful for the married man to sleep with his wife and to have intercourse with her. . . ."

ALONSO DE ZORITA (c. 1575)

Alonso de Zorita, also sometimes called Zurita (1512–c. 1590), was born in Spain and studied law at the University of Salamanca. He arrived at Santo Domingo in 1545 appointed as *Oidor* of the Court, and after two years went to Nueva Granada with a similar appointment. His fair handling of Indian affairs gained for him three years later the appointment at the Guatemala Audiencia, and he was appointed to the High Court of Mexico in 1554. Zorita remained in Mexico until 1564 when his deafness and poor state of health made it necessary for him to return to Spain, retiring to Granada. There he wrote two important works on the social and economic history of the Mexican Indians *Breve y Sumaria Relación de los señores de la Nueva España* first published in French by Ternaux-Compans (1840) and afterwards in Spanish by García Icazbalceta (1891); a recent English translation by Keen (1965) has appeared with an extremely biased introduction. Zorita also wrote a *Historia de la Nueva España* published with notes by Serrano y Sanz (1909) which seems to have been based on certain manuscripts of Fray Andrés de Olmos (+1571) a Franciscan friar very learned in the Nahuatl language. Zorita mentioned in his works interesting references about sodomy and confession among the pre-Columbian Mexicans.

1909 edition, Chapter XI, p. 167

p. 167: ". . . Fray Andrés [de Olmos] in his Relation says . . . that they also had a sort of confession and penitence privately in front of their idols to appease them and to obtain what they wanted, and that on occasions they were used to evil ends . . ."

DIEGO MUÑOZ CAMARGO (1576)

Because of his Indian extraction and the scarcity of information about the Tlaxcaltecs, the bitter enemies of the Aztecs, it is wise to present the testimony of Diego Muñoz Camargo (1524–c. 1614). He was born in Tlaxcala the son of a Spanish Conquistador and a native girl, was educated in Mexico city and by 1537 was already teaching the Christian doctrine in his native town. Muñoz was married to a Tlaxcaltec princess and was governor of his province four times, the last time in 1613. He wrote in 1576 a *Historia de Tlaxcala*, published in a well annotated edition by A. Chavero in 1892; his judgements are fair and sometimes even harsh on the Indians, but not in respect of sexual behaviour.

1892 edition, pp. 137–138, Chapter XVI

p. 137: "[The Tlaxcaltecs] were proud of having many wives ... but they did not make marriages between brothers and sisters.

p. 138: "They considered as a great abomination the nefarious sin, and the sodomites were despised and considered very low, and treated like women; but they did not punish them, instead they said to them ... You cursed and wretched men, is there by any chance lack of women in the world, you *bardajes* taking the office of women! Were it not better for you to be men? Finally, though there was no penalty for those sins *contra natura* those guilty were abominated and thought bad omen and awful. Neither did they marry their mother, aunt or stepmother ..."

Muñoz Camargo, furthermore, confirmed the human sacrifices among the Tlaxcaltec's rituals and the self-mutilations in cases of guilt. He described most of the drugs today known to produce hallucinations, *peyotl*, the cactus containing mezcaline, *nanacatl* the mushroom containing psylocibin, and other drugs used in ceremonies of divination.

1892 edition, p. 142, Chapter XVII

p. 142: "They drew blood from the tongue if they had offended with it talking, and from the eye lids for looking, and from the arms if they had been lazy, from the legs, thighs, ears and noses according to the guilt they erred and fell, excusing themselves with the devil; and finally they offered him the heart as the best of his body if they did not have anything to give, promising to give him as many hearts of men and children to appease the wrath of their gods or to reach, or obtain other aims they wished; and this served them as vocal confession with the perverted enemy of the human race ..."

1892 edition, p. 134, Chapter XVI

p. 134: "[The Tlaxcalteos] likewise had things which they ate and drank for purpose of divination, with which they fell asleep and lost their senses, and with which they had frightful visions, and saw the devil with these things they took; one thing was called *Peyotl*, another herb *Tlapatl*, another seed they call *Mixitl* and the meat of a bird called *Pito* in our language, they call it *Oconenetl*, that the meat of this bird eaten provoked all these visions. The same property is possessed by a small and tall mushroom which the natives call *Nanacatl*. Of these things the lords used more than humble people: leaving aside the wines they had, because when they got drunk in their drunkenness they saw likewise great and very strange visions, though drunkenness was very much forbidden among them and only those very old and ancient drank it, and when a youth drank it and got drunk he died for it, and thus it was given only to the oldest in the Republic or when these took place a very celebrated festivity it was given with great temperance to qualified men, old and honoured in war matters . . ."

FRANCISCO HERNANDEZ (1577)

The work on the Mexican Materia Medica by Francisco Hernandez (1517–1587) is without any doubt the most systematic and thorough study undertaken during the Spanish Colonial period. He was born in Puebla de Montalvan, Toledo and studied medicine in Alcalá de Henares. Hernandez practised medicine at Seville around 1553, afterwards at the celebrated Monastery of Guadalupe in Extremadura and finally at the Hospital of Mendoza in Toledo. In 1567 Philip II made Hernandez physician to his chamber and in 1570 appointed him Protophysician of the American possessions. Hernandez, however, only visited Mexico and from 1571 to 1577 was engaged with his son and several Indian experts in the classification and medicinal trial of all the drugs animal, vegetable and mineral of New Spain. His original work, unfortunately, was destroyed during a fire at the Escorial, though a summary by N. A. Recco under the title *Rerum medicarum Novae Hispaniae Thesaurus* was published by the Lincei in Rome (1628–1651) and also by Gomez Ortega (1790); recently all his works have been published in Mexico (1960). The descriptions left by Hernandez of drugs producing hallucinations or affecting behaviour are modern, follow the strictest botanical rules of his time and represent the Mexican beliefs about their properties. They include the *peyotl*—containing mezcaline, *esqua* or *toloatzin*—a Datura with scopolamine, the mushrooms *nanácatl*—with psylocibin, *oloiuhqui*—similar to Morning Glory, and several others which are extremely potent.

1790 edition, Vol. I, p. 74; Book I, Chapter CXXXIII

"*Aquiztli* or herb which adorns. The aquiztli is a vinelike twining plant with leaves similar to those of the *tzitzin* or *elme*; its fruit is acinus with red peduncles, it has a sour taste and is naturally cold, dry and astringent. It is also said that this plant drives those who eat it mad. It grows in Xicotépec."

1790 edition, Vol. I, p. 211; Book III, Chapter XXVI

"*Poyomatli* . . . There is another root of the same name which induces a strange madness and through which the Indians believe that secrets and the future are revealed to them. . . ."

1790 edition, Vol. I, p. 296; Book VIII, Chapter XLIII

"*Esqua* is a bush with ramified roots from which sprout stems six cubits long, misshapen, knotted and green in colour, the leaves are hairy like those of nightshade (it may well be of the same species) but more pointed, its fruit is similar to the date and contains a stone. Having fasted all day and purified the house, the Indians eat the fruit to enable them to find things that have been lost or stolen, and to see, even shut up in the house, a picture of the thief. The leaves, ground and applied, cure inflammation. The Michoacanenses call it *esqua* and the Mexican *toloatzin*. It grows in temperate or cold regions such as Patzcuaro and Mexico and it is naturally a cold, damp plant although the root is fairly sweet."

1790 edition, Vol. II, pp. 357–358; Book IX, Chapter XCV

"On the *nanácatl* or a kind of mushroom. There are in New Spain so many varieties of mushrooms that it would be too wearisome to describe or depict each one, therefore we will now deal with some of them in detail and leave for another occasion what is pertinent to the doctrine or complements the natural history of the New World. Briefly, then, some mushrooms grown in these lands and called *citlalnacame* are deadly; there are others named *teihuintli*, which do not cause death ingested, but produce temporary insanity manifested by immoderate laughter; they are tawny in colour, acrid and of a strong though not disagreeable smell. There are others which, without producing laughter, engender all sorts of visions such as war and demons . . . those which, because they cause intoxication, are called *teihuintli*. These are dun coloured and they produce senseless laughter and visions."

1790 edition, Vol. III. p. 18; Book XIII, Chapter XXIV

"*Nacázcul*. It is a species of *tlápatl* found in the province of Huexotzinco. In the early stages its guilt is thorny but later these thorns are shed. It is round and divided, like the melon, in four parts. The seed is tawny in colour and resembles that of the radish . . . care must be taken not to exceed the stated dose as this would produce alienation, visions and delirium. Some people call it *toloatzin*."

1790 edition, Vol. III, p. 19. Book XIII, Chapter XXXV

"*Tlápatl*. Its roots are white and ramified, its fruit round and similar to a chestnut bur, its leaves like those of the vine, wide and divided by deep lines, and its flower white, long and capsule shaped. It is like the *nacázcul*, naturally cold and lacks a distinctive taste or smell . . . A few drops on the pillow brings sleep to those who suffer from insomnia, and taken in large quantities its brings on madness. It is found everywhere but mainly in Tepecuacuilco and Mexico."

1790 edition, Vol. III, pp. 31– 32; Book XIV, Chapter I

"On the *ololiuhqui*, or round-leaved plant. The *ololiuhqui*, which some call *coaxihuitl* or herb of the serpent, is a vine-like plant with fibrous roots, cylindrical, narrow green stems and leaves which are also narrow and green but heart-shaped, long white flowers and a round seed which resembles coriander, from which it takes its name. It is hot to the fourth degree . . . When the Indian priests wished to simulate a conversation with their gods and receive replies to their questions they partook of the plant which produced delirium and apparitions of phantoms and demons. This property can be said to be similar to Dioscorides's *Solanum manicum*. It is found in the open country of the warmer regions."

1790 edition, Vol. III, pp. 70–71; Book XV, Chapter XXV

"On *peyotl zacatecano* or soft woolly root. It is a medium-sized root which produces neither branches nor leaves above ground, but merely a down which is attached to the root. For this reason it was not possible to draw it. It is said that there is a male and a female of the species. It is sweet to the taste and of moderate heat . . . If we are to believe a theory which is given great credence among the Indians, this plant gives to those who eat it the power of foreseeing and foretelling the future. Whether, for example, enemies were to attack the following day, whether happy times were ahead, who stole a utensil or any other object, and many other things which the Chichimecs try to find out through the medium of this drug. In addition, when they wish to know where to look for the root they eat another one which tells them. It grows in warm humid areas."

By carefully surveying Hernandez's work it is possible to gather through the medicinal plants used by the Mexicans, the mental syndromes they recognized and the manner in which he as a 16th century physician was able to interpret them. Some of Hernandez's ideas, and even the way he described the pharmacological action of tobacco and coca, for instance, can hardly be improved today.

1790 edition, Books and chapters indicated

Book III, Chapter I: "Of the *Atlipozonzapitzahoac* or foam of sedative water . . . is good against the heart irritation, the seizure, the anxiety and the fevers.

Book XVI, Chapter LXXIV: "Of the *Qualancapatli* or medicine for the irate man . . . it is administered . . . to whom is sick because he in anger or has received some insult; that is the reason of its name.

Book XIV, Chapter XVI: "Of the third *Oceloxochitl* . . . They say that the root . . . removes the sadness of the heart, particularly if due to another drug.

Book III, Chapter CXIII: "Of the *Tolpatli* or the reed medicine . . . It is said that reconciles love if the man sprayed with it touches the hand or the body of the woman he loves.

Book VI, Chapter XXXII: "Of the *Cutiriqui* . . . They say that stimulates venereal lust, that reliefs fevers, removes jealousy and reconciles the love between spouses.

Book VII, Chapter X: "Of the second *Cunguricua* ... The Indians say that the pod when eaten reconciles the love between spouses and makes it firm.

Book XV, Chapter XXXVI: "Of the *Pinahuihuitzli* or bashful herb ... They say that reconciles love ... the sap of the root ... produces sleep.

Book XVIII, Chapter CXLIII: "Of the *Tetechmomatiaui* or medicine of love... They also say that ground and mixed with *tlapatli* reconciles love.

Book V, Chapter I: "Of the *Tomatl* or plant with acinus fruits ... these fruits have been called the fruits of love.

Book IX, Chapter XX: "Of the first *Huapahuizpatli* or medicine for stress. They say that anointed cures stress and the pain of the whole body.

Book IV, Chapter LIX: "Of the *Tecomahaca* ... strengthens the brain and weakened nerves.

Book X, Chapter CXLVII: "Of the *Tlaliztacpatli* or whitish and small medicine ... the root is [used] against delirium and fevers.

Book IV, Chapter XLIV: "Of the *Tecopalquahuitl pitzahoac* or tenuifolio ... the sap of this tree ... they say it cures those who have delirium without having fever.

Book XVII, Chapter CXXIII: "Of the *Tetlahuelicpatli* or medicine for those who are delirious ... The juice of the leaves is usually administered to those who are delirious or insane.

Book I, Chapter CXVI: "Of the *Acaxilotic* or spike of maize's cane ... when applied to the head alleviates those insane.

Book VI, Chapter CXLII: "Of the *Poztecpatli* or medicine for fractures ... washing with it the legs of those insane they get cured.

Book VI, Chapter CLII: "Of the *Iyauhtli* or herb of the clouds ... alleviates those insane and those frightened and stunned by lightning.

Book XVIII, Chapter LXXXV: "Of the third *Tlaloelilocapatli* ... when applied to the head alleviates insanity.

Book IV, Chapter V [Animals]: "Of the *Hoitztócatl* or thorny spider ... spider which sting causes insanity.

Book I, Chapter XXXVIII: "Of the first *Acxoyatic* or herb like the spruce ... they also say that it is inebriating and it is mixed with drugs that induce rest.

Book II, Chapter CIX: "Of the *Picietl* [tobacco] or herb *yetl* ... with it the head is strengthened, sleep is produced, pain is calmed, the stomach recovers its force, the headache is cured, the feeling of sorrow and travail becomes dulled, and the soul is invaded entirely by calm of every faculty (which we could almost call inebriation).

Book XXI, Chapter LXXII: "Of the plant called Peruvian *Coca* ... it extinguishes the thirst, nourishes extraordinarily the body, calms down hunger when there is not abundance of food and drink, and takes away the fatigue in the long journeys. They use also [the leaves] mixed with *yetl* as a pleasure, when they remain in their villages and homes to induce sleep or obtain intoxication, peace and oblivion of all the sorrows and cares.

Book XI, Chapter XXXVII: "Of the *Quauhyayahoal* . . . when it is applied on the head alleviates those frantic or insane, takes away the fevers . . . and recovers those injured by lightning, apoplectics and those who have lost their senses by any other cause.

Book XXI, Chapter   : "Of the *Capancapacua* . . . they say that a decoction of its leaves drank cures mental alienation.

Book II, Chapter I [Animals]: "Of the *Hoactzin* or bird that utters a sound like its name . . . the fumes of its feathers returns reason to those who came out of a disease somewhat insane.

Book XIII, Chapter LI: "Of the *Neyoltzayanalizpatli* or medicine for fainted heart . . . the leaves in water are administered to those frightened.

Book II, Chapter XLIII: "Of the second *Tlepatli* . . . it cures excitement of the mind and the ailments of the heart caused by it.

Book XXI, Chapter XXX: "Of the *Coatli Xochitlanensis* or *Coanenepilli* . . . the root . . . expels the retained semen and almost out of its proper container as result of the images induced by dreams . . . and also protects the day it is taken from witchcrafts, traps, and noxious foods from whores.

Book IV, Chapter LX: "Of the *Tlahoelilocaquahuitl* or tree of madness . . . the evil spirits fear very much this tree and avoid it; it frees from spells.

Book XX, Chapter XXVI: "Of the *Xochitlapitzalli* . . . the bark . . . if taken in too much quantity produces sometimes persistent madness.

Book XVII, Chapter LXXXIII: "Of the *Tlahoelilocapatli* or medicine for madness . . . any part of it cooked with copali and xochiocócotl cures a twisted mouth or any other part of the body relaxed.

Book IV, Chapter XXVIII [Animals]: "Of the spiders *Laualaua* . . . its sting . . . turns mad to those affected.

Book XXIV, Chapter XXVII: "Of the *Teotlacxihuitl* . . . taken with . . . *atonahuizpatli* or *yolilácatz* alleviates those recently mad.

Book XX, Chapter XLIII: "Of the *Xochitl* . . . (according to the veterinary in Oaxaca) recovers the lost memory and takes away the headache with admirable speed.

Book I, Chapter XXIII: "Of the second *Acocoquilitl* . . . it is said that . . . induces sleep, specially if mixed with other herbs which we will mention in the chapter of the *Tecochitixihuitl*.

Book II, Chapter CXLII: "Of the *Cochiztzápotl* or somniferous *tzápotl* . . . the fruit eaten induces sleep, which is the reason of its name.

Book III, Chapter LVII: "Of the *Xochiocotzoquahuitl* or the liquidambar tree of the Indies . . . mixed with tobacco strengthens the head . . . induces sleep and mitigates headache . . .

Book V, Chapter LXXII: "Of the *Cozolmecatl* or rope of the cradle . . . the root . . . alleviates the head and induces sleep.

Book VII, Chapter XCIV: "Of the *Cochizquilitl* or soporiferous green ...
its juice crushed and instilled in the mouth of the babies induces sleep
in them; from this comes its name.

Book IX, Chapter LXII: "Of the *Ahuahuauhyo* or herb like the *Ahuauhtli*
... alone or mixed with other herbs induces sleep.

Book XVIII, Chapter XLIX: "Of the *Tecochitixihuitl*. It is a soporiferous
herb, from where its name comes ... applied with milk to the temples
and the head induces lethargic sleep.

Book XVIII, Chapter L: "Of the second *Tecochitixihuitl*. The juice ...
with woman's milk if applied to the forehead to those unable to sleep
due to excessive heat, it induces sleep in a wonderful manner.

Book I, Chapter XXII [Animals]: "Of the *Mazame* or deers ... [the
bezoar stones] cure the stroke and epileptic seizures and applied to
the fingers induce sleep.

Book VI, Chapter XXIII: "Of the *Tzoyac* or that smells burnt ... Smoking
small children with the fumes of the leaves when they have been
frightened, perhaps by strengthening the head and the stomach, controls or dissipates the vapours of fear.

Book XIX, Chapter XXIV: "Of the *Tzopelicpatli* acatlamensis ... its fumes
cure those who due to a fright get thinner little by little, because they
say that by provoking sweat they recover their health.

Book XIV, Chapter XCVI: "Of the *Tzitzicazpatli* or medicine like nettle
... it is taken against the falls and blows and against sudden night
fears ...

Book III, Chapter VII: "Of the *Ocopetlatl* from Quauhtla ... the leaves
crushed and taken with water dissipate false fears, alleviate sadness
and cure faints.

Book VI, Chapter XLIV: "Of the *Tlaolli* or maize and of the drinks and
kinds of cakes they use to make with it ... they take putting first chilli
those with fainted heart or excess of bile who are almost always sad.

Book XI, Chapter XIX: "Of the *Yolcocolpatli* or medicine for a sick
heart ... it is taken for those ailments resulting from heart diseases.

Book I, Chapter CVI: "Of the *Acaxaxan* or marshy and tender plant which
if crushed, crumbles between the fingers ... it helps in dismay, vanishes
groundless fear and strengthens the fainted body."

DIEGO VALADÉS (1579)

Very few authors were in a better position to understand the concept of
confession among pre-Columbian civilizations and its adaptation into the
Catholic dogma than Diego Valadés (1533–c. 1590). He was the son of
the Conquistador Diego Valadés who went to Mexico with the soldiers
sent by Narvaez, and an Indian girl, and was born in Tlaxcala. Because
of his extraction he soon mastered, besides Spanish and Latin, three
Indian languages—Nahuatl, Tarascan and Otomí. Around 1550 Valadés
entered the Franciscan Order and spent several years in missionary work

among the Chichimec Indians. In 1571 Valadés went to France to attend the Council of the Franciscan Order, and afterwards visited Spain, but in 1575 he became Solicitor of his Order in Rome. He wrote several religious works in native languages, but from the point of view of cultural transfer the most important is the *Rhetorica Christiana* first printed at Perugia in 1579, reprinted there in 1582 and 1583 and translated into German in 1590. This book contains 28 plates engraved by the author explaining psychological phenomena and theological problems within the pictographic tradition of the ancient Mexican techniques used in the codices. They refer to doctrine, Mexican history and ethnography.

1579 edition, p. 189

"... It follows this that it is not really burdensome to hear the confessions of the Indians, since usury, commerce and contracts, to which the Spaniards give attention, are alien to them; their more usual sins, however, are deceitfulness, lust, drunkenness and theft, but momentary only, for the Indians never commit serious theft, nor is this remarkable ..."

CODEX RAMIREZ (*c.* 1580)

There is certain confusion about the author of the Codex Ramirez, which was used and transcribed into his works by D. Durán, and was named after the celebrated Mexican historian Jose Fernando Ramirez (1804–1871). Ramirez was born in Hidalgo de Parral, Chihuahua, and died in exile in Bonn, Germany, because he had been the minister of Foreign Affairs during the short lived rule of Emperor Maximilian in 1864. The given title of the Codex Ramirez, which was published in 1878, is *Treatise of the rites and ceremonies and gods which the Indians of this New Spain used in their infidelity.* The only part of interest apart from the sections used in their entirety by Durán, is the record of *Ololiuhqui* being used among the Aztecs for purposes of divination.

1878 edition, Chapter III, p. 112

"Of the temple of this idol Tezcatlipoca where we deal as a whole and together about the ceremonies and order of dignities and priests which existed.

"... They put jointly with this herb [tobacco] and ashes some scorpions, and spiders alive, and millepedes, and they mixed them and crushed them together, and after all this they put a seed ground which they call Ololiuhqui which the Indians drink just to see visions, and which has the effect of depriving of judgement ..."

PEDRO GUTIERREZ DE SANTA CLARA (*c.* 1580)

The details gathered by Cieza de León were confirmed in another chronicle written by an obscure, though reliable, Conquistador of Peru.

Pedro Gutierrez de Santa Clara (1522–1603) was the son of a converted Jew, Bernardino de Santa Clara who participated with Cortés in the Conquest of Mexico, and a Mexican Indian girl; Pedro had at least five other brothers and sisters of mixed blood who inherited his father's Mexican estate. He joined Gonzalo Pizarro's forces around 1542 and participated in the Conquest and the Civil Wars of Peru. Gutierrez de Santa Clara wrote the *Quinquenarios o Historia de las Guerras Civiles del Peru* (*c.* 1580) dedicated to the Viceroy of Mexico, Marquis of Montes-Claros, and died in Mexico shortly afterwards. Perhaps his Mexican ancestry gives the *Quinquenarios* less prejudice on Inca history than works by Peruvian writers, and although his narrative has been considered timid, Gutierrez de Santa Clara is an honest chronicler with excellent literary style. His text mentions the large sodomitic area at Manta in North Peru, the legend of the sodomite giants and, what is very important for the interpretation of the Virú and Mochica sodomitic pottery which had passed unnoticed by archaeologists, that sodomitic pottery representations of nose and lip mutilation were a sign of religious office, and not of punishment for sexual aberrations.

1963 edition, Vol. 166, p. 215. Book III, Chapter L

[Temples of the Sun built by Topa Inga Yupangue]
"... They castrated and cut the noses and lips of the Indians who served in these temples, and they killed them very cruelly if they had dishonest conversation with them [the vestals of the sun god] ..."

1963 edition, Vol. 166, p. 259; Book III, Chapter LXVI

"Chapter LXVI. Of how certain giants arrived at the Province of Manta, who came from some islands of the South Sea, and afterwards they were burnt by celestial fire, and account of other things in the land ...
"... Because these devilish [giants] had been so long without women, and because the demon had misled, and blinded them and distracted them away from natural reason, they had got very drunk, and proceeded from this the nefarious sin [sodomy], and they were like that for many years in this devilish vice, so they were not ashamed and they did not mind to use it publicly. The natives (of Manta province) when they learnt that these Indians of Lucifer used this cursed sin, they said that those [giants] were dogs and brutal animals, or that they were demons who had left hell for this world in the shape of men to the amazement of the world. It seems to me that the Indians of Manta we see in our days, learnt from their ancestors and from these great giants this diabolic and heinous vice, because in these days they use it in their rites and ceremonies and in their drunkenness. Juan de Olmos, domiciled in the village of Puerto Viejo, burnt great numbers of these perverse and devilish Indians, because he was the Chief Justice then and there, though the town was within his jurisdiction, to

make them abandon this pestiferous and devilish vice, but he never got any profit from it. The natives say that when these giants were one day engaged in certain heinous sacrifices and using the nefarious sin, a very handsome young man came flying from heaven with great shine and that he shed so much fire over them that he burnt all alive, but a few escaped because they were underground."

CRISTOBAL DE MOLINA (c. 1580)

Cristobal de Molina of Cuzco (c. 1529–1585) was born in Baeza, Spain, and from 1556 was a priest in Cuzco; in 1565 he became parish priest of the Na. Sa. de los Remedios Church attached to the Natives' Hospital, but under Viceroy Toledo, because of his knowledge of the Quechua language, he was soon appointed Ecclesiastical Inspector. Molina accompanied the Bishop of Cuzco Sebastian de Lartaún to the Third Concilium of Lima in 1583, and prepared for that purpose a *Relación de las fábulas y ritos de los Incas* first published by Markham (1873) in English. The work of Molina of Cuzco dealing with the religion and calendar of the Incas must not be confused with that of another Cristobal de Molina of Santiago de Chile (1494–1580) who wrote *Relación de ... el Perú* dealing with the conquest and population of Peru.

1873 edition, pp. 14–15

"... There were also other sorcerers who had charge of the *huacas* among whom there were some who conferred with the devil and received his replies, telling the people what they wished to know or privately to certain persons who asked for this request, but very seldom gave correct answers. According to the accounts they give all the people of the land confessed to the sorcerers who had charge of the *huacas*; and these confessions were made public, to know if they confessed the truth: The sorcerer cast lots and in this way with the aid of the devil, found out who had confessed a lie, and upon these they inflicted severe punishments. Those who had grave crimes to confess which merited death confessed them in secret to him.

"The Incas and the people of Cuzco always made their confessions in secret and generally they confessed to those Indian sorcerers of Huaro who were employed for this office. In their confessions they accused themselves of not having reverenced the sun, the moon and the huacas, with not having reverenced the feasts of the Raymis which are those in each month of the year, with all their hearts; with having committed fornication against the law of the Inca not to have the wife of another or to corrupt any virgin, or to take her unless given by the Inca, and not because fornication was a sin, because they did not consider this to be so. They accused themselves of murder and theft, which they considered a serious crime, and likewise to murmur, especially if they had been against the Inca or against the sun."

1873 edition, pp. 63–64

"... There were several forms of apostacy during this time, some danced and gave out that they had the *huaca* in their bodies. Others trembled for the same reason. Others shut themselves up in their houses and shouted. Others flung themselves from rocks and were killed and others jumped into the rivers, thus offering themselves to the *huacas* ...

"... When any Indian is sick they call these sorcerers to find out if they will live or die. Having pronounced upon the case, they order the sick man to take white maize called *calliçara*, red and yellow maize called *cumaçara*, yellow maize they called *paro-çara* and other sea shells they called *mollo mollo* of all the colours they can collect which they call *ymaymana-mollo*. When these things are collected the sorcerer grinds the maize with the *mollo* and gives it ground in the hand to the sick man to blow it so he may offer it to the *huacas* and *vilcas* with these words: 'To all the *huacas* and *vilcas* of the four parts of this land, my grandparents and ourselves receive this sacrifice wheresoever you may be and give me health". They also make him blow a little *ioca* to the sun offering it and praying for his health and likewise to the moon and the stars. Then with a little gold and silver of little value in his hand, the sick man offers to the creator spilling it (or throwing it) away. Then the sorcerer orders him to give food to the dead placing it on their graves, if there is in a place where it can be done, and pouring out *chicha* and if not in a corner of his house. Because the sorcerer gives the patient to understand that disease has arrived because the dead are starving. And if he is able to go on foot to some junction of two rivers, the sorcerer makes him go there and wash his body with water and flour of white maize, saying that he will there leave his illness and if not in the house of the sick man. At the end of the ceremony the sorcerer makes a speech telling him that if he wishes to escape from that illness he must confess then and there all his sins without concealing any, and they call this *hichoco*."

DIEGO DURAN (1581)

Several suggestions have been made concerning the sources used by Diego Duran (*c.* 1537–1588), but it must be remembered that, although he was born in Seville, he arrived as a child in Mexico in 1542. Duran grew up in Texcoco, an area rich in ancient traditions, and in 1556 entered the Dominican Order of the Convent of Mexico City. After years of missionary work he produced several books concerning Mexican antiquities, in 1570 the *Book of the gods and their rites*, in 1579 the *Mexican calendar* and from 1570 to 1581 his most important study *Historia de los Indios de Nueva España* which was published by J. F. Ramírez (1867–1880) from the original MS preserved in Madrid. Duran was very much impressed by the close relationship between parents and children within the Aztec family, and by the existence in their religion of certain rituals like confession and communion very similar to the Sacraments of the Catholic Church. He also left in his *History of Mexico* a description of the use of hallucinogenic drugs, *ololiuhqui* and *teonanacatl* which were taken for divination and in ritual ceremonies.

1880 edition, Vol. II, Chapter LXXXI, p. 36

"... in honouring the fathers and the mothers, and relatives and priests and old people there is no nation in the world and has never been a people who honoured their elders with more fear and reverence than this one [of Mexico]. Those irreverent to old people, fathers, or mothers lost their lives, and thus what these people asked and taught to their children was to revere the old in every dignity and position they were ..."

Chapter LXXXII

p. 101: "Of the god call Tezcatlipoca and the manner he was solemnized. "... the people who regretted their faults and sins asked in that day [of the festivity] that their sins were not known ..."

1867 edition, Vol. I, Chapter LIX, p. 431

p. 431: "... Once the sacrifice was over, the steps of the temple and courtyard weltered in human blood, and everyone departed in order to partake of raw mushrooms, with that eaten all lost their senses, and were in worse condition than if they had drunk a lot of wine; so inebriated and out of judgement were they that many of them killed themselves by their own hand, and with the power of those mushrooms saw visions and had revelations of the future, for the devil spoke to them while they were intoxicated ... History has it that from that day Montezuma summoned all kings and enemy chieftains for a celebration thrice in every year; the first was the feast of chieftains, the second the feast of flags, and that remaining was the feast at which they partook of the mushrooms, being called the feast of revelation ..."

GASPAR ANTONIO CHI (1582)

This Maya Indian, born Gaspar Antonio Xiu (*c.* 1531–*c.* 1610) at Maní, Yucatan, was the son of the *Ah Kin* or priest Napuc Chi who died with other relatives at the famous massacre of Otzmal in 1536. Chi was the godson of the wife of Montejo, the Conquistador of Yucatan. He studied at the Franciscan Convent in Mérida protected by Bishop Landa and knew, besides his native Maya, the Spanish and Nahuatl languages. Chi wrote a *Relación sobre las costumbres de los Indios* in 1582 known first through an abstract published by Lopez de Cogulludo (1688) and translated from the original Maya by Roys; this translation has been published by Tozzer (1941). Chi's account containing the laws of the Maya, mentioned both by Landa and Cogolludo, was prepared by order of Guillen de las Casas, the Governor of Yucatan, when Chi was the official interpreter, and although his testimony according to Tozzer (1941) is biased because of his Indian extraction, Chi was well informed.

1941 edition, pp. 230–232

"... Nor is it true that in this province they committed unnatural crime [sodomy] or did they eat human flesh ... They did not imprison anyone for debt although they did for theft and for adultery, but only if they took the offenders in the act these were condemned to death or imprisoned ... there was another prison ... in which they put children and others of greater age condemned to death and for sacrifice ...

"The oath, it was nothing else than cursing ... for it was believed that they did not lie in order not to curse themselves ... Today many perjure themselves, not understanding the gravity of the oath ... They punish vices with severity. The man or woman who committed adultery received the penalty of death, and they killed them with arrows ... They greatly hated this vice ...

"He who corrupted any maiden or violated any woman received the penalty of death ...

"He who assaulted a married woman or the daughter of anyone while she was under the authority of her parents or broke into her home received the penalty of death ... the thief remained enslaved until he was redeemed ..."

MIGUEL CABELLO DE BALBOA (1586)

Born in Archidona, Andalusia, Miguel Cabello de Balboa (1535–1608) first entered a military career and fought bravely in Flanders up to 1558. Returning to Malaga he entered the Augustinian Order and in 1566 went to South America devoted to missionary work. Cabello was in Quito from 1574, worked in the mission of San Juan, valley of Ica from 1580, and in 1594 went to Camata where he died. He was very interested in the customs of the Chuncho Indians and wrote about them, though his best known work was the *Miscelánea Antártica* written between 1576 and 1586, but published in 1920. It is worth recalling that Cabello mentioned there the Indian practice of confession.

1920 edition, Chapter I, p. 4

p. 4: "... In some provinces they had confessors to whom they confessed without reserve all their faults, and who imposed upon them a penitence ..."

JOSÉ DE ACOSTA (1589)

The work of José de Acosta (1540–1600) occupies a very important place in the history of American anthropology and natural history. He was born in Medina del Campo, Spain, entering the Society of Jesus in 1553; owing to his clear intelligence, Acosta began in 1567 to teach theology in Ocaña. In 1571 he went to America and after teaching at Lima he accompanied Viceroy Toledo during his travels through Peru. In 1576 Acosta was elected Provincial of the Jesuits in Peru, and in 1583 he took a very active part in the III Council of Lima, being the historian of its proceedings published in 1591. Acosta was recalled by Philip II to Spain, visiting Mexico on the way, and he went to Rome where he played an ill-fated role against the election of C. Acquaviva as General of the Jesuits in 1592. Acosta's best known work is the *Historia Natural y Moral de las Indias* published in Seville (1590) where among other things he describes the natural history of America, the action of coca leaves, and the syndrome of altitude. From our point of view the important points are his description of confession among the Peruvian Indians and his views on Indian rationality first presented in his *De procuranda indorum salute,* published in Salamanca (1589). Acosta gave detailed consideration (1590) to establishing a parallel between the structure and sacraments of the Catholic Church and those of the Mexican and Peruvian Indians. Chapter 23 (pp. 358–360) in the *Natural and Moral History of the Indies* (1590) is dedicated to "How the Devil tried to reproduce the Sacraments of the Holy Church". And Chapter 24 (pp. 360–364) refers to "The manner the Devil tried in Mexico to reproduce the feast of *Corpus Christi* and the Communion used by the Holy Church."

1590 edition, Book IV, Chapter 22, p. 250

p. 250, Chapter 22: "Of the Cocoa and the Coca.

p. 251: "... In Peru ... grows the Coca which is by far a greater superstition and seems a thing of fiction.

"... The practice is to keep it in the mouth, and to chew it sucking it without swallowing: they say it gives them great strength and it is most singular pleasure to them. Many important people consider it superstition and a thing of pure fiction. I to tell the truth do not persuade myself that it is just imagination, on the contrary I believe that in effect it gives strength and support to the Indians, because effects can be seen that cannot be attributed to imagination, such as marching double journeys with a handful of *coca*, sometimes without eating anything else, and other similar works ..."

1590 edition, Book V, Chapter XXV, pp. 364–368

"Of the confession, and confessors used by the Indians. The same father of lies wanted to mimic also the Sacrament of Confession and in his idolatries to be honoured by a ceremony very similar to that used by the faithful. In Peru they believed that all adversities and diseases came because of sins committed, and to remedy that they used sacrifices: and besides that they also used oral confession in almost all the provinces, and they had deputed for this higher and lower confessors, and reserved sins for the higher ones, and they received penitences, sometimes hard, particularly if the man who committed the sin was poor and had nothing to give the confessor; and this office of confession was also held by women. In the province of Collasuyo the use of Shaman confessors whom they call *Ychùri* (or *Ychùiri*) was, and is, more extended. They maintain that it is notorious sin to hide any sin in the confession, and the *Ychùris* or confessors find out, either by casting lots, or looking into entrails of some animal if any sin is hidden and punish it by striking him in the back with a stone a number of blows until he tells everything, and they give him the penitence and make the sacrifice. They use also this confession when their children, wives, or husbands, or headmen are sick, or when they are in great troubles; and when the Inca was ill they confessed in all the provinces, particularly the *Collas*. The confessors were committed to secrecy, but with certain limitations. The sins of which they mainly accused themselves were, first killing somebody other than in war, also robbery, also taking somebody else's wife, also giving [dangerous] herbs, or witchcraft to harm. And they held it as a very notorious sin to be careless about their *huacas*. And not to keep their feasts, and to speak badly of the Inca. And not to obey him. They did not accuse themselves of internal sins or acts, and according to some priest's accounts, after the Christians arrived in the land, they accused themselves to their *Ychùris* or confessors, even of their thoughts. The Inca did not confess his sins to any man but to the Sun, for it to give to Viracócha and be forgiven. After confession the Inca carried out certain ritual ablution and finished the cleansing of his faults: and it was in this way, being in a running river he said these words: I have told my sins to the Sun, you river receive them, take them to sea where they can never be found. These washings were performed by the rest who confessed with a ceremony very similar to that used by the Moors called by them *Guadoi*, and by the Indians *Opacúna*. And when it happened that some children died, the father thought he was a great sinner saying that it was due to his sins that the children died before the father. And these after confession carried out the washing ceremony called Opacúna (as we have said) they had to be flogged with certain type of nettles by a monstrous Indian, hunchback, or deformed from birth. If the wizards, or witches by their lots or omen said that some sick man was going to die, they did not hesitate to kill their own son, even if he was their only one, and by that they expected to gain their health, saying that they offered in sacrifice their son instead. And after the Christians arrived in this land this cruelty has been found in some parts. It is an interesting thing, that this custom of confessing secret sins has been preserved and the performance of such harsh penitences such as fasting, the giving of cloth, gold, silver, remaining in the mountains, or receiving hard whipping in the back. And nowadays some of ours [Spaniards] say that this pestilence of confessors or *Ychùris* is found in the province of Chicuyto, and that many sick people go to them. But, already thanks to the grace of God they are being undeceived and learn the great benefit of our Sacramental confession, and they come into it with great devotion. And in part it has been the providence of the Lord to allow its use in the past so that confession was not difficult to them: and thus the Lord is glorified in everything, and the mocking demon is deceived . . ."

After this Acosta describes the confession in Japan where the sinners were placed in scales near an abyss.

BLÁS VALERA (1590)

There is an anonymous account *De las costumbres antiguas de los Naturales del Peru* written by a Jesuit around 1590, which has been attributed to Blás Valera (1551–1597) where several references to sodomy were included. Padre Valera, born in Chachapoyas, was a mestizo, the son of one of Pizarro's captains and a *mamacona* or Indian girl from the Inca court. Valera studied in Trujillo—an area where sodomy was notorious—and became a Jesuit. He died in Cadiz shortly after Drake's attack. His work was first published in 1879 and like several other texts written by authors of Inca extraction praised the Indian past. Valera's account of the *Ancient customs of the Peruvian natives* mentions, in referring to the *Ichuri* or confessor of sins, that one of the faults reported in confession was:

1968 edition, p. 165

". . . to commit the nefarious [sin or sodomy] with man or beast . . ."

Dealing with the civil life of the ancient Peruvians Valera produced an introduction exculpating them of the blemishes some historians have mentioned; this is quite revealing because of his repeated references to sexual deviations.

1968 edition, p. 174

"The customs and habits of a nation and the people of its republic must not be measured for the actions of some of them or vicious ones, but for what the whole community does or feels it ought to do, and by the laws issued and executed. Because even if we see five or six thieves or homicides, or we hear that this one or that one used the nefarious [sin or sodomy], or has sacrificed his son, we must not condemn the whole nation . . . From here (the feasts of triumph or *hailli*) began what serious authors have written, that they [the Incas] did not respect first grade kinship, consanguity or affinity, and that the problem reached such a degree that they *etiam* [even] used the nefarious [sin or sodomy], and that the children did not wait just up to the years of puberty; this is in part true, considering that the Peruvians during the period when they lacked the Inca government, did not have anybody to control them . . . the Inca permitted certain vices publicly and he did not enquire about secret ones even if he learnt of them, to avoid greater vices more harmful to the republic . . . He allowed in those meetings for drinking and drunks, the presence of prostitutes . . . to avoid incests, adulteries, rapes and nefarious [sin or sodomy] . . . All the care of the Inca was not to have abductions of women, raping of girls in the villages, or with virgins *Ucllas* [Vestals], nor adulteries, incests, or sins against nature [sodomy] . . . because in finding something like that the law was executed without mercy killing adulterers incestuous or nefarious [sodomites] . . ."

Finally there is a short reference in Valera which confirms the castration of certain priests mentioned by Gutierrez de Santa Clara,

1968 edition, p. 163

" . . . The confessors of the virgins who were kept in the temples had to be either *eunuchs* or men who had proved perpetual chastity, and they usually were old men . . ."

1968 edition, pp. 168–169

"Indian priests.

" . . . Many of them offer themselves since childhood, not only with continence until old age, but being virgins . . . Many of them or most of them were eunuchs, whom they call *corasca*, because they castrate themselves in reverence to their gods, or have been castrated by others while they were boys, to be in service in their office . . ."

JUAN DE CÁRDENAS (1591)

Juan de Cárdenas (1563–1609) was born in Seville and went to Mexico in 1577; after studies in philosophy he in 1581 became Bachelor of Arts, and in 1584 Bachelor of Medicine at the University of Mexico. During four years Cárdenas practised medicine in Guadalajara, Mexico, in charge of the Hospital of San Miguel, but in 1588 he returned to Mexico to become doctor of Medicine in 1590. In 1591 Cárdenas published in Mexico the *Primera parte de los problemas y secretos maravillosos de las Indias* where he discussed some interesting biological problems, including an excellent analysis of the action of hallucinogenic drugs upon the human body. After repeated contests, in 1595 and 1598, Cárdenas was appointed professor of Medicine at the University of Mexico in 1607, but he died two years later.

1591 edition, folios 234–246, Chapter (XV) last

"Last chapter. In which it is declared utterly whether it can be witchcraft in the herbs, and what are witchcrafts.

"... For us is left only to declare this that it is experienced in the Indies of the *Peyotl*, of the *Poyamatl*, of the *Ololiuhqui* and even of the *Picietl* that many affirm, mostly Indians, Negroes, and dull stupid ignorant people, that if these above-mentioned herbs are taken by mouth they imagine and see the Devil, who talks to them and declares of things to come; it is now convenient to investigate if some herbs or roots exist in nature the virtue of which could be so effective and powerful that by means of them we force the devil to come at our call, or by them we forsee things to come. In reference to this, it occurs to me that the answer is that there is part of this in the herb, and there is part that should be attributed to the devil, I declare furthermore, when one of these herbs that I mentioned, or any other that could exist, similar in virtue is taken by mouth or use is made of them, the herb produces, due to its properties and naturally, three things in the human body, and everything else is illusion and the work of the devil. The effects that the herb has are the following: in the first place, inasmuch as these herbs are within themselves extremely hot and strong and at the same time are composed of parts extremely subtle, strong and hot, in entering into the stomach the natural heat starts to alter and heat them, and in heating them makes ascend and distributes in the cerebrum and every way in the pores of the body, they start to heat, perturb and disorganize the animal spirits of the body, taking the man out of his judgements, as is done by the wine, the *picietl*, and to conclude every herb, and even a drink, and any sustaining material strong and vaporous and this is the first effect that the herb or root makes out of its own virtue. The second effect that the said herb has, is to cause annoying and painful dreams in the man who takes it, and this is caused by those same thick and vaporous fumes of the same herb, which although at the beginning may be subtle, in thickening with the coldness and humidity of the cerebrum, and so came to cause sleep, not smooth and easy and pleasant as the one that comes and is caused out of the soft and humid vapours of the sustaining materials, but a sleep horrible and terrifying as is naturally caused by fumes strong and painful. The third effect of the aforementioned herbs, or of their painful fumes, is to disturb and disorganize the species that are in the interior senses of the cerebrum and perturbing them are represented in the imagination, no species and forms of things that are enjoyable, and entertaining the so-mentioned imaginative potency, but instead terrifying and awful things, and therefore they imagine species of figures of monsters, bulls, tigers, lions, and ghosts, in conclusion painful black fumes, strong and heavy are the ones that cause such a sleep, and the ones that move the species in the fantasy, it is understood that they will not represent in the imaginative species of beautiful things, pretty, colourful and pleasant, but on the contrary, of wild beasts and horrible things, as the figure of the devil should be represented by the figure of a horrible monster; and so that all of these effects of throwing away the judgement of the one who takes it, to cause horrible sleep, and to represent a species of horrible things in the imagination, it can be made out of its own virtue by every herb of the ones above-mentioned, and therefore there is reason and cause to be able to make it. The one thing that the herb or root cannot make without having a pact and communication with the devil, is what I am going to say now, in the first place the devil to come at the call of the wicked man who searches for him, this is something that the herb cannot do, and it is completely false to say that the herb out of its virtue makes the devil appear; the second, to say that due to the virtue of the herb we know of things to come or secrets that have occurred, it is a notable error that the devil says or declares this, that I understand it, as in effect was told and declared in ancient times by the mouths of the oracles, those false gods, but that the herb out of its virtue could make neither one of these things, I have it as falsehood and lies: what I imagine in relation to this is that when the devil brings blindness and deceit to some of these wretched ones he must advise them to make use of some of these herbs, not because that with their virtue he must come at their call, but that with them they may get inebriated, and get out of judgement, and getting out may lose the fear of a thing so horrible and ugly as must be the devil, and being like that out of judgement of being half astonished, the devil comes to communicate, deceive him and tell or answer about what he requests, and this is the cause why the Indian priests of this land, in order that they might consult with the devil, used first to take the smoke of the strongest *picietl* that they were able to find, and so was ordered by the devil, and it was that they faster might get inebriated and lose the fear with the inebriation; furthermore, when we read or hear said that the sybils and the priests of Apollo, Jupiter and Diana became furious when wanting to give answers of their gods, it must be that they became furious with some strong herb, that the devil ordered them to take, and being furious with it, lose the fear, and the devil came and gave answer; and so everything I say is true with no more token and certainty of it than to see by experience that the man who uses the above-mentioned herbs with good intent, I mean to say with the purpose of healing some disease, because these herbs are very medicinal, the most that can happen, what we said above, due to some virtue the herb produces therefore half inebriation with it, and to cause the mentioned herb-sleep, and at the most to represent to him among dreams things annoying and painful; but not that he may really see the devil and know things to come, on the contrary this occurs in the one who uses these herbs with an evil intent, as Indian braves and squaws who are called witches, because such as these take them with the purpose of seeing the devil, and knowing things that they did not know, to such as these God permits that the devil presents himself to them; but as I say this is not by virtue of the herbs, because this exceeds its limits . . ."

JERÓNIMO DE MENDIETA (1596)

He was born in Vitoria (c. 1524–1604) and entered the Franciscan Order in Bilbao. Mendieta arrived in Mexico in 1554 and studied Arts and Theology at Xochimilco where he also began to master the Nahuatl language. He visited several areas of Mexico, such as Toluca, Tlamanalco, Huexotzingo and after a short trip to Spain in 1570 he returned to Mexico where he died in 1604. Mendieta wrote a *Historia Eclesiástica Indiana* from 1592 to 1596 using excellent sources and the writings of several members of the Franciscan Order, among them Andrés de Olmos, Toribio de Motolinia, Francisco Ximenez and Bernardino de Sahagún. The information gathered by Mendieta on Indian beliefs and the introduction of the Catholic faith among them is solid and of interest in medical history.

1870 edition, pp. 281–284; Book III, Chapter XLI

"Of some manners of vocal confession which the Indians had in their infidelity, and how they fitted the sacrament of confession of the Church.

"In some provinces of this New Spain the Indians in their infidelity used a manner of vocal confession, and this they made to their gods, twice a year, withdrawing themselves to a corner in the house, or in the temple, or by going to the mountains, or the springs, each one where he felt more devotion, and there they gave signs of the greatest sorrow, some with many tears, others joining their hands as when we show great regret, twisting and intertwining the fingers one with the other, making wry faces, confessing their faults and sins. And during the days lasting in this exercise, they never laughed nor admitted any pleasure, but all they did was to have and show sadness, sorrow and unhappiness. They also confessed sometimes their sins to the physicians and to the sorcerers to whom they went asking for remedy or advice in their needs. Because the physician who was called to cure a sick man, if the illness was light, he put some herbs or things used for remedies; but if the disease was acute and dangerous, he said: You have committed a sin. And he bothered and worried him so much by repeating it, that he was forced to confess what he had perhaps done many years before. And this was considered as the main medicine: to throw out the sin from the soul to obtain the health of the body. They did the same when they asked advice from some sorcerer or soothsayer, about what they could do to have children, why they lacked them; because this was one of the things they wanted most and asked from their gods. The sorcerer or soothsayer casting their lots answered them, that the gods had not given them children because of their sins, and they confess them to him. And then he ordered penitences to them, usually they were to be away from their wife's bed forty or fifty days; not to eat anything with salt; to eat dry bread not fresh, or just maize in grain; to be a certain number of days in the field in some cave already appointed, to sleep on the ground, not to wash during certain times. Finally, they believed that all their hardship and needs were due to their sins . . ."

ANTONIO DE HERRERA (1601)

The materials and first-hand reports surveyed by Antonio de Herrera y Tordesillas (1559–1625) give particular accuracy to his work. He was born in Cuellar, Spain, and after completing his studies became secretary to the Spanish Viceroy in Naples, Vespasiano de Gonzaga. The Viceroy in turn recommended Herrera to Philip II for the appointment of royal historian of Spain and the Indies. He first published an *Historia de Portugal* 1591 and *Historia general del mundo* 1601, but his most important work was the *Historia general de los hechos de los Castellanos en las Islas y Tierra Firme del Mar Océano* 1601–1615, better known as Herrera's *Decades*, which were reprinted and translated several times. The value of this monumental history lies not only in its detail and the wealth of reports quoted, but also in the balanced judgement and honest standpoints taken by the author, because Herrera, in spite of the shortness of the time available and the wealth of official documents, was able to select sound and relevant information. There are many reports of Indian customs, and notes on sexual behaviour and religious practices which have considerable interest, particularly as the original drafts of these reports were in some instances subsequently lost. Herrera died in Madrid after serving as historian to three Spanish Kings.

1601 edition, Vol. I, p. 88, col. 2; Decade I, Book III, Chapter IV

"[Year] 1494. Chapter IV. It continues the previous one concerning the Hispaniola and the customs of the Indians.

p. 88, col. 2: ". . . Of the customs of this people: in marriage they used one wife whom they respected but used many others in intercourse for different manners of beastly and abominable sins, with each one in its own way, and among them there was never disagreement. They were vicious about the nefarious sin, a thing the women hated very much; the women were chaste with the natives but lustful with the Castilians. The men did not use [intercourse] with mothers, daughters, or sisters, but in the other degrees did not have any respect".

1601 edition, Vol. I, p. 296, col. 2; Decade I, Book IX, Chapter IV

"Chapter IV. Description of the Isle of Cuba and the most notable things found there.

p. 296, col. 2 [Year 1511]: ". . . the people of the Hispaniola, Cuba, San Juan [Porto Rico] and Jamaica did not use the nefarious sin and it is true that neither ate human flesh: and although [Fernandez de] Oviedo holds the opinion that they were sodomites, men as reliable as he deny it, and censure him for it . . ."

1601 edition, Vol. II, p. 84, col. 2; Decade II, Book III, Chapter V

Chapter V: "Of the things in the provinces of Tierra Firme, their rites and customs.

p. 84, col. 2. [Year 1518]: "... Sodomy was hated [in Tierra Firme] and those who used it were greatly despised ..."

1601 edition, Vol. II, p. 162, col. 2. Decade II, Book VI, Chapter XVI

Chapter XVI: "Of other notable things of Tlaxcala.

p. 162, col. 2. [Year 1519]: "[In Tlaxcala] those who committed the sin of sodomy were put to death, although it was used in other provinces ..."

1601 edition, Vol. III, p. 128, col. 2; Decade III, Book III, Chapter XV

"Chapter XV: It continues the religion, usages and customs of other nations of the New Spain.

p. 128, col. 2. [Year 1522]: "[In the town of Ixcatlan] there were penalties for all the vices: the property of the thief, after the judgement was given as compensation to the offended. They did not punish the sodomite, and those full of sins were forgiven for as many sins as offerings presented at the temple ..."

1601 edition, Vol. III, p. 153, col. 1; Decade III, Book IV, Chapter VII

"Chapter VII. Fray Blas de Iniesta went to explore the Massaya volcano and the most notable things in the province of Nicaragua.

p. 153, col. 1. [Year 1522]. [In Nicaragua]: "there were public women and in the place where they existed they stoned the sodomites ..."

1601 edition, Vol. III, p. 172, col. 2; Decade III, Book IV, Chapter XVI

"Chapter XVI. Of the customs of the Mexicans and others of the New Spain.

p. 172, col. 2. [Year 1522]: "[the Mexicans] had their laws to punish crimes: they stoned the adulterers, although this penalty was changed to hanging. Though some people say in Mexico that those who committed the nefarious sin were put to death, others say that they did not pay attention to it for punishment, but it is true that among them it was a despicable thing to be called *cuy lumpult*, that means consenting sodomite, and because of it they had fights with swords and shields and the challenge was allowed ..."

1601 edition, Vol. III, p. 181, col. 1; Decade III, Book IV, Chapter XIX

"Chapter XIX. It deals with the Otomies and Xilotepec: and how the cattle multiplied in these lands.

p. 181, col. 1. [Year 1523]. [Among the Otomies]: "theft, the nefarious sin, adultery, and rape of women were punished by death ..."

1601 edition, Vol. IV, p. 23, col. 2; Decade IV, Book I, Chapter X

"Chapter X. A general account of the provinces of Castilla del Oro and customs of their natives.

p. 23, col. 2. [Year 1527]: "the children [of the concubines] were considered bastards and supported by the legitimate sons: they despised sodomy and insulted those who used it . . ."

1601 edition, Vol. IV, p. 44, col. 2; Decade IV, Book II, Chapter VII

"Chapter VII. Francisco Pizarro lands again on the shore and talks once more to the Indians, and two Castilians stay with the Indians.

p. 44, col. 2. [Year 1527]. [The giants in Santa Elena]: "the native women could not stand them and the natives had meetings to throw them out because they were loathsome and used very much the nefarious sin, in front of the people without shame or fear of God, and it is said that He punished them with the fire from the heavens when they were all together using that sin, leaving but a few bones of unbelievable greatness which can be seen today . . ."

1610 edition, Vol. IV, p. 125, col. 2; Decade IV, Book VI, Chapter I

"Chapter I. Juan de Ampues went around Coro and the customs of the Indians of that land, and the arrival there of the Germans.

p. 125, col. 2. [Year 1529]: "Concerning the rites and customs of the Indians [of Venezuela] it will be without end to tell the variety of their abominations; some of them who inhabit the mountains near Coro had all the wives they wanted and many had intercourse with their daughters, cousins or relatives and used the nefarious sin; they did not have law or reason, and only cared for food and drink. To the sodomites the only penalty was to serve in the role of women, that is to grind the corn, to spin and to cook meals . . ."

1601 edition, Vol. IV. p. 187, col. 1; Decade IV Book VII, Chapter XI

"Chapter XI. Nature of the Isle of Puna, and the reason for the war between its natives and those of Tumbez.

p. 187, col. 1. [Year 1530]: "the people ate human flesh, they were very vicious, inclined to the nefarious sin, and brothers did not abstain [from intercourse] with their sisters, and had other beastly sins . . ."

1601 edition, Vol. IV, p. 242, col. 1. Decade IV, Book IX, Chapter XI

"Chapter VII [i.e. XI] Nuño de Guzman continued his discovery, how he withdrew and the villages he settled.

p. 242, col. 1. [Year 1531]: "All this land [of Mexico] from Piastla to the Culuacan river . . . the houses were covered with hay very much adorned and the ridge of the houses with paintings, especially men joined with women and men with men, because they were very inclined to the nefarious sin . . .

p. 243, col. 2. [Year 1531]. In Chametla ... they worshipped idols, ate human flesh, and had other abominable vices which thanks to God have been driven away from them ... ."

1601 edition, Vol. V, p. 115, col. 2; Decade V, Book IV, Chapter V

"Chapter V. Of the offerings, sacrifices, fasts and beliefs of the Indians their counting of the year and months.

p. 115, col. 2. [Year 1533]: "the ceremonies of these sacrifices during their heathenism they did not lead an honest life, nor in their marriages ... everything was mixed up ... and there was nothing but killings, deceit, thefts, unfaithfulness, travesty of sexes, revolts, troubles, adulteries and filth ... ."

1601 edition, Vol. V, p. 162, col. 2; Decade V. Book VI, Chapter I

"Chapter I. The Conquistador Pedro de Alvarado went with his army back to Peru and landed his people in the limit of Caraques, and decided to go to Quito.

p. 162, col. 2. [Year 1534]: "Captains Pacheco and Olmo when they governed these provinces [of Puerto Viejo] burnt some sodomites and in this way they frightened them [the Indians] in such a manner that they left this great sin."

1601 edition, Vol. VI, p. 96, col. 2; Decade VI, Book III, Chapter XVI

"Chapter XVI. Sebastian de Belalcazar settles the city of Santiago de Cali and the village of Tymaná, and goes discovering down the great river.

p. 96, col. 2. [Year 1537] [In Cali]: "they hated the abominable sin, they married nieces and some lords married their sisters."

1601 edition, Vol. VI, p. 149, col. 2; Decade VI, Book V, Chapter VI

"Chapter VI. Of the life, customs and religion of the Indians of this Nuevo Reyno de Granada.

p. 149, col. 2. [Year 1538]: "the moral life of these [Moxcas] Indians is of average reason, because they punish the crimes, particularly homicide, theft and the nefarious sin, of which they are very clean ... ."

1601 edition, Vol. VII, p. 85, col. 1; Decade VII, Book IV, Chapter II

"Chapter II. Felipe Gutierrez and Diego de Rojas went to their discovery and the discord they tried to put between them.

p. 85, col. 1. [Year 1542] [In Tacuiman]: "they are great sorcerers, they believe there is nothing beyond birth and death, they hate sodomy ... ."

1601 edition, Vol. II, p. 207, col. 2; Decade II, Book VI, Chapter XVI

"Year 1519. Chapter XVI. Of other interesting things of Tlaxcala ... and they sold children just born or two years old, to fulfil their promises and offerings in the temples as we offer candles, to be sacrificed and obtain their wishes, and this served them as vocal confession . . ."

1601 edition, Vol. III, p. 154, col. 1; Decade III, Book IV, Chapter VII

Vol. III, p. 154: "Year 1522. Chapter VII. Fray Blas de Iniesta went to explore the volcano of Massaya and the most interesting things of the province of Nicaragua.

". . . the priests do not get married, but for those who listen in confession to the sins of others and give penitence according to their guilt, and they do not reveal the confession under penalty of punishment . . .

1601 edition, Vol. III, p. 216, col. 2; Decade III, Book V, Chapter XII

Vol. III, p. 216: "Year 1524. Chapter XII. Francisco Hernandez de Cordoba settled Granada in Nicaragua: what happened between his people and Gil Gonzalez Davila . . . they sacrificed men and women and penitences, they bled their tongues and anointed with blood the idols as an offering; they confessed to their pope those things they considered sins, and in that way they thought became free [of guilt] . . ."

1601 edition, Vol. IV, p. 205, col. 2; Decade IV, Book VIII, Chapter VIII

Vol. IV, p. 205: "Chapter VIII. It deals with the province of Guatemala and the manner it is now governed by the Royal Court.

[Year 1530] "It happened that an Indian complained against a Mayor of his nation because without his own permission had punished his wife on account of eight adulteries, and ordered him to pay the penalty, therefore making him to suffer the affront and taking besides his money, the case being that during the time of his idolatry, when a woman was going to have a child, the midwife ordered her to tell her sins, and when this did not induce childbirth, ordered the husband to tell his own, and if this did not produce results, she took his trousers and put them on the flanks of the pregnant woman and if she did not give birth, the midwife bled her and sprayed it at the four winds making some invocations and ceremonies: and being the said woman delivering a child, confessing her sins, a minor police official who was hiding overheard what she said, and after she had the child accused her of adultery, because their ancient ceremonies still last . . ."

Decade IV, Vol. IV, p. 210, col. 1, Book VIII, Chapter X

"to confess women in parturition has already been said."

1601 edition, Vol. IV, p. 266, col. 2; Decade IV, Book X, Chapter IV

"Chapter IV. Which continues the notable things of Yucatan
Vol. IV, p. 266. [Year 1531]: "the plagues and misfortunes suffered by these people, they knew happened because of their sins: and to escape

from them they used confession in their disease and in any danger of death, such as in parturition or in similar things; they publicly declared their sins, and if they neglected it their relatives reminded them; if the priest was present to him, if not to the fathers and mothers, to the wives, to their husbands. The accused themselves of theft, of homicide, of lewdness, of false testimony, and if they did not die, it occurred plenty of troubles between husbands and wives; they did not confess sins of intention, although they considered evil . . ."

1601 edition, Vol. IV, p. 279, col. 2; Decade IV, Book X, Chapter XI

"Chapter XI. Of certain peculiarities of the province of Chiapa in New Spain.
Vol. IV, p. 279. [Year 1531]: "to perform marriages . . . the pope advised them [those contracting] to declare the [evil] things they have done up to that time: the groom said the thefts, though they did not considered it sinful, but just things found, he mentioned those things pertaining to lewdness, and if he had had intercourse with the bride, and with how many women and how many men, because they did not consider this an abomination: the bride also declared without shame, also in proper order [all sins], and after finishing the relatives arrived with presents . . ."

1601 edition, Vol. V, p. 115, col. 2; Decade V, Book IV, Chapter V

"Chapter V. Of the offerings, sacrifices, fasts, beliefs of the Indians [of Peru] and count of the year and months.
Vol. V, p. 115. [Year 1533]: "they held in Peru that all the misfortunes came because of sins, and the remedy was to use sacrifices and used to confess vocally, and there were confessors and gave penitence, and sins reserved for the high [priest] and women also confessed: and some provinces held the opinion that it was a grave sin to conceal any sin during confession: and sick people also used the confession or when they were in any trouble, and the confessors, with certain limitations were bound to secrecy; they accused themselves of killing away from war, of theft, of to take the neighbour's wife, to give herbs, witchcraft, and to neglect worshipping their idols, not to keep their feasts, to speak evil of the king, to disobey him; they did not accuse themselves of internal sins: the Inca only confessed his sins to the Sun . . ."

FERNANDO DE ALVA IXTLILXOCHITL (1605)

Fernando de Alva Ixtlilxochitl (1570–1649) has been accepted as the most reliable historian of the Toltec and Chichimec migrations, which preceded the Aztecs in central Mexico. He was born in Teotihuacan and was a direct descendant of the Acolhua kings of Texcoco, one of whom gave considerable help to Cortés during the Conquest of Mexico. Ixtlilxochitl, as he is generally known, was for six years a student at the College of

Santa Cruz de Tlaltelolco, and eventually was made governor of Texcoco. As a result of his persistent search for pre-Columbian hieroglyphic pictures, native maps and ancient manuscripts, he gathered a unique collection of Mexican historical documents; at his death the heirs gave this collection to Sigüenza y Gongora, and afterwards it became part of the Jesuits' Library in Mexico City. Mexican pictographic codices recording historical facts had been systematically destroyed—Tlacaélel prior to the Spanish arrival had done so to assure Aztec cultural hegemony; the Tlaxcaltecs also burnt the Acolhuan codices kept at the royal houses of Nezahualpilzintli in Texcoco; and after the Spanish Conquest Archbishop Zumarraga in Mexico and Bishop Landa in Yucatan completed the destruction on religious grounds. Ixtlilxochitl had the good fortune of working with certain sources which are no longer extant, and this gives considerable value to his writings. As Chavero (1891) has pointed out, his works can be divided in two parts: (a) Miscellaneous accounts which are drafts and versions of the same events written from 1600 to 1608, and (b) the *Historia Chichimeca* written from 1608 to 1616 which is a complete and well developed study. All these works were written in the Nahuatl language and their annotated translation into Spanish made by Francisco Rodriguez. Most of the Ixtlilxochitl data can be confirmed by the Annals of Cuauhtitlan and Quauhtinchan, and some chapters of Sahagún on the Toltecs and Chichimecs; later on, his notes were expanded by Veytia. The variants of Ixtlilxochitl's *Toltec Relations* indeed provide glimpses of the cultural fall of the Toltec preceded by sexual corruption comparable to that of ancient Rome.

1891 edition, Vol. I, p. 43

p. 43: "Brief relation of everything that happened in New Spain and of many things that the Tultecs learned and knew ... Fifth Relation. Of the Tultec kings and his destruction. [First tells how king Tecpancaltzin raped Xochitl when she brought the honey made from maguey, and they had a son Meconetzin, in the year Ce Acatl or A.D. 900, later known as King Topiltzin]

p. 47: "It was forty years since Topiltzin began his rule [A.D. 977] ... he had committed very grave sins, and with his bad example the whole city of Tula and all the provinces and cities, and lands of the Tultecs [were contaminated]; and the women went to the temples and to the cities with sanctuaries and false gods in pilgrimages and had intercourse with the priests and committed other grave and abominable sins; among them a very principal lady of Tula went to Cholula to visit the temple of that city, ... and especially to a temple dedicated to god Ce Acatl, where there were two priests, one Ezcolotli and the other Texpolcatl, who, as I have said, the false priests of the Tultecs professed chastity, and was a most grave sin to break it. And so, Texpolcatl, seeing this lady, who had also professed [chastity] courted her, obtained her friendship, and she gave birth a few years later to a child named Yzcax, who afterwards, with his descendants, inherited this dignity of false high priests or popes ... the inventors of these sins were two brothers, lords of various parts, very brave and great necromancers called, the elder Tezcatlipuca and the young Tlatlauhquitezcatlipuca, who afterwards the Tultecs revered as gods. Persisting the king, all his court and subjects in great sins, and doing the things they knew in their evil ways, they persuaded them to grave sins and obscene and abominable deeds ..."

1891 edition, Vol. I, p. 75

p. 75: "History of the Chichimec Lords until the arrival of the Spaniards. First Relation.

"... they only married to one woman, and she was not a close relation, such as sister or aunt in second degree, and if they were not one of them, they married relations.

p. 237: "Ordinances of Nezahualcoyotzin

"1st. The first that any woman who committed adultery to her husband, if seen by the husband, she and the adulterer be stoned to death in the *tianguis* [market]; and if the husband did not see it, but heard of it, to present his complaint, and if it found true, she and the adulterer be hanged.

"2nd. The second that any person who forced any boy [committed sodomy] and sold him as slave be hanged.

"7th. The seventh that any daughter of any lord or knight found bad, to die for it ...

"12th. The 12th no lord to get drunk under penalty of losing office ...

"13th. The 13th anybody found to be sometic, to die for it.

"14th. The 14th that any man or woman who acted as procurer of married women, to die for it.

"15th. The 15th that if it were found anybody to be a sorcerer, using witchcraft, doing it by way of words, or with intention of killing somebody, to die for it and their estate to be given away."

1891 edition, Vol. I, p. 323

p. 323: "Relations Ninth and Tenth

p. 324: "3rd. The nefarious sin was punished in two ways: To the one acting as a female, they removed his entrails from the bottom, was tied down to a log and the boys from the town covered him with ash, until he was buried; and then they put a lot of wood and burnt him. The one acting as a male was covered with ash, tied down to a log until he died.

"4th. The adulterer was killed by crushing his head between two stones ..."

PLATE I

FIG. 1. Mochica drinking vessel portraying sodomy. Art Institute of Chicago.

FIG. 2. Chimú drinking vessel portraying sodomy. Art Institute of Chicago.

FIG. 3. Virú drinking vessel portraying sodomy. Art Institute of Chicago.

FIG. 4. Mochica drinking vessel portraying sodomy. Art Institute of Chicago.

1892 edition, Vol. II, p. 185

"Chichimec History.

p. 185: "Chapter XXXVII: It continues the description of the houses of Nezahualcoyotzin and the temples they had inside.

"... and in these temples there was one where he had many women secluded and locked up and likewise were educated some daughters of lords and citizens...

p. 187: "Chapter XXXVIII: It deals with the eighty laws established by Nezahualcoyotzin and the way he ordered to keep them.

p. 213: "Chapter XLIII: [It is the story of Nezahualcoyotl (1402–1472) falling in love with Azcalxochitzin, who was her cousin in first degree, and engaged to be married to Quaquauhtzin. Nezahualcoyotl, to get rid of him, sent Quaquauhtzin to fight the Tlaxcaltecs and when he died obtained the love of Azcalxochitzin]"

1892 edition, Vol. II, p. 236

"Chapter XLII. It deals with some prophecies and sentences by King Nezahualcoyotzin.

p. 236: "... in a year like this [A.D. 1467], this temple [of Huitzilopochtli in Texcoco] which is now inaugurated, will be destroyed ... then evil, pleasures and lewdness will reach their summit and men and women will give themselves to lust from their tender years... To save our children of these vices and misfortunes you should lead them from childhood into virtue and work..."

1892 edition, Vol. II, Chapter LXIV

[The story of Nezahualpiltzintli (1463–1515) who married Chalchiuh-nenetzin, the daughter of Axayacatzin, king of Mexico, when she was very young. She had many lovers whom she killed and made statues of them. Once Nezahualpiltzintli recognized one of her jewels in a young man and suspecting her betrayal visited her apartment one night. Nezahualpiltzintli found his wife with her three lovers, Chicuhcoatl, Huitzilihuitl and Maxtla, and put the four to be strangled in public.]

GREGORIO GARCÍA (1607)

The work of Gregorio García (1554–1627) is interesting for its comparative study of customary law of the Jews and the American Indians. He was born in Cozar, near Toledo, and after entering the Dominican Order in his youth went in 1592 to Mexico and Peru where he carried out missionary work for 12 years. After his return to Baeza, Spain, in 1604 he wrote the *Origen de los Indios* published at Valencia in 1607, where he examined the theories put forward by Las Casas, Acosta, Garcilasso and others concerning the origin of the American Indians, the possibility of their being a tribe of Israel, and he tried to prove that Quetzalcoatl had been St. Thomas the Apostle.

1607 edition, p. 276; Book III, Chapter VI, 2

p. 276: "Item, in the same Leviticus (18 and 20) it was the law that those who committed the nefarious sin should die. The Indians of New Spain kept this law, without missing one point, and they executed it with great severity; they had the same penalty with the woman who laid down with another, because it was also against nature."
[from Torquemada Book 12, Chapter 2, Volume 2, and Book 2, Chapter 52, Volume 1]

1607 edition, p. 281; Book III, Chapter VI (6) last

p. 281: [In Mexico]: "They punished also the sometics and the penalty was death, and if a woman sinned with another she was strangled, and for greater punishment drowned. This abominable and nefarious vice was practised in two or three provinces, where it was publicly permitted and there were public houses of men. The wretched ones did it because the devils they worshipped had made them believe they did the same and that therefore it was legal and good. But despite all this, this sin was always considered something abominable and ugly, and although it was not punished among those who used it, those who committed this sin were held as infamous. In Mexico and Texcoco the sometics were greatly punished. The sin of bestiality was never seen or heard of among the Indians, hence there was no law against it, neither was there against idleness, because I do not think they knew, or comprehended that sin.
[from Torquemada Book 12, Chapter 4, Volume 2, and Garcilasso Book 9, Chapter 8, and Book 1, Chapter 13, Volume 1]
[from Torquemada Book 12, Chapter 11, Volume 2, and Book 3, Chapter 6, Volume 2]

GARCILASSO DE LA VEGA (1609)

Most of Cieza de Leon's views were confirmed by the writings of the Inca Garcilasso de la Vega (1539–1616) on the Inca history. He was the son of a Conquistador and an Inca princess, and went to Spain after having received an excellent education at Cuzco up to the age of 21. The works of the Inca, as he is usually known, were written in Montilla and Cordoba, sometimes reflecting his resentment against the Conquistadors owing to the humiliations he suffered at the Royal Council of the Indies, more because of the assistance given by his father to Gonzalo Pizarro against the Crown than because of his own illegitimacy. The *Comentarios Reales de los Incas* (1609) and to a lesser extent his second part *Historia general del Peru* (1616) are among the great sources for an understanding of the pre-Columbian Andean civilizations. The Inca gave his interpretation to the European culture from the unique standpoint of a man educated at the sources of both civilizations. In his *Royal Commentaries of the Incas* he discussed the attitude of the Inca rulers towards prevalent sodomy among the population in the northwest of Peru, and referring to the life of Manco Capac's son Sinchi Roca he said as follows:

1609 edition, folio 42; Book Two, Chapter XVI

"The life and deeds of Sinchi Roca, the second Inca king.

"He called together the principal *curacas* appointed by his father ... they were in need of being delivered of the bestial customs and nefarious action in which they lived."

Further on while describing the conquest of the Inca commander Auqui Titu during the reign of Inca Capac Yupanqui, Garcilasso de la Vega mentioned the settlements of sodomites.

1609 edition, folio 71, i.e. 68; Book Three, Chapter XIII

"Chapter XIII. They conquer many valleys on the seacoast. They punish the sodomites.

"... The Inca general Auqui Titu and his commanders after reducing all those valleys to the service of the king without giving battle, reported all the events; and in particular they informed the king that investigating the secret customs of the natives, their rites and ceremonies and their gods, which were the fish they caught, they had found, that there were some sodomites, not in all the valleys, but in some of them, and not all the inhabitants, but some in particular who secretly practised this vice. They also reported that there was no more land to conquer in that direction because they had closed the coast right down to the South with the Conquest left behind. The Inca was very pleased with the account of the Conquest, more so because it was done without bloodshed. He ordered that after leaving there the usual system of government, they should return to Cuzco. And in particular he ordered that a careful search was to be made for the sodomites and when found they to be burnt alive in the public square, not only those proved guilty, but also those indicted by circumstantial evidence, however slight. Furthermore, their houses should be burnt and pulled down, the trees in their lands burnt and pulled up by the roots so that no memory should remain of such an abominable thing, and it would be proclaimed as an inviolable law that thenceforward they should keep away from falling into such crime, because the sin of an individual would destroy the whole town, and would burn all the inhabitants, as individuals would lead to the burning of all.

"This was done as the Inca directed, to the great wonder of the natives of all those valleys at the new punishment of the nefarious [sin]; this was so hated by the Incas and their people that even the name was odious to them and they never uttered it; any Indian among those from Cuzco, even though not an Inca, who in anger, in dispute with another, said it [the word] as an abuse, was regarded as disgraced, and for many days looked upon by the rest of the Indians as something vile and filthy for having used such a word in his mouth."

Referring to the campaign in the highlands of the same Inca Capac Yupanqui, Garcilasso comes once more upon the practice of sodomy.

1609 edition, folios 138–139 verso; Book VI, Chapter XI

"Of other provinces subdued by the Inca, and of their customs and the punishment of sodomy.

". . . And in the province of Huayllas he punished very severely some sodomites who very secretly practised the abominable vice of sodomy. As until then this sin had not been found or heard of among the Indians of the mountains, though it was known in the plains, it caused great scandal to find it among the Huayllas, and that scandal gave rise to a saying among the Indians at that time which is still in use as a stigma of that people, that says: *Astaya Huayllas*, meaning, Go hence Huayllas implying that they still stink of their ancient sin, which though practised by few, and in great secret, was well punished by the Inca Capac Yupanqui."

Finally Garcilasso de la Vega quotes (1609 edition, folios 234–235, Book IX, Chapter IX) Cieza de León's Chapter LII "On the giants of those parts and how they met their death", including the way they introduced the practice of sodomy into ancient Peru.

The works of Garcilasso de la Vega the Inca, a term used to designate both the ruler and tribe of the Cuzco's highlanders, who was the most knowledgeable of the Peruvian writers, gives considerable support to the honest accounts of Cieza de León. The Yungas, or Indians who settled in the coastal valleys from Tumbez to Arica, where the pre-Inca civilizations Viru, Nazca, Mochica and Chimú developed over ten centuries prior to the Spanish arrival, indeed practised sodomy, and so did the Huayllas in the highlands. The Inca Garcilasso de la Vega takes pride in reporting the conquests of his Inca ancestors and the measures taken by Capac Yupanqui to eradicate sodomy both in the coastal valleys and in certain highland areas. However, the Inca penalties of burning for sodomites was so similar to the Spanish law that Garcilasso's honesty was later questioned in this respect.

Garcilasso also reported vocal confession.

1609 edition, folio 32; Book I, Chapter VI

"Chapter VI. What an author said about the gods they had.

". . . And from this comes that in one region it was used the vocal confession to clean themselves of their faults: in others to wash the head of the children."

1609 edition, folios 38–40 verso; Book II, Chapter XIII

"Chapter XIII. Of some laws that the Incas had in their government.

". . . those who broke the law even if their offences were not known, many times occurred that those offenders accused by their own conscience, came to publicize before the Justice their own hidden sins; because, besides the belief their soul was to condemn, they firmly believed that due to their faults and sins came all the evils to their nation, such as diseases, deaths, bad years and any other general or private misfortune, and they said, that they were trying to appease God with their death, so He would not send more evils into the world because of their sins; And from these public confessions I understand that the Spanish historians wish to state that the Indians of Peru confessed in secret, as we Christians do, and that they had commissioned Confessors; that is a false report of the Indian which they tell to soothe the Spaniards and flatter them, answering questions according to the wishes they guess in those asking and not as it is the truth: that honestly there were not secret confessions among the Indians (I refer only to those of Peru, without interfering with other nations, kingdoms or provinces which I do not know), but the public confessions we mentioned, asking for exemplary punishment."

REGINALDO DE LIZÁRRAGA (c. 1611)

It is worth recording the remarks of Reginaldo de Lizárraga y Ovando (1540–1615) despite the fact that they are those of a passing traveller. He was born in Medellin, Spain, and went to America when 15 years old. Lizárraga arrived at Quito in 1555, moved to Lima and after receiving Holy Orders in 1560 he entered the Dominican Order. He travelled extensively throughout the old Viceroyalty of Peru from Tumbez to Concepción; in 1572 he went to Chuquisaca and in 1584 sailed in pursuit of Hawkins. Lizárraga was consecrated Bishop of La Imperial in Chile, a see which he only occupied until the end of 1602 owing to the Araucanian revolts. Finally, in 1606 he was made Bishop of Paraguay, arriving in 1608 in Asunción, where he died. Lizárraga's *Descripción breve de toda la tierra del Perú*, completed about 1611, and published in 1907 does not pretend to be a deep study of the area, but nevertheless it gives some interesting biological and archaeological information, particularly that pertaining to the ruins of Trujillo which he believed to have been built by the same culture as the builders of Tiahuanaco and Huamanga. His remarks about the people show the deep-seated customs and beliefs wherever he went.

1908 edition, p. 5

"Chapter IV. Of Santa Elena point
p. 5: "... the Indians say that according to their ancestors, the newcomers [giants] came from they knew not where, they did not have women, and the native women could not stand them: they [the giants] fell into the vice of sodomy, which God punished sending upon them fire from heaven and thus they were all finished. This nefarious vice does not have any other medicine ...

"Chapter V. Of the town of Guayaquil

pp. 10–11: "The Chonos [Indians] have a bad reputation about the nefarious vice. They wear the hair a bit high and cut up to the top of the neck, hence the other Indians sneer at them part as a joke and part truly calling them Chonos dogs, queers, as I shall tell later . . .

"Chapter VI. Of the Chicama valley.

p. 12: "The Lampunas [Indians insult the Chonos by saying] Hallo! Chono dog, queer, pointing out their nefarious sin. This I saw and heard.

"Chapter LXXXXI. Of the road from Porco to Arica

p. 110: "The nation most dishonourable that can be seen.

p. 111: "They have no shame in making procuresses of their wives, who are so frightened that in fear of punishment they bring [women] to them and all sleep together . . . They are very much inclined to the sodomitic vice and as soon as their wives become pregnant they fall into it easily, hence Our Lord has punished the Yungas leaving very few of them in the valleys, as we have said . . ."

MARTIN DE MURÚA (1611)

Martin de Murúa was probably born in Guernica (*c.* 1530–1620), and after entering the Mercedary Order went as a missionary to Peru around 1557. He worked in the Aymara area of highland Peru, near Lake Titicaca, and was priest of Huata, Capachica and Huarina. Murúa also received high offices within his Order at Cuzco and Arequipa. By 1611 he had finished a most important book, the *Historia General del Perú* where he offered a detailed study on the origin and customs of the Inca, and which was printed in part in 1922–1925; the definitive edition from the original MS at the Wellington collection was published by Ballesteros Gaibrois (1962) with an excellent preliminary study. Murúa's history contains one of the best descriptions of the ritual for confession among the Incas, and mentioned a hysterical condition or dancing mania, similar to tarantism.

1962 edition, pp. 95–98; Chapter XXIV

"Chapter 24th. Of the confessions used by these Indians.

"The devil did not forget to try that, in the same way the Christians keep the law of the Gospels according to the truth of the Roman Catholic Church, confess our sins to the true priests to whom Our Lord Christ left the jurisdiction and keys to open and close the Heaven and forgive our sins, in the same way the Indians revered him, due to possessing them, making them to confess their sins and tell them to the priest they had, and by all possible means, to give him the honour and to have them blind till the end of their miserable lives.

"These unfortunate and ignorant people had a belief that all their illnesses, sufferings and persecutions were due to sins they had committed; this was an ancient and well kept custom, to believe that their misfortune and misery, even those of nature, came and were due from their own sins, or from their parents, from whom they suffered them, as it appears in the question asked to Christ by his disciples about the blind man from birth, but there Christ undeceived them from this erroneous belief, because many times to show and prove the marvellous works of God, He sends hardships and persecutions as we also saw in Job and Tobias.

"For the remedy of their diseases these Indians used different sacrifices, according to their quality, and they also used, in almost all the provinces of this kingdom [Peru] to confess vocally and they had to this aim confessors of high and low commissions, and sins which were reserved to be confessed to the high priest, and they gave them [the sinners] penitences some time rough and severe according to the severity of their sins, and this was done especially if the Indian in confession was poor, and did not have anything to give the confessor he attended. Women also had this office.

"This use of confessors and sorcerers was more common and usual in the province of Collao, and were called *Ychuri*, and they held that it was a very serious thing and sinful to hide any sin during the confession, and the confessors found it out by casting lots, looking into the entrails of some animal if they concealed any sin, and when they thought that they had not told the truth and omitted something, they punished them by striking blows with a stone in their backs, until they declared the whole truth and then gave them the penitence and made sacrifices for their sins.

"Of this confession they also used when their children and wives fell ill, or their headmen or when they had considerable hardships, and when the Inca fell ill. Then all the provinces confess for him, particularly the *Collas*. These confessors, although barbarians and ignoramuses, were compelled to keep the secret of confession, but there were in this certain limitations, that it seems that in many things they guessed what was coming to this kingdom and how they were going to practise vocal confession to clean themselves of their sins.

"The sins they considered more serious and important and they accused themselves more frequently were these: to kill some Indian privately, outside war; the second was to take away from somebody else the wife, because this was a serious case; the third was to give poisonous herbs and witchcraft in food or drink, to kill somebody else; the fourth was to steal or assault or take away by force something belonging to other: They had for very serious sin to neglect or disregard the worship of their *huacas* and idols, not to keep the solemn feasts ordered by the Inca, and also to say or show lack of respect for the Inca, and when he ordered something not to obey with punctuality. These were the things they confessed more especially, without regard or account of actions and internal sins and thoughts. The Inca was exempt of this obligation of confession, who did not confess his sins to any other person, but to the Sun, his father, so he could tell his Maker and forgive him. When the Inca had confessed his sins in front the Sun's image, he made certain sort of washing, in a way that meant that he was purified and had finished cleansing his faults. And this was done in the following manner: He went into a stream with rapid current and said these words: 'I have told my sins to my father the sun, you river with your currents take them swiftly to sea, where can never be found,' and with this he concluded. The rest of the Indians also used these washings with the same or almost the same ceremonies; they called them *opacuna*. And if somebody's children happened to die, they considered him a great sinner, and said that because of his sins it occurred all the way around, that the children died before the father, and those in that case, after confession and having carried out the washings mentioned, they were flogged with certain nettles which prickled very hard, by an Indian with hunchback or deformed from birth, or someone with some monstrosity or notorious defect."

1962 edition, pp. 116–119; Chapter XXXII

"Chapter 32nd. Of the sorcerers and witches used by the Indians.

". . . They frequently suffer a dancing disease, they call it *taquioncoy*. To cure it they call the sorcerers, and they get cured of it by means of millions of superstitions and by confessing with the sorcerers.

1962 edition, pp. 119–124; Chapter XXXIII

"Chapter 33rd. Of the soothsayer and fortune teller there were among the Indians.

". . . During the childbirth time of their wives, the husbands and even the wives used to fast, avoiding certain foods and they confessed with sorcerers and made sacrifices to the *huacas*, or hills, or their idols, offered to obtain that the child be delivered without lesion or ugliness of any kind. And this matter of fasting was very common and for different purposes; in famine and hardships, abstaining of certain foods, and mixing in them different ceremonies . . . In several places, whether they are sick or healthy, they used to go washing to streams and springs making certain ceremonies, with the belief that in this way they washed their souls of sins committed and that the stream of the rivers carried them away, and they took the *hichu*, which is like feather-grass, and spitted, confessing their sins to the sorcerers, and in this way they believed they were left clean and purified of the diseases they had . . ."

1962 edition, p. 59; Chapter XI

". . . In the last few years since the Indian men and women have been instructed by learned confessors, and having experience in confessing by these strings and *quipus* they make their general confessions according to the commandments and afterwards every time they confess they bring out their *quipus* and following them they declare their sins. This indeed has been a marvellous and very effective way to make their confessions more complete and to satisfaction they tell the truth (of which we always had suspicion), being reminded better and with memory of their sins, and more relief of those giving the sacraments. To this effect is thought in general, or because the confusion of their mind and the little meditation they have of their lives, or due to the ability they have in lying (which it is considerable) or because their awful inclination, malice, and incitement of the devil, they make most confession null or diminished, hiding the sins they have committed or after confessing them denying their number, even if they know it, or the circumstances which greatly increase their severity, or they change the species, and even when they say they cover them out of fear, they also lie in this, because even if there is a priest rude and rough, most of them treat them [the Indians] with love in confession trying to extract their sins softly, and many times they are the cause they drive the confessors out of reason, being caught in the most open lies while saying, to excuse their sins, things which are impossible . . ."

JUAN DE SANTA CRUZ PACHACUTI (c. 1613)

Juan de Santa Cruz Pachacuti Yamqui Salcamaygua (fl. 1600) was also entirely Indian, not of Inca extraction but from the Collahua who had been subjugated by the Inca. He was a descendant of the headmen of Orcosuyo and in his account *Relación de Antigüedades deste Reyno del Perú* written *c.* 1613 and first published in 1869 by Jimenez de la Espada, Santa Cruz gives a balanced view of the Inca rulers and customs of Peru prior to Spanish arrival. The account praised some of them for their wise government, but Santa Cruz also brought to light some of the sexual perversions and abuses of the rulers with his candid reports.

1879 edition, p. 252

"Sinchi Ruca Inca 2º Inca

". . . This unhappy Sinchichiruca they say always enjoyed pleasures, and say he ordered them to look for *chotarpo* [the male] *vanarpo* to get use in fornication, and this is why there were so many *vacanquest* where the Indians arrived with those presents. This unhappy Inca they say only had but one son Inca *Lluquiyupanqui*.

1879 edition, p. 253

"Iloqque Lupanqui 3º Inca

". . . they say he kept long fasts, and he did not have relations with women until very old, he forbade fornication and drunkenness . . . he ordered all men to shave their beard to be like him beardless . . . and he had raised many boys who were not to have relation with women.

". . . He made great justice . . . to adulterers and liars, to those who committed fornication, those who committed it with animals, to sodomites, thieves, . . ."

1879 edition, p. 310

"Huascar Inca, 11° Inca

". . . Huascar Inca . . . being in the square of Pomapampa ordered to take out [from the temples] all the *ucllas* [virgins] in four manners into the square; and then being all [the virgins] among such great number of *apocuracas* and every sort of people of the kingdom, ordered one hundred *llamallamas* and *hayacuchos* Indians to come forward; while they were playing their comedies, he visited all the virgins, looking at each one, and ordering the *llamallamas* to assault each one the virgins, to use the [sin of] bestiality in public act, like the sheep of this land; and watching the virgins being assaulted in this manner, he made exclamations raising his eyes to heaven, of this all the great lords of the kingdom felt very sorry, and had the said Huascar Inca for half demented . . ."

Pachacuti Yamqui, like Huaman Poma, had a limited knowledge of the Spanish language and he mixed Quechua words and used Indian syntax in his texts. From his writings it seems that physically the Inca Sinchi Ruca had an effeminate distribution of hair, large bone structure and the writers are doubtful about the supposed late procreation of his descendant. Concerning the Inca Huascar, the sexual abuse and perversions described by Pachacuti Yamqui in the Pomapampa square leave no doubt about his nature: the Inca ruler ordered the dancers to commit public sodomy with the virgins in charge of the Temple of the Sun. Huascar was accused of this desecration shortly before he was assassinated by the generals of his brother Atahualpa (1500–1533).

FELIPE HUAMAN POMA DE AYALA (c. 1615)

Felipe Huaman Poma de Ayala (1534–1615) was the son of a headman of the Lucanas and a descendant of the tenth Inca ruler Tupac Yupanqui. He had a rebellious nature and because of his ancestry received the privilege of listening to the complaints of the Indians against the abuse of the Spaniards. Despite his mature age, he left his village and for some 20 years was engaged in visiting the Indians in the Guamanga region, teaching and protecting them. At the end of his long life Huaman wrote a *Primer Nueva Crónica y Buen Gobierno* (published in facsimile, 1936), full of resentment against the Spanish haughtiness and cruelty, which despite its unbalanced judgement is very interesting. To Huaman the Incas were perfect rulers and no fault or sexual excess was tolerated by them.

1936 edition, p. 59

"Third age of the Indians.

"... Of how among their women no adulterer was found, there was not whore or *puto* [sodomite] because they [the Incas] had a rule that ordered that such women were not supposed to get nourishing food or to drink *chicha*, they had this law and in this way they never became with lust like a mare or adulterous in this kingdom the Indian women."

1936 edition, p. 70

"Fourth age of the Indians.

"Of how there were not true or false wizards, people who gave poison, nor adulterers, or whores neither *putos* [sodomites] apostate, or liars because they were killed alive with great suffering under penalty of stoning or being thrown away on a precipice."

1936 edition, p. 129

"The Fifth Coia [Queen] Chinbomama Cava was [the] first to be married to Capac Yupanque. This beautiful and peaceful lady after being married suffered the heart malady [epilepsy] and each day they say suffered three attacks and shouted and attacked the people and bit them and scratched her face and pulled her hair. With this illness she was left very ugly and [he] could not govern the land, and so they say that the above mentioned her husband Capac Yupanque asked the Sun his father for another lady and wife, to get married, to have [normal] life and to be able to rule his kingdom, and so they say his father the Sun ordered him to marry his other younger sister, Cucichimbomama mi cay yanci. They say that the said lady with the heart malady was eaten by a son and died and her sickly life lasted few years, and she was very poor and she did not leave a testament nor made she *euna cusca* of anything. And so afterwards [he] ruled [with] her younger sister Cucichi[m]bo-mama micay coya and he enlarged his kingdom and this lady was very respected and honoured who was the second wife Coya [Queen] of the said Inga in this kingdom.

p. 185: "Ordinances of the Inga Topa Inga Yupanqui ... women should never be allowed to act as witnesses because they are deceitful and liars and *pusillanimous picisongte* ..."

p. 237: Priest confessors

1936 edition, p. 280

p. 280: "Sorcerers who suck. Other sorcerers sleep and between dreams they talk to the devil who tells them everything they want and ask for ... the sorcerers as priests who served in those Guamanies and around Apachitas, common *huacas*, idols gods of which there were many in the kingdom, these priests served as confessors, they deceived the people saying what to eat and to drink, and that the *huacas* spoke without being true, and thus the whole kingdom had *huacas* idols, and those who

did not have them were killed. Everything I write [about] the popes
I know because I was in the service to Cristobal de Albornoz general
inspector of the Holy Mother Church [and] destroyed all the *huacas*
idols and witchcraft in the kingdom, he was a Christian judge."

1936 edition, p. 282

p. 282: "Superstitions. The Indians during the Inca period believed in
dreams and from there when they dream *acu-nina* they say are going to
be ill, and when they dreamt of *chicollo-yuaychan* and of *chinaco* they
say will live, when they dream *acuyraqui—mayuta chacata chinpani—
yntiqui llavanun* they say their father or their mother is going to die,
when they dream *quiro ymilloc ciu* that their father or their brother
will die, *llamata nacani* the same, when she dreams *rutuscamrani* is
going to be a widow ...
p. 209: "Aclla the virgins
p. 312: "Punishment of lewd virgins by hanging them from their hair."

JUAN DE TORQUEMADA (1615)

The Franciscan friar Juan de Torquemada (*c*. 1557–1624), who arrived in
Mexico as a child, was a chronicler of the ancient history of Mexico
respected for his reliable records. In 1609 he began to write the *Monarchia
Indiana*, first printed at Seville (1615) and reprinted in Madrid (1723).
Although he moralizes about the accounts given of the Mexican Indians,
his work is full of important observations and news which include a
report on sodomy among the Maya Indians of Vera Paz, Guatemala.

1615 edition, Vol. I, p. 422; Book XII, Chapter XI

"Chapter XI. Of Laws pertaining to lewdness, and fornicating people,
and it is declared what punishments and penalties they received and
were corrected ...
"... Some in those provinces were found with the nefarious sin
[sodomy] and thus there was law, that prohibited it, because, though
it is true that they did not always use this bestial vice, at the end this
corruption was introduced, as many others do, in the republics, and
this happened in the following way. There appeared to them a devil
under the figure of a young man, who was named Chin, though depending on the variety of languages, he had several and different names, and
he induced them to commit it [sodomy] with another demon in their
presence, and from there came that many among them did not consider
it a sin, saying that since that god (to say it properly, filthy and vile
demon) did it, and persuaded them it was not a sin; but they cannot be
excused of having committed the most deadly sin of all which can be
called bestial; because if this is a sin in the way of generation, it is
seen that the natural law induces and teaches it to be illicit, because
it does not follow the end nature intended.

"Convinced therefore that it was not a sin the custom started among parents of giving a boy to their young son, to have him for a woman and to use him as a woman; from that also began the law that if anyone approached the boy, they were ordered to pay for it, punishing them with the same penalties as those breaking the condition of a marriage . . ."

After this text, which very closely follows the manuscript of the *Apologetic History of the Indies* by Bishop Las Casas—during that time kept at the Dominican convent of St. Gregory in Valladolid, Spain—Torquemada embarks upon a lengthy dissertation on the extent of sodomy in biblical times and ancient civilization. Torquemada also gave accounts of anthropophagy.

1615 edition, Vol. II, pp. 124–126; Book VII, Chapter XIX

"Chapter XIX. How was done the sacrifice of men slain in the service of the devil.

"There was a stone at the top of the temple . . . In this stone were carried out the sacrifices of men very frequently . . . Six ministers of Satan came out, four to hold the feet and hands, one for the head and throat . . . another who was the most important and supreme had the knife . . . to whom and nobody else was given the office to open the men by the chest and tear out the hearts . . . he tore out the heart and still beating showed it to the sun . . . the old priest had licence to eat the hearts . . . the body . . . was cooked, and with other foods, they made a very solemn and joyful banquet."

1615 edition, Vol. II, pp. 127–129; Book VII, Chapter XXI

"Chapter XXI. How they sacrificed children to the devil making them to die in different ways.

". . . This same sacrifice was done, not in any way or in few occasions, but with strange and excessive number among these Western heathens . . . The first time . . . at the beginning of the year . . . two children one boy and one girl three to four years of age . . . they did not eat them as usual, like in other sacrifices, but they were kept in a stone box . . . In the eighteenth month . . . they gathered all the children they had purchased during the year . . . whom they kept killing for three months, which in our calendar are February, March and April . . . After being sacrificed these children . . . their bodies were eaten by the headmen, lords and priests. And they never removed the child from the mother until the day he had to be sacrificed . . ."

FERNANDO DE AVENDAÑO (1617)

Fernando de Avendaño (1577–1655) was born and studied in Lima, receiving Holy Orders in 1606. He was at first priest in small Indian communities such as San Pedro de Carta and San Francisco Yguari, becoming

acquainted with the Quechua language and the primitive religious practices of the Indians; in view of this background the Archbishop of Lima
appointed him General Inspector of Idolatries from 1617 to 1623, a period
during which Avendaño produced a most interesting report. After his
visits to Indian villages in order to learn their secret practices he was
made Canon of Lima Cathedral in 1633. Before that date, however, he was
lecturer in Arts, and in 1630 received the Chair of Theology at the
University of San Marcos, Lima, where he became Rector in 1642. The
appointment of Avendaño in 1648 as Qualifier or Judge at the Holy Office
of the Inquisition coincided with the publication of his *Sermones de los
misterios de nuestra Santa Fé Catolica en lengua castellana y general del
Inca*, Lima 1648. Both the *Account* and the *Sermons* by Avendaño are of
great interest in the interpretation of Indian practices and beliefs among
the Incas because of his solid theological training and his research into
the Indian way of thinking. The *Account* was published by Jimenez de la
Espada (1881).

1881 edition, Vol. I, p. 205, note b

"Account of P. Fernando de Avendaño, visitor of the Archbishopric of
the kings [Lima] Peru, sent to his prelate D. Bartolomé Lobo Guerrero
on 3rd April 1617.

"Around *Corpus Christi*, when it could be better located [the constellation of] the Pleiades *Oncoymitta*, when the corn froze and they
lost the seed sown ... the high priest warned the headman and the
other priest of the idols ... and began [the feast] by confessing, and
having first confessed the priests of the idols one with the others ... the
priest sat down and the penitent carry *mullu* which is a ground sea shell
and *paria* which are purple powder [vermilion] and *llaxa* green, and
coca which is a leaf and *sancu* or *parpa* which are cakes made of maize
and lard of the sheep of the country and *chicha* ... and they confess of
theft, of having more than one woman, of killing other people; and in
many provinces they accuse themselves of attending matters of the
[Catholic] Church; and at the end of the confession, the priest minister
of idolatry told them to mend their ways and to commit themself truly
to their *huacas*, and gave them the little stone with the powders to blow
them off and offer them to the sun or the huacas; and in other provinces
they wash in the river, assuming the water washed away their sins,
and they burnt the cakes and the lard, and spilled the *chicha* in offering the idol; and the priest ministers of idolatry used to impose penitence in their own way and fasts; and these confessions used in their
diseases and other travails ... At the end of the confessions they offered
rabbits called *coy* and the sheep of the country ...

"After the sacrifices they began fasting, sometimes during two days,
others five, and the wizards used to fast thirty days, and this fasting
consisted only of not to eat with salt or ají [red pepper] and to abstain
of sleeping with their wives ..."

ANTONIO DE REMESAL (1620)

Antonio de Remesal [c. 1570–1619] was born in Allariz, Orense and in 1593 he entered the Dominican Order in Salamanca. It was not until 1613 that Remesal first went to America and spent two years doing missionary work in Guatemala. It was there that he began writing the *Historia ... de la Governación de Chiapa, y Guatemala*, concluded in Oaxaca in 1617. Remesal then moved to Mexico obtaining the approval of another historian, Fr. Juan de Torquemada, and returned to Spain; his book was printed in Madrid the year of his death. Although most of Remesal's work refers to the missionary progress of the Dominican Order in the Maya and Zapotec areas, there are a few naïve observations about Indian behaviour on aspects so striking to the newcomer, which are worth recording. Remesal also wrote about the confessions used by the Indians.

1620 edition, p. 302. Book VI, Chapter VII

"[In Chiapas] ... to relieve the needs of their bodies they had less care than dogs or cats, because they urinated in front of each other, while in conversation being seated as they were, and the first times they attended a sermon they left the ground wet and muddy no less than a sheep's corral ..."

"... Because they did not lose any of their ancient vices, particularly lust, but acquired some of those in the Christians as well, which they did not consider faults, and he who before baptism did not rob, swear, kill, lie, or carry away women, if he did such after baptism he said: I am becoming a bit Christian ..."

1620 edition, p. 314; Book VI, Chapter XI

".... In many parts of this New Spain it was found the confession of sins. Those of Tlaxcala ... were served as vocal confession of the guilt they had ... it was the way of confessing the Spaniards found in the province of Nicaragua. They told their sins in secret to the priest who could not reveal them ... In Yucatan was also found the confession of sin ... In this province of Chiapa they used to confess and to tell in secret their sins. When the women were near parturition or delivering and men and women getting married, it was necessary to confess first. The jurisdiction of this confession did not reach sins of the mind, but they were only concerned with acts, thefts, homicides, false statements, lies, and all sort of sexual sins. Those women in childbirth and marriage were sometimes confessed by other women, but both men and women did not keep the secret of confession of Nicaragua. Just finishing the confession after the delivery and they said her adulteries. They confessed the bride and said in front of everybody: Our daughter has sinned ..."

PABLO JOSÉ DE ARRIAGA (1621)

The work of this Basque is one of the best published sources for the study of the South American Indian mind. Pablo José de Arriaga (1564–1622) was born in Vergara, Spain, and entered the Society of Jesus receiving Holy Orders at Madrid in 1579. After teaching in Spain he was sent to America, arriving in Peru in 1585. Arriaga was Rector of the Jesuit college of Saint Martin in 1588, but returned to Rome as solicitor of the Peruvian Jesuits at the Council of 1601. Upon his return to Lima he was commissioned by the Archbishop Lobo Guerrero to search, together with P. Fernando de Avendaño, into the primitive practices and beliefs of the Incas, which he later on published as *La extirpacion de la idolatría en el Perú* (1621). Shortly afterwards Arriaga left for Spain and was drowned in the Caribbean Sea during a storm in 1622. Among many interesting details Arriaga offered an excellent description of confession among the pre-Columbian Inca and their attitude to suicide.

1621 edition, p. 17; Chapter III

"Chapter III. Of the ministers of the idolatry.

"... Macsa o Villac are those who cure with a thousand lies and superstitions, usually preceding a sacrifice to the *huaca* or *conopa* which belongs to the patient ...

"... *Aucachic,* named in Cuzco *Ychuris* is the confessor; this is not an office by itself, but always annexed to that of *Villac* or *Macsa* already mentioned.

"... All these offices and positions are common to men and women, even confession, because there are women who are great confessors. But usually the principal offices are taken by men. And I know of an Indian who was the cook and butler of a priest, who was the confessor of the whole village, and the Indians said: 'Such a one is a good confessor, gives little penitence, and such a one is no good, because gives great penitence'"...

1621 edition, p. 27; Chapter V

"Chapter V. What feasts are made to the *huacas.*

"... During fast all Indians men and women confess with those in that office, sitting down on the ground, the one who listens and the other who confesses, in places specially in the field to that effect. They do not confess internal sins, but theft, to ill treat another and to have more than one wife (because to have one, even if they are not married, it is not considered a sin); they accuse themselves of adulteries, but simple fornication under no circumstances is considered a sin; they accuse themselves of having revered the God of the Spaniards and not to have attended their *huacas*; the wizard tells them to mend their ways etc. And they place upon a flat stone the powders of the offering and make [the penitent] to blow them away, and with a little stone they

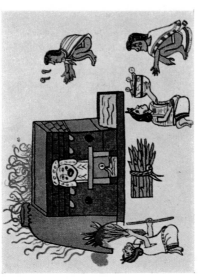

Plate II

Fig. 5. Aztec representations of anthropophagy. *Codex Magliabecchi*, folio 61 (73).
Fig. 6. Aztec medical confession. *Codex Magliabecchi*, folio 66 (78).
Fig. 7. Aztec medical confession and steam bath. *Codex Magliabecchi*, folio 65 (77).
Fig. 8. Aztec self-mutilations and penance. *Codex Magliabecchi*, folio 67 (79).

call *Pasca*, that means forgiveness, that the Indian carries, or the penitent has, they rub the head with ground white corn, and they wash the head with water in some stream or where two rivers join, which is called *Tincuna*. They consider a great sin to hide the sins during confession and the confessor is very diligent in finding out. To this aim in several places follow certain ceremonies. In some, when the Indian arrives at the confessor he says 'Listen the hills around, the plains, the eagles flying, the owls, that I want to confess my sins'. And he says all this holding a head of *mullu* put in a thorn with two fingers of the right hand; raising up the thorn they tell their sins and at the end they give it to the confessor, who receives it, and nailing it down into the blanket, he presses it until the bead breaks down and looks in how many parts broke, and if it broke in three the confession was good, and if it broke in two the confession was not good, and tells them to turn back to confess their sins.

"In other places to verify the same they take a handful of *hicho*, from where it comes the name *Ychuri*, meaning he who gathers straw, and the confessor divides it in two parts, and gets drawing one straw from one side and one from another, until he finds out whether are left even numbers which means the confession was good, but if odd numbers then is bad. In other places they guess it by the blood of the *cuyes* [guinea pigs] and in villages nearby the confessor tied up the hands in the back of the penitent after confession and tying up the rope forced him to tell the truth. Today in front of me an Indian told the Visitor that the confessor pressed him to tell his sins with a stick and other with a rope. They get as penitence the above mentioned fasts of not to taste salt or *ají* [red pepper] or to sleep with their wives, and one told that he had been given this fast during six months. Beside the feasts they use to confess when they are sick with the same wizards in the way described, because they believe that their *malquis* and the *huacas* are angry on account of their sins and this is why they get ill."

1621 edition, p. 32; Chapter VI

"Of the abuses and superstitions of the Indians.

". . . They do not think of those who hang themselves for what they really are. But for something beyond human, and they implore to them and call them for certain things, and it could be this was one of the reasons why in some places they hang themselves so easily, like that young and principal Indian who was having a good time a few months ago in a drinking feast with some Indian girls he had an evil friendship, he said one day near the evening at the end of the feast, and they thought he was teasing: I want to see who among you cares for me and comes to hang herself with me, and with this he left the house, and after searching for him in one place and another they thought he had gone far, he was found hanged near his own house.

"And it was a bit more than a month that having the Inspector imprisoned a sorcerer with handcuffs, without questioning or pressure in any way, on the contrary treating him well, and giving him to eat from his own table two days he had been a prisoner in his own room, he left one night without being noticed, and with a piece of a very thin rope, of those they carry in their head, called by them *huaraca*, he hanged himself at the door of the house, in such way that he was left kneeling, and I found him in this way and met him across our room, when I got up next morning at dawn. We made him to be pulled out dragged by his legs outside the village and to burn him to make example for the others."

ALONSO RAMOS GAVILAN (1621)

There are very few first-hand accounts about the meaning of chastity vows in ancient Peru; one has survived in the book by Alonso Ramos Gavilan (fl. 1621) who was born in Peru, where he entered the Augustinian Order. He was for many years a missionary in the area surrounding Lake Titicaca and around 1618 he went to Lima under the protection of the Viceroy Prince of Esquilache and P. Calancha. Ramos wrote the *Historia del . . . Santuario de Na. Sa. de Copacabana* printed in Lima (1621) where he gives important details of ancient Peruvian religion and social customs.

1621 edition, p. 99

"Chapter XIX. Continuation of the same matter concerning curious things [Of the Virgins dedicated to the Sun there were in Peru]

p. 99: ". . . these virgins dedicated to the Sun . . . had to keep perpetual virginity . . . and to confirm this I wish to tell an outstanding case which took place over nine years ago around 1611 in the village of Uracha, a journey from the city of La Paz, where the teacher of Cathecism was the Priest Ruiz López de Frias Cuello. He certified to many people the death in the village of an old Indian woman, who in his belief was over 120 years old, and in her confession told him that she was not baptized and that she was a virgin; on his asking her the reason, she declared that she had been dedicated to the Sun, and for this reason no Indian dared to have evil relation with her . . ."

1621 edition, p. 103

"Chapter XX. Of other things which there were in Copacabana and the good government of the Inga aiming at the good service of the temple of the Sun.

p. 103: ". . . the Inga knowing that the people of Lupaca were lascivious and dishonest, and liked to dress like women, used great punishments to turn them to the right policy, and hence many times took away from them cattle and food, in order that their need and hunger should make them more subservient and more inclined to work."

CODEX OF THE BACABS (*c.* 1625)

The manuscript first entitled *Ritual of the Bacabs* by Gates is a Codex of 212 octavo pages in Maya language written on linen paper, the last two pages being on the back of a printed indulgence dated 1779. According to Roys (1965), who has published the Maya transcription with an annotated English translation, this Codex of the Bacabs, now preserved at Princeton University Library, is a copy of an earlier text, *c.* 1625. The Codex is a book of Mayan incantations addressed to the four Bacabs or gods. In it the Indian physician asks them to remove the disease from the sick, sometimes in a peremptory manner, because he considered diseases as personified entities. In the curative incantations references are made to the *mut* or animal omen assigned by the Mayas to every person, and also to a plant, both of them referring to the sign of the patient's birthday. The psychiatric value of the incantations of the Bacabs lies in the fact that the Maya physician, by assuming knowledge of the personified disease afflicting the mentally ill, and the fauna and flora related to the evil spirit, in the eyes of the patient was in a commanding position to influence the diseases of the mind. The most frequently accepted cause of mental illness among the Maya were *ik* or wind, air, breath, or spirits entering the person. Of course, there are in the Codex many obscure references to lust, and sexual desires responsible for seizures, asthma and other ailments which could be cured by medical incantations.

1965 edition, pp. 3–6

I.

"The words for jaguar-macaw-seizure; the madness of the seizure. Hun-Ahan [One Lord], Unique Lord of the sky, he would be the creation, he would be the darkness when you were born. Who was your creator? Who was your darkness? He created you did sun great lord, snatcher of the eye of the sun, when you were born. Who was your mother? Who was your begetter, father, when you were born? Red Ixchel, white Ixchel, unique point of the lancet, unique point of the genitals. That was your mother; that was your begetter, your father ... Drunkard-seizure are you. Lust of creation, madness are you. Cock-macaw-seizure are you. Deer seizure are you ... These then are his mother, his lewd father, when he arrives in the heart of Metnal [underworld] ..."

1965 edition, pp. 9–11

III.

"The incantation for macaw-seizure and convulsions; also traveller-seizure and fever, whether it is his mouth, not his tooth, whether froth flows from his mouth, this is to be said. This is a certain command, which begins when you recite it. A very good command, a good incantation. First One Ahau, Unique Four Ahau would be the day.

One Ahau would be the night. Then occurred the birth in four divisions of the sky; then it occurred in the four divisions of the clouds. Meanwhile, this would be said: I curse you, ye god, ye Bacabs, when ye command the Bacabs. How great is his insolent talk, when you command him. This is the command of the gods; this is the command of the Bacabs: Seven heaps grasped! This would be said: I curse you, creation! Koko-bird! This would be his shameless talk; this would be his insolent speech. What is your pain or grief?..."

1965 edition, pp. 11–12

IV.

"The words for erotic-seizure. Mad will be the speech of the man because of the fever. The man has an impulse to run because of his madness also. Unique Four Ahau is the day for the creation of the great fierce one. High is the door of his green arbour, where the origin of the lust of birth, the lust of creation took place. Firmly set was his red haft, when there occurred the birth of the *on*, the *nicte*; when there occurred the birth of the humming bird-nicte.

"Oh, I curse you father dwarf-man wind together with erotic-seizure." This would be recited over the man who talks very madly. He runs afflicted with a convulsion. This shall be recited over him twiced recited."

1965 edition, pp. 17–18

VI.

"The lewd madness of seizure. Unique Four Ahau is its day; unique [One] Ahau is its night; the lewdness of night, the lewdness of day, there in the sky, there in the clouds. Firmly established is his acantun. Four days prostrate is the serpent of creation. Four days it turns about [where it is] placed, planted. You are the lewdness of seizure, curses upon you!... I suddenly grasp you for the fourth time in my incantation when I stand erect..."

HERNANDO RUÍZ DE ALARCÓN (1629)

Hernando Ruíz de Alarcón (fl. 1629) was born in the silver mine area of Taxco, Guerrero, Mexico and was brother of the celebrated writer Juan Ruíz de Alarcón (1580–1639); he studied Philosophy at the University of Mexico and received Holy Orders; after several years in the Oaxaca area, by commission of his bishop, Ruíz de Alarcón was engaged on the analysis of primitive religious practices and superstitions among the Indians of Iguala in Guerrero. Later, in Atenango in the same area, he carefully collected the aboriginal texts in Nahuatl and Spanish *Tratado de las supersticiones de los naturales de esta Nueva España* written in 1629 and published by del Paso y Troncoso in Mexico (1892). It would be difficult to find another author, apart from Sahagún, who can be compared with Ruíz de Alarcón for his analysis of Mexican psychology, and the survival of their ancient behaviour. He left a detailed description of the use of hallucinogenic drugs, the medical art of suggestion and incantation and many other pre-Columbian practices which exemplified the value of psychiatric procedures in these ancient civilizations.

1892 edition, p. 127

p. 127: "Dedication to the Archbishop of Mexico

"... and some [vices] which were not allowed in their gentility, such as drunkenness, which had in their gentility death penalty.

"And drunkenness which at present is so frequent among them... and it is today the greatest of their vices, the complete destruction of their corporal health, and therefore the worst and main obstacle towards their preservation and growth.

p. 134: "Chapter II. Of the idolatries and abuses, and notice of things they attribute divinity, specially *ololuihqui, piciete* and *peyote.*

"... the *ololuihqui* is a kind of seed like lentils produced by a type of vine in this land, which when drunk deprive of the senses, because is very powerful, and by this mean they communicate with the devil, because he use to talk to them when they are deprived of judgement with the said drink, and deceive them with different hallucinations, and they attribute it to a god they say is inside the seed, called *ololuihqui* or *inexpalli*, which is the same thing..."

1892 edition, p. 142

p. 142: "Chapter VI. Of the superstition of Ololuihqui.

"The so-called *ololuihqui* is a seed like lentils or meris which when drunk deprives of judgement, and it is a marvel the faith these wretched natives have in this seed, because drinking, seek its advice like if it were an oracle, for every one of the things they wish to know, even those which human knowledge cannot reach, because almost everyone of them who are hectics, phthysic, with diarrhoea, or any other chronic disease, readily attribute it to witchcraft, and to get out of this doubt or similar ones, such as things robbed, and their aggressors, seek advice in this seed by means of their deceitful physician, who some among them have for office to drink this seed for such consultations, and such physician is called *Pàyni*, because of his office, and he is well paid for it, and bribe him with food and drink in their own way. If the said physician does not have that office or wants to be excused of that trouble, he advises the patient to drink himself the seed or somebody else, to whom they pay as much as the physician, but the physician sets day and hour when it has to be drunk, and tells him for what purpose is drunk.

"Lastly, either the physician or the other is his place, to drink the said seed, or *peyote*, which is another small root about which they hold the same faith than with this other seed, they lock themselves alone in a room, which is usually their oratory, where nobody must come in all the time which lasts the consultation, lasting while the consultant is away from his sense, because they believe that the *ololuihqui* or *peyote* is revealing them what they want to learn; and in passing that drunkenness or deprivation of judgement, they come out telling two thousand lies, among which the devil usually mixes some truths, with which he keeps them completely deceived and mistaken.

"It is a fact that who drinks *ololuihqui* loses his judgement very briefly because too much strength in the seed, afterwards with his judgement altered it is offered the task made to purpose, and there is the sentence where the devil inclines him to who is not lacking skill for those tricks, perhaps he condemns the innocent, perhaps he discovers the guilty, perhaps he comes out with so many crazy ideas that cannot be made anywhere else, and the wretched ones believe everything, whether is revealed by the devil, or representation of their fancy caused by the talk given, because they attribute everything to the divinity in the *ololuihqui* or *peyote*, to whom for this reason they revere and fear so, that they do as much as possible, and care that this do not reach to be noticed by the ecclesiastical ministers, especially if they are judges who can forbid and punish them as I said . . .

1892 edition, p. 153

p. 153: "Second treatise. Chapter II. Of the spell they use to induce sleep.

"In the incantation to induce sleep they aver that the charmed one remains in such way, that he is unable to wake up no matter what, even if they do anything to him, or they have experienced as they certified is true that it is work of the devil, particularly as it is always aimed at some mortal sin, such as theft or adultery; the words they used are:

"Myself, whose name is darkness, so I can deliver from nine parts then come soon charming sleep, so I can bring my sister nine times. I priest (or demon, fable of the antiquity) whose sister is the goddess *Xochiquetzal*, although she was very much watched by the priests and the rest of the people, the prince and the most powerful, so it was impossible to get in, I invoked the sleep shouting, and with that all went to the nine depths [i.e. the watch fell deeply asleep]. Because I am the youngman. I to whom the joints crackle, and foolishly shout everywhere. Yea, come now, priest or demon One flint (*Ce tecpatl*) go and see if my sister is already sleep, to whom I am going to take away so my youngman would not be wanted, so none of her brothers would not want me when I take her to the nine depths, that I must take [her] to the centre of the earth to give her there to darkness [i.e. to sleep] so even if she returns to four parts, I should not feel that I am war itself, to whom everything is a joke and jest with everyone, changing them one into the other, making them unconscious. I who am war itself, jester of everyone, who want them to surrender so they will be drunk lost in darkness [i.e. sleep].

"They aver that with these words not only fall asleep those exorcised, but that they seem unconscious, and thus they do anything they wish with them, carrying and taking them to other places.

"They also aver that they will not wake up unless the spell is broken, and to break the spell they use other words meaning that what they said in the first spell was not true but make-believe, and they assented as perpetual was only temporal, the words are as follows:

"To bring these from the earth's centre, and from the four parts, and so may not be true that I spelled them, and changed into others, and that slept and went to the nine depths, nor that I took them to the sleep or darkness. Yea here, that I return and remove the sleeping spell, I who have sought nocturnal drunkenness.

"With this they say the spell is broken and the charmed are awoken, and in order not to forget the devil his arts, after these words in the papers there is *in nomine domine* [In God's name] where the devil manifest his ambition."

1892 edition, p. 180

p. 180: "Fourth Treatise. Chapter I. Of the spell and words they use to appease anger.

"Having dealt with the spells these natives use in their business, and actions pertaining to inanimate things, or are aimed to things not free, it seemed to me [to deal] in the last place with the spells and words they use in business and things which are aimed to human communications, and to those who have reason and free will, where they pretend to have entry and even dominion, by means of words used for different effects, and for what we have to deal in this chapter, which is to command the condition and even the state of will, pretending that who is in anger be appeased, or that who is fretful and ready to anger, should not be like that, and on the contrary, who is peaceful, do not be, who is actually in love, despise and dislike whom he loved before; although this referred could be aimed to good end, like if the wife in a bad marriage pretend the husband to part from the one who is motive in her bad marriage, or if the man who is disliked by his wife, pretended her love according to the law of marriage. Even then, it would never be legal to use those means, according to the common axiom: *non sunt facienda mala, ut inde everiant bona* [it is not by doing wrong that in the end comes good]. But the damage is even greater, because the one leading this dance always goes in such a way that evil gets bonded and aimed to more evil; and so it is well established among these miserable and blind ones to use the superstition of the spell and to invoke in his favour, and this to prepare and means of other sins, because used them currently for evil friendships and adulteries, pretending to remove from the husband the love and affection for his own wife and place her in something wrong, or that the wife abhor her legitimate husband, or that the husband be like insensible to offences against the matrimonial faith, tolerating them, as if they were not his own. To this aim they use a procedure which includes two things, they are potion and words, and although may be of many kinds the two things included in this procedure, I will only put down one kind, because, to those who have to deal with its remedy, they will have enough information with what I will say here, and to put down all the procedures they use it is not necessary and could be stumble and occasion to the evil ones to greater sins, because one of the things they use as medicine to which they attribute part of the effect, are certain grains of maize, which are placed the beginning of the cob, and the aforementioned grains had their points against their growths, turned away and to the other side of the rest in the cob, and they attribute this contrary trend to a contrary effect in the inclination and will towards affection and hate. They apply to these maize grains the second part of this procedure, which are words exorcising the maize, in their judgement, give them new strength and virtue to obtain the effect of exchange they pretend; these words are, therefore:

"Come here, illustrious and esteemed man, a god who will appease the heart burning [of anger] you will exile from it the green anger, the yellow wrath I will banish and drive away because I am the priest Prince of Charms who will give to drink the spelled one the potion that changes heart (by charm).

"This spell cast to apply the medicine, grinding the exorcised maize, they make a drink their own style, such as *atole* or cocoa, and give it to drink to whom they pretend to change their will or affection, and so to introduce discord they use contrary words and give the drink in the way I have just described.

"The deceit and superstition is readily seen and unless definite agreement is entered into, or at least implied, those means never would obtain the aim."

1892 edition, p. 181

p. 181: "Fifth Treatise. Chapter II. Of another spell to attract and entice.

"Of the kind referred is the superstition used to attract enticing the will of somebody and is used by those in love if it is to their advantage, and fits here properly, and this superstition is based only in words to which they attribute the virtue to surrender at their will anybody they fancy, they say [these] words of the spell:

"In the crystal hill where the will meet, I search for a woman and sing to her loving songs, fatigued by the care I have for her love and so I do my best about it. I bring in my help my sister the goddess Xochiquetzal [Venus] who comes gracefully surrounded by a snake and another as a girdle and has her hair gathered by her ribbon. This loving care made me tired and crying yesterday and the day before yesterday, and this makes me afflicted and unhappy. I think she is truly a goddess, truly beautiful and delicate. I must obtain her not tomorrow, not some day, but now this moment, because I in person order and command it. I the young warrior who shine like the sun and have the beauty of dawn; am I by chance just any kind of man? Was I born among mallows? I came and was born through the flourish and transparent sex of woman etc . . .

"The other words are of such nature, though somehow disguised, that for modesty and [not to offend] chaste ears, are not put down; lastly to end they say:

"Truly is worth to be considered a god[dess] because she is of the prettiest in the world, I will not reach her tomorrow, or any other day, but soon now, that I in person order it, the young fighter; perchance do I bring war? Mine is not war but the conquest of women."

1892 edition, p. 182

p. 182: "Fourth Treatise. Chapter III. Of the evils and illnesses produced by illicit loves.

"Among the gentile superstitions which remain among the Indians, it is not the least damaging the fiction about diseases caused by illicit loves and forbidden desires, which is the matter contained in this chapter, and although it is dealt in it with the pretended cures of these maladies, it seems that belongs and should be included in the Treatise of the superstitious doctors and their frauds, despite this, I decided to put it here because this fraud is based upon affectation of the free will, we shall see in its discourse. This chapter has two parts: the first contains the fiction of diseases and evils called or named of illicit loves and desires, and its cause and manner of falling in these diseases; the second part contains the superstition of the cure and remedy of such diseases and evils. In respect to the first part the cunning of the enemy, that taking advantage of the opportunities to harm us, has introduced and established that many illnesses arise from illicit love and desires, i.e. to be in bad condition a third party; and having to remove this idea, that it would be much better for everybody to be good, the enemy, changing everything into evil, and making and manufacturing poison even from the good doctrine, has produced two evils: the first is that due to the profit those liars, who pretend to be physicians, soothsayer, learned and mending agents of these illnesses, have in the treatment of the pretended cure of them, there are many who want that office; the second and more serious damage is that with this motive they introduce and persuade that to sin is a good thing, because it seems that if from the outside in the skin of this superstition are manifested diseases and evils produced by sins, examining with care its interior and the damaging intention of the enemy, this corporal and temporal damage is only pretended by participation of those assisting and participating, without considering those of the soul and eternal of the guilty, the other by wishing to establish for certain that such diseases and evils have for cure and remedy to commit other similar or greater offences, sins which level or surpass the pretended cure of them, and in order to understand this better:

"To notice first (and this is the first part of this chapter) that the diseases and damages which pertain to this chapter, are three: the first, of children who get usually frightened and shout as if they were seeing some dreadful thing, the same when they wake up shouting and crying as if frightened, when without apparent accident they lose their senses and look like dead and others hurting [themselves]; and these ailments are commonly called in Castilian epilepsy or falling sickness; the second is when anybody either due to advanced age, or because he has sickly constitution or weakness in the stomach, or being hectic of consumption, goes little by little getting thin; the third species has more latitude and the enemy takes more advantage of it for the second aim, which is to persuade guilty evils to avoid those of sorrow, and as a remedy for temporal ills they fall into eternal penalties with harm and death of the soul.

"And so any disease or ailment commonly judged by our physicians as incurable, these liars say that are due to excess of faults in the mate, either his wife or her husband, or either their friend or friends, and to this kind of diseases they add and include those which we usually call unhappiness and hardship, such as poverty and bad events, i.e. frost of seed bed, rotten of seeding, damage to the maize and wheat by animals, to lose and fall in precipices the beasts, to be unable to find outlet for the merchandises, or not to gain in their deals, and even not to cook properly their meals and drinks, things which in one way or another nobody can escape of; these, therefore, they call diseases and ills caused by the excess faults of the mate as said, and in the Mexican language they call it *tlàçolmiquiztli*, which means, ill due to love and lust; they give the same name to the diseases of children mentioned above, although for falling sickness they usually say *tlàçolminiquiliztli*, which means almost the same, only indicates losing the senses; the second species of illness by weakness and wasting away they call *netepalhuiliztli*, which means to depend on other and better interpreted illness by depending from other.

"Now it rests to say how they pretend to receive these ills and diseases and afterwards of their pretended cure which is the second part of this chapter.

"There are two types of persons who pretend to be subject to these diseases either children or adults, both men and women; the children they aver suffer the aforementioned ailments because at their childbirth attended or was present a person of loose or dishonest life, or because that person arrived to the mother while they were in the womb or after birth in her arms.

"In the adults give as a cause, if they are married or in concubinage, the excess of adulterers and concubination in the mate, and call *tlàçolmiquitztli* to the ailments contracted in their belief on this account and those of children in the previous paragraph, but if the sick adults are not married or in bad ways, in such case they say got sick due to one or two reasons: the first, when the sick person was in the company of others, arrived there or mixed with them another one of bad way of life, or going in the wrong way and in concubinate; the second cause they say it is due, when the sick man was in the company of others, one of them wanted to obtain a woman and coveted something or something belonging to others, and because this third person was unable to obtain his desire, usually causing in him much melancholy and sadness, they say like the philosophers aver by sympathy and redundancy, they infect their companion and give him that ailment of wasting and getting thinner, which they call *netapahuiliztli*, as we have said before: let us go now to the lie of how to cure these diseases, which is the second part of this chapter: to all this ailment they apply the same remedy which they call *tetlaçolaltiloni*, meaning: bath for the illness caused by loves or lust; although they have it for sole remedy they do not exclude the one used against the ills due to excess in offences which is to level or exceed them, and this is just plain gentile blindness.

"Baths, extended lie and general cure of these ills, are carried out in the following manner: The soothsayer gets fire, copal incense and water and places a clean cloth upon a mat, makes the sick man to stand near it; afterwards he talks to the fire and later to the water."

BUENAVENTURA DE SALINAS (1630)

Like those of las Casas, the books of Buenaventura de Salinas y Cordoba (*c.* 1592–1653) were passionate in defence of the Indians and full of historical information about the Incas. He was born in Lima and became an outstanding student at the San Marcos University where he eventually became Professor of Latin and Rhetoric. In 1615 Salinas had been appointed secretary to the Government of Peru, but left this position to enter the Franciscan Order in 1616. In 1639 he was the Solicitor in Rome of the Peruvian Franciscan province, in 1640 he became Rector of Studies in Naples and in 1645 was made General Commissary of the Franciscans in Mexico and died there in Cuernavaca. He wrote a *Memorial de las historias del Nuevo Mundo* printed in Lima (1630), with deep insight into Indian customs.

1630 edition, Chapter I [pages unnumbered]

"Origin of the first Indians who inhabited Peru, how long their barbarousness lasted and the policy of the Inca Kings during their monarchy. [sig. b₁ *recto*] ... This fourth age lasted more than one thousand and one hundred years crowded with insolence and barbarousness, sown with the [sodomitic] abominations of certain Giants who arrived in the plains following the coast from Tucuman strait... [sig. b₂ *verso*] ... Lloguiyupangui ... had perfidious inclination, he was

lascivious and given to idleness ... [sig. b₃ *verso*] ... Pauchacutic Inga
... was given to all sort of abominations and during his time most of
them were sodomites, and this is why God locked the skies so that
there was no rain in seven years.

Afterwards Salinas offered a quotation alleged to be taken from a work
by Jean Bodin which is extremely important but the source is incorrect:

1630 edition, signature C₂ verso

" ... And Juan Bodino who refers in the *Theatrum vitae humanae*
volume 27 book 4 page 4189 says of these priests [in the temples of the
Sun] that they went through long fasts, dedicated to the contemplation
of the Sun and the Stars to whom they pray for the kingdom. There
were many monasteries of virgins and those [men] in their care had the
nose and the lips cut, and were castrated, having death penalty if they
were lascivious ... "

GIOVANNI ANELLO OLIVA (1631)

There are details on ancient Peru in the work of Giovanni Anello Oliva
(1572–1642) which are not to be found in any other chronicle of Peru,
because he was fortunate in receiving information from Catari, the
quipucamayo, or Inca keeper of records by *quipus*, in Cochabamba. Oliva
was born in Naples entering the Company of Jesus in 1593; he went to
Peru with P. Claver in 1597, received the Holy Orders in Lima and
visited many points of Peru: Juli, Potosí, Arequipa; he died in Lima. In
1631 Oliva concluded *Vidas de ... la Compañia de Jesus en el Peru*; the
first of its four parts is in fact a history of Peru to which the General of the
Order refused publication. A copy of the manuscript was finally printed
in 1895.

1895 edition, p. 11; Book I, Chapter I, paragraph 2

p. 11: " ... it grows in the Andes. The most appreciated herb of the
highest esteem among the Indians, called *coca* considered their only
support, not just because satisfied their hunger, but because it dupli-
cates their strength in any work. Therefore while they perform any
[work] they have it in the mouth persuaded that as long as they have
they will be encouraged to work. Because of this the use they make of it
is very great and just in Potosí goes up to a million and a half per year
the amount consumed ... "

1895 edition, p. 25; Book I, Chapter II, paragraph 1

p. 25: " ... In this time Otoya, the other younger brother to Tumbe and
brother of Quitumbe who had remained in Sumpa ... proceeded with
his vices until some giants arrived in that land; they were as deformed
and ugly in their appearance as they were cruel in their deeds. They

oppressed the land and became masters of everything because having Otoya a prisoner they had his subjects confused and frightened. But soon God delivered them of this oppression and tyranny with a punishment sent by the heavens against these giants, who because they had no women used the nefarious sin. Because of this flakes of fire rained down in such a manner that they consumed and burnt all of them, delivering the inhabitants of that land from such toil though [they were left] without their head to govern them, because Otoya died in prison . . ."

1895 edition, p. 42; Book I, Chapter II, paragraph 5

p. 42: ". . . Mayta Capac Amaro . . . was a man of strange condition of whom the *quipucamayo* and chronicler Catari tells a most extraordinary thing, that he had such a distaste for relations and intercourse with women, even the most beautiful, he was naturally withdrawn from all, and despite being married to Mama Curi and Ilpaycoya, who was the prettiest princess of that time, he never lived with her. But Garcilasso de la Vega in the First Part of his Commentaries says that at the time of his death he left his heir a legitimate son whom he had among others from his wife. The reader may believe of these opinions the best to his liking . . ."

ANTONIO DE LA CALANCHA (1638)

Because of his birth and deep knowledge of Indian affairs the work of Antonio de la Calancha (1584–1654), although very much devoted to the affairs of the Augustinians, has a number of interesting observations. He was born in Chuquisaca and entered the Augustinian order in 1598, studied theology at the College of San Ildefonso in Lima, and eventually became its Rector in 1622. Calancha was also Prior of the convents of Arequipa and Trujillo, and wrote the *Coronica moralizadora del orden de San Augustin en el Perú*, published in 1638, containing important views on sodomy and religious practices, and a brief reference to the confessions used by the Inca Indians.

1638 edition, p. 556. Book III, Chapter II, paragraph 13

p. 556: ". . . These Indians of the valleys were very inclined to sodomy and today are not free from this contamination, the wives being their accomplices. If during the time of their heathenism the men were the accomplices, today many cover under the cloak of marriage the treason done to nature, depriving from generation what is given to lewdness. The Inga to remedy such abominable impulse made a law, enforced without pity, which not only burnt the agents but their farm, house, cattle, clothes, and everything belonging to them, and if by chance anyone of their blood and family had notice of it, they burnt all their descendants, paying the ignorants as well as those who knew it.

"Then, when they burnt many of them, there were thousands and and thousands of Indians, and now without killing any of them, the villages are annihilated without Indians. God punishes when Justice does not judge. Those who live today in the villages of the Virgin [of Guadalupe, in the Valley of Pacasmayo] do not show this vice, nor do we know of them having idols or idolatry . . ."

1638 edition, p. 377; Book II, Chapter XII

". . . With these [wizards] and with the witches they confessed, and [the confessors] gave them harsh penitences and to give gold, silver, clothes, or food to the *huacas* or holy places and to keep fast three or four or six months continuously . . . The matter of confession was theft, adultery, to kill by poison, and the highest faults were not to serve God or to break something ordered by the Inca . . ."

The narrative of Vasco Nuñez de Balboa is also reproduced by Calancha (1638):

1638 edition, p. 29; Book I, Chapter XXIX

". . . the Company [of Vasco Nuñez de Balboa] entered into an allied village [in Castilla del Oro] where they saw men dressed like women; Balboa learnt that they were sodomites and threw the king and forty others to be eaten by his dogs, a fine action of an honourable and Catholic Spaniard. This is reported by Geronimo Benzoni in his *America* (in book 4) . . ."

This account does not appear in Benzoni's *Historia del mondo nuovo* (1565) which only contains three books, but in Anglerius' *Decades* (1530), as has already been indicated.

PEDRO SANCHEZ DE AGUILAR (1639)

A descendant of Spanish Conquistadors, Pedro Sanchez de Aguilar (1555– c. 1640) was born in Valladolid, Yucatan, and received his first education from an Indian, in turn a descendant of Maya rulers, Gaspar Antonio Xiu. Sanchez de Aguilar studied in 1588 at the University of Mexico graduating as a Doctor of Theology. After entering the priesthood he returned to Yucatan to practise missionary work at Chancenote and Valladolid; in 1602 Sanchez de Aguilar had to rule the bishopric of Yucatan. He went to Madrid in 1612, to be appointed in 1619 bishop of Las Charcas in the Viceroyalty of Peru, where he died. Sanchez de Aguilar's most interesting work *Informe contra Idolorum cultores del Obispado de Yucatan*, published in Madrid 1639 and reprinted in Mexico (1892), is important for the analysis of surviving pre-Columbian beliefs and practices among the Mayas.

1892 edition, p. 84

p. 84: "Witchcraft

"... They also use to call certain old Indian sorcerers who heal by words of their infidelity to woman in parturition, to whom they confess and [also] to some sick people. I was unable to investigate this, of which I feel very sorry ...

p. 91: "... During the early discoveries they considered the Indians un-fitted to receive the Holy Sacraments because they thought [they] were beasts ...

p. 115: "XV That this prosecutor, cure the sick people and help them to a good death ... because when lacking this consolation and help they despair and are strongly tempted by the devil to hang themselves."

BERNABÉ COBO (*c.* 1642)

He was born in Lopera (1580–1650), went to the West Indies in 1595 and remained in Santo Domingo for four years. Cobo was a member of the Society of Jesus and arrived at Lima in 1599; from 1609 to 1613 he studied at Cuzco, where he received the Holy Orders, and became interested in the ancient history of Incas. In 1629 he visited Mexico to return in 1642 to Lima, where he died. Cobo's *Historia del Nuevo Mundo*, not published until 1890–1895, considerably expands Acosta's history in a systematic way, and his discussion of the confession among the Peruvian Indians is done in great detail.

1890 edition, Vol. I, p. 473–477; Book V, Chapter XXIX

"Book V, Chapter XXIX. "Of the Coca

p. 473: "In this kingdom of Peru there is nothing better known than the *Coca* ... The *Coca* is a shrub no greater than the dwarf apple trees in Spain ... its leaf, which the Indian esteem and price so highly is in size and shape similar to that of a lemon ... In ancient times the natives of Peru planted and cultivated the *Coca* in the manner of vines, and the leaf was so highly esteemed that only was used by kings and noblemen, and offered it in the sacrifices they usually did to the false gods. To the peasants it was forbidden to use it without licence of the governors. But after the rule of the Inca Kings ended and with it its prohibition the common people gave themselves to it with the desire of those wishing to eat the forbidden fruit ... The use of this leaf is in the following manner: The Indians make little balls of it crushed like a fig, and they ordinarily carry them in the mouth, between the cheek and the gum, sucking the juice without swallowing the leaf; and they aver that gives them so much strength that while they have it in the mouth, they do not feel thirst, hunger or fatigue. I verily believe that most of the things they manifest is their imagination or superstition, though it cannot be denied that it gives them some strength and encouragement because we can see them work double with it ... Its temperament is hot and dry, with very good styptic action; usually chewed, keep the teeth from corruption and caries, bleaches, fix and reinforce them. It happened to me that calling once a barber to pull me out a molar because it moved and hurt me considerably, the barber told me it was a pity to take it out, because it was sound and healthy; and being present a religious friend of mine, he advised me to chew *coca* for a few days. I did it, and the toothache went away, and the molar became firm like the rest. The sap of the *coca* strengthens the stomach and helps digestion."

1890 edition, Vol. IV, pp. 89–93; Book XIII, Chapter XXIV

"Of the opinion they [the Incas] had about their sins, how they confess them and penitences and fasts they made.

"It is a thing of great admiration to see how the Devil introduced among the Indians the use of the vocal confession so universally extended which became one of the ceremonies most welcomed among them and exercised with most devotion. They entirely confessed everything they thought to be sinful; although they were greatly mistaken about their judgement of sins. Because, in the first place they never considered internal acts, such as wishes, licentious tendencies, either to be told in confession, or to be considered sins.

"In external acts they believed there were many fashions of sin. Those considered most were: to kill one another away from war, or violently, with witchcraft or poison; to rob, to neglect the care of their *huacas* and places of worship; not to keep the feasts or celebrate them; to speak evil of the Inca, or not to carry on his wishes. Although they considered it a sin to take the neighbour's wife and to corrupt a virgin, this was not due to think that fornication itself were a sin, but it was to break the order given by the Inca, who prohibited this. They believed that all the misfortunes and adversities which came to men, were due to their sins and therefore those who were the greatest sinners suffered the greatest tribulations and calamities and when to somebody's children died, they believed his sins were very great, founded in that according to the natural order, parents should die first than their children; and not only they believed that their suffering came because of their own sins, but they also thought that when the king was ill or suffered other adversity, it was due to the subject's sins not those of the king's; this is why when they learnt that he was ill all the provinces confessed, especially those of *Collas*, and made great sacrifices for his health. Those persons commissioned to practise the office of confessors were usually the wizards and sorcerers in charge of the *huacas*, either men or women, because the females also learnt this ministry. These confessors had their own hierarchy and order from the highest to the lowest, and sins reserved to the highest. Although this vocal confession was generally used in all the provinces of the Inca empire, it was more practised in those of *Collas*; and it seems that they were the inventors because everywhere the *Collas* were considered the best teachers in this office. The practice of confession was compulsory to all kinds of people except the Incas, who were not forced to confess their sins to anybody; they based this on the fact that they were descendants and kinsmen of the king with whom *Viracocha* had relation, it was unfair that if they sinned were to be easily forgiven, but they should die for it if their offences were manifested; but to confess to the Sun, as a mediator with Viracocha, so they could be forgiven; although they better agreed that it was not convenient that they [the Inca] told their faults to other men, or anybody learnt their failures. Finally, anyhow, they [the Incas] did not confess vocally but in the manner said; and afterwards they used a washing, assuming that in that way they finished cleansing their faults, going into a stream and saying these words 'I have confessed my sins to the Sun, and *Viracocha* because he begot me he forgave me; you river receive them and take them to sea never to be found.' The time they confessed most frequently was before sacrifices, and after confession and fulfilling the penitence, they made their offerings. And this business of confession and offering sacrifice, was not only done during their own illness, but that of the wife, the husband, the son or important people, such as the headman or any of similar office. The confessor was bound to secrecy, although with certain limitations, and the penitent to tell the truth, because they were convinced that it was a very serious fault to hide any sin in confession, and the confessors were judges of this fault, and investigated whether the confession was complete and true, by means of lots they cast such as little stones or by looking into the entrails of some animal, and if the lot was bad and by the research the sorcerer thought the penitent was lacking in completeness and due clarity, he then punished him, striking a number of times in his back with a stone, and forced him to turn back to confess until the said confessor thought the confession was good; and this done, he gave the penitence according to the severity of the sins; and sometimes these penitences were very harsh, particularly if the sinner was a poor man and had nothing to give to the confessor. All of them were told after confession to go and wash in a river, in the same way it has been told was done by those of Inca caste; because these washes were generally used by those who confessed their sins to the Sun, and by those who confessed in the ordinary way, and beside the washings they imposed other penitences, which were usually some days of fast in their fashion. When the confessor judged the penitent to be a great sinner, such as those whose children died, he increased the penitence in this way; that he should search for a person born deformed and marked by nature, and this person went with the penitent to the river where he had to make the customary washing up, and after he finished washing in the usual ceremony, the deformed one flogged him with nettle; and just for this purpose there were in Cuzco certain small Indian deformed half of their body, with huge hunchbacks born that way. Finally, there were in this rite and ceremonies many other rules and regulations, all meant to abuse.

"Both to fulfil the penitence imposed in confession, and by devotion to request from the gods something desired, they afflicted themselves and suffered hard and rough experiences, nothing was worse penitence than fast, which was very different from ours; because it was not to abstain during a certain period of time of all food, or to eat less times or in less quantity than usual, but only to abstain during all the time of fast from salt and *ají* which were their spices and most exquisite sauces; and if they abstained from these things, even if they went loose reined in other matters, they thought did not break fast. It is true that some times and in serious cases they added to abstain some days from eating meat, to drink *chicha*, and reach their wives, which they had for extreme rigour, but the usual and ordinary fast was as above; no more than the abstinence of salt and *ají*."

FERNANDO MONTESINOS (1644)

There is a certain amount of controversy regarding the work of Fernando Montesinos (*c.* 1600–*c.* 1645). He was born in Osuna and after receiving Holy Orders went to Peru in 1628 as the chaplain of the celebrated Viceroy Count of Chinchon, whose name is associated with Cinchona. Montesinos had a most active life in Peru, travelling continuously for 15 years, first as secretary to the Bishop of Trujillo, then as priest in Potosí, ecclesiastical inspector in Arica, missionary in Tarma in 1637, chaplain in Lima until 1639, and other church appointments at Cajamarca in 1640, Trujillo in 1641 and Quito in 1643. As a result of his observations at the mining area of Potosí he published a *Beneficio común … de metales* Lima (1638), and, due to his participation in the Inquisitorial proceedings against the Jews, the *Auto de la fé … en Lima … 1639* printed at Madrid 1640. His important works were the *Anales del Perú 1498–1642* and his *Memorias antiguas historiales y políticas del Perú* written in 1644 after Montesinos returned to Spain and became the Vicar of Campana, near Seville. He was a good scholar and collector of documents, particularly those on pre-Columbian Peru gathered by the Bishop of Quito Luis López de Solís (*c.* 1530–1606). Montesinos also relied on the manuscripts of P. Valera, and the well known chronicles by Cieza de León, Zárate and Garcilasso de la Vega. Despite his errors in the correlation between the Biblical sequence and Peruvian history, and his belief that Peru was inhabited by the descendants of Noah and his grandson Ophir, Montesinos shows extraordinary vision in the interpretation of Peruvian history. His critics fail to understand that Montesinos, as Gibbon did 150 years later with the Roman Empire, pointed out that the rise of the Inca hegemony was also the result of the moral and political decay of the Mochica and Chimú cilizations, where among other things, sodomy was prevalent.

1882 edition, p. 54

Chapter IX. "What happened during the time of this king [Ayar Tacco Capac] in Cuzco and the origin of the giants in Peru.

p. 54: "The spies also told how very big and very tall men had arrived at the point we call Santa Elena and mastered that land of Puerto Viejo, and that the natives were fleeing from them because they made bad use of their bodies. In my opinion was not to flee from sin, because they were also given to sodomy, but for the damage they suffered from their instruments, because with them they took their lives away. But the excesses of the giants were such that the divine justice took care of its punishment, and chastised them in an instant by sending fire from Heaven which suddenly burnt them . . ."

1882 edition, p. 85

Chapter XV. "Of the events during the time of Tupac Cauri Pachacuti the seventh and other Peruvian kings.

p. 85: ". . . Nine years after the reign of Tupac Cauri Pachacuti the seventh completed three thousand five years after the Deluge. This king began to take the lead and tax some cities and provinces; but the natives obeyed with resistance because they were so corrupted in matters of religion and customs that he had to conquer them, because he said that if that people communicate with his own, they would contaminate them their great vices, particularly idolatry and sodomy, to which they were given like beast without control.

p. 88: "During the times of this King [Toto Cozque] came in great number of people from Panama and the Andes, reaching Cuzco and other places of those provinces and made settlements there. They live like beasts, very much given to sodomy, without policy or government and ate human flesh . . .

p. 89: "Near death [Toto Cozque] gathered his sons and told them how those vices of sodomy and to eat human flesh were against the ancient laws, and that Illaticí Huiracocha had always punished it and would punish them if they were not little by little leaving them . . ."

p. 90: ". . . during the time Inti Maita Capac . . . Pachacuti, the eighth of this name the vices ended by corrupting good customs and sodomy was a political sin. There was not obedience, men live without discipline and like beasts, lasting several years until the Incas took over this kingdom . . ."

1882 edition, p. 91

Chapter XVI. Origin of the Inca kings and the manner they took over the Government.

p. 91: "Every day the things of Peru went for the worse and the kings of Cuzco were just kings by name, because the vices had removed the sense of obedience, discipline had disappeared and confusion had been introduced. The worst of them was the vice of bestiality [i.e. sodomy], origin of every unhappiness in the kingdom. This sin lasted from the years of the Deluge until the year —— of our redemption for over —— continuous years. The women regretted the most this misfortune to see their nature deceived and their pleasure unsatisfied. In their meetings they dealt in nothing but their miserable state and low esteem they had reached, burning of jealousy, watching how men communicated among themselves the favours and pleasantries which the women only deserved; they gave and took measures to remedy this, used herbs and devices but to no avail to change the men's desires."

Montesinos then tells how Mama Ciuaco decided to make his son Inca Roca a king and covered him with gold leaf. Then Inca Roca remained hidden in the Chingana to appear shining in the sunshine three times as the incarnation of the son of the Sun, and thus became accepted as king by the Incas in Cuzco. Inca Roca had been told by his mother Mama Ciuaco that the military exercises and the natural laws ordered by Illaticí Hiura Cocha had made Cuzco flourish and overcome their enemies but.

1882 edition, p. 93

p. 93: "... All this has been turned down and twisted by the bestiality [sodomy] that barbarous people has introduced in this kingdom and led to the miserable state you can see ..."

In turn Inca Roca told his people

1882 edition, p. 99

p. 99: "Vices and bestialities have been the fire which has been consuming the greatness [of Cuzco] ... instead of following the road of men you walk the way of animals leaving courage so effeminate, that you forgot what it is the sling and the arrow ..."

1882 edition, p. 103

"Chapter XVIII. The marriage of Inca Roca and penalties established against sodomites.
p. 103: "because his father the Sun commanded that in order to increase the number of those living, due to those destroyed by pestilence and past famine, he should be married and his example followed by the rest, with most severe penalties for those who wasted the human semen ..."

Then Inca Roca married his sister, the daughter of Mama Ciuaco.

1882 edition, p. 104

p. 104: "After this marriage next day were married six thousand people and a severe law was issued against the sodomites: those who were caught in this sin or tainted with it even lightly, were burnt publicly in the square; furthermore were to be burnt their homes, the trees of their estates, and these to be uprooted, so no memory of such abominable thing could remain, and that from then on nobody dare to commit such a crime under penalty that for the sin of one person would be devasted the whole town, excluding those who informed of it . . ."

1882 edition, p. 115

p. 115: ". . . Sinchi Roca the fifth Inca was very clever and ordered to preserve the laws of the ancients. During this time was very extended the nefarious sin; the kings put little remedy to this avoiding conflict with their subjects; those who regreted most were the women . . ."

p. 120: ". . . Very much in vogue was witchcraft during the time of Sinchi Roca, as we have seen due to sodomy . . ."

PEDRO DE VILLAGOMEZ Y VIVANCO (1649)

Villagomez was born in Castroverde del Campo (1590–c. 1660) and studied Law and Canons in Salamanca and Seville. He lived in Seville for over 20 years, where he became Judge of the Holy Office of the Inquisition until he was appointed Bishop of Arequipa in 1632. During that time he inspected the University and the Courts of Lima and was elected Archbishop of Lima in 1641, and was also Rector of San Marcos University there between 1655 and 1656. Villagomez's inquisitorial and theological training together with his high office in Peru were the bases for his book *Exhortaciones e instrucción acerca de las idolatrías de los Indios* published in Lima (1649), where he described the confession practised by the Indians.

1919 edition, p. 152; Chapter XLIII

p. 152, Chapter XLIII: "Of the ministers of idolatry
paragraph 7: "*Aucachic*, who in Cuzco are called *Ichuris*, which means the confessor. This office is not by itself, but annex to *Villac* or to the said *Macsa* (they are those who cure with thousand lies and superstitions). They confess to all those of their *ayllo* even their wife and son. These confessions are always at the time of their *huacas*'s feasts and when they have to go on a long journey . . .

p. 154: "All these offices and ministeries are common to men and women, even confession, because there are outstanding confessors among women. But it is more usual the main offices to be held by men.

p. 155, paragraph 17: "The high ministers usually say (when they see an Indian man or woman suffer a sudden illness and lose their senses and look like crazy) that the accident occurred because the *huacas* want him to be their *Villac* or priest; and when he recovers they make him fast and learn the office, based upon the fact that when they [the priests] talk to the *huacas* they are usually out of their senses, because the devil makes them dumb with his talk, or with the strength of the *chicha* they drink when they want to talk to the *huaca,* and for his motive, they readily select for those offices those who have the heart's malady [epilepsy] ..."

1919 edition, p. 158; Chapter XLIV

p. 158, Chapter XLIV: "Of the feasts made by the Indians to the *huacas*
"... the *pacaricue,* and from that night begins the fasting by not eating salt, *ají,* or to sleep with their wives, and in some parts this usually lasts five days, and in others more, according to different traditions"

paragraph 3: "During the fasting the Indian men and women confess with those holding that office, sitting on the ground the one listening, and the one who confesses in places they usually have in the field specially designed to that effect. They do not confess internal sins, but theft, to abuse others, and to have more than one wife (because to have one even a concubine it is not considered a sin). They accuse themselves of adulteries, but just fornication it is not thought at all sinful; they accuse themselves of worshipping the God of the Spaniards, and not to revere their *huacas*; and the sorcerer tells them to mend themselves etc. And they place on a flat stone the offering powders, and make him to blow them away, and with a little stone they call *pasca* which means forgiveness, carried by the Indians or kept by the confessor, they rub his head with white ground maize and work his head with water in some brook, or at the junction of rivers which they call *tincuna.* They consider a great sin to conceal their sins during confession and the confessor is very diligent to find out; for this purpose they have several ceremonies; In some parts in arriving the Indian to the confessor he says: listen the hills around, the plains, the condors flying, the owls and owls, that I want to confess my sins. And all this is said while he holds a bead of *mullu,* pierced by a thorn with two fingers of the right hand, raising the thorn upwards, he tells the sins and at the end he gives it to the confessor; this one takes it and piercing the cloth with the thorn, pushes it until it breaks and if it broke in three the confession has been good, and if it breaks in two the confession has not been good and tells him to go back to confess his sins."

paragraph 4: In other parts to find this out, they take a bundle of *hicho* (from where the name *Ichuri* comes, who is the one who picks straw) and the confessor divides in two parts, and begins to take a straw from one side and one from the other until only remains a pair, then the confession is good, but if it is odd is bad. In other parts they guess by the blood of *cuyes* [guinea pigs] tying hands behind the penitent, when he finish confession, and stretching with a string the confessor forces him to tell the truth, or by giving him blows with a stick the confessor press him to tell all his sins, or by flogging him with a rope. They give for penitence the said facts, not to eat salt, or *ají,* nor to sleep with their wives. Beside the feasts they also use to confess with the same sorcerers when they feel sick in the manner described, because they believe that their *malquis* and *huacas* are angry on account of their sins and this is why they get ill."

paragraph 5: "They also have another manner to purify themselves without telling [their sins] to another, that is to rub their head with their *pasca* and wash their head in a river; then they say that the water carried away their sins."

1919 edition, p. 204

p. 204: "Chapter LV. Of the reading and the context of the Proclamation against Idolatry . . .

p. 214: "If they have confessed or they confess with the sorcerors ministers of idolatry when they are ill or in other sufferings or occasions; and they have washed, or wash their head with a small stone they call *pasca*, or with ground maize, killing a *cuy*, and inspecting the blood in the entrails of the said *cuy* certain signs pretending to guess things to come . . .

p. 239: "Chapter LXI. How must proceed the search of idolatries.

p. 240: "Have you confessed with him?

p. 241: "If they have confessed with some sorcerer.

p. 251: "Chapter LXIV

p. 254: ". . . The sorcerers, confessors and fortune teller and other ministers of the devil, who have for office to pervert the rest of the Indians . . . be placed and locked in a place away from the rest.

SIMÃO DE VASCONCELLOS (1663)

Very few early references on the intellectual aspects of Tupi-Guaraní tribes can be found. Simão de Vasconcellos (1596–1671) recorded some comments in his *Chronica da Companhia de Jesu do Estado do Brasil* first published at Lisbon 1663. He was born in Porto, but went to Brazil as a child, entering the Society of Jesus at Bahía in 1615. After a short trip to Portugal P. Vasconcellos returned to Brazil and was Rector of the Jesuits' Colleges at Bahía and Rio de Janeiro, where he died.

1668 edition, p. 181, paragraph 133

"In their marriages they do not have respect for their degree to kin among feminine relatives; on the contrary, the daughter of a sister, usually the wife of the uncle, or the wife of the late brother . . .

p. 82: "they have many wives and as among them there is no problem about the dowry they think they do a great favour by marrying those women."

ALONSO DE LA PEÑA MONTENEGRO (1668)

A comprehensive view of the American Indian mind and its behaviour with respect to dogma and religious practices appeared at the middle of the 17th century in the book of Alonso de la Peña Montenegro (c. 1610–1688). He was born in Padron, Coruña, and studied in Santiago de Compostela where he became a Doctor of Theology. In 1632 he entered as scholar at the College of San Bartolomé, University of Salamanca, and shortly afterwards, in 1633, moved back to Santiago. The king elected Peña bishop of Quito in 1652, an area he also had to rule politically from 1658 to 1663. At the request of some missionaries in his diocese, bishop Peña published a guide entitled *Itinerario para Parochos de Indios*, Madrid (1668), reprinted many times in Spain, France and Holland, discussing the role of the priest in dealing with pagan beliefs of the Indians. The book is full of interesting observations and his initial review of the problem of illegitimate children of the priests shows that sexual laxity had also reached the Catholic Church there. Peña considered that the first vice to be eradicated among the Indians was sodomy and bestiality. He emphasized several other points on sexual matters, the damage caused by alcoholism, and the extensive practice of dream interpretation. He also reviewed the rationality of the Indian mind and their ability to receive the Sacraments of the Church.

1678 edition, p. 182; Book I, Treatise X, section VIII

"Care which the Evangelist Minister must have in taking away certain vices and sins from those converted.

"... The first vice which must be removed is the sodomy and bestiality, because as Antonio de Herrera says, *Decade I book 3 Chapt. 4 p. 88*, in talking about the Hispaniola isle and the Coro isle, is very common among those barbarians. And Garcilasso Inga says about the Indians of Peru they were very much inclined to the nefarious sin and Fray Pedro Martyr, Decade 3 in *Historia Generali Indiarum chapt. 62*, tells that during the conquest made by Blasco Nuñez de Balboa in the Province of Nicaragua he found so stained that land of this vice that many Indians were dressed like women, to indicate by their garments their obscenity, and that Captain was so incensed by that, that threw to the dogs forty of them he captured, to die dismembered with admiration and approval of the other Indians. I say that among the barbarians must be sought with care this sin, accepting is common among most of them, and so serious that it is against nature by antonomasia."

p. 183: "... It is also common abuse among the Indians, and it must stop, that women do not care for their virginity *ante nuptias* which among all nations in the world is respect and honour, on the contrary they have it for affront, and they consider themselves unhappy if nobody has wanted them, as Acosta reports on the Indians of Peru, *De proc. Ind. sal. book 6 Chapt. 20. Virginitas, quae apud omnes mortales in pretio de honore est, apud hos vilis et indecora habetur*; and so the virgins before marriage seek the first one that come across to corrupt them, infernal custom ...

"... From this custom of their infidelity has remained now the abuse the Indians have, that they do not get married unless they had evil intercourse first for several months with the one is going to be their wives, to know by experience if she is going to be adequate for their marriage."

1678 edition, p. 213; Book II

"The nature and customs of the Indians ...
p. 220: "Section IV. If commit mortal sin those who call the Indians *putos* [sodomites], thieves, drunkards, etc.

"The contumely is a serious thing ... is mortal sin ... This accepted, I say that usually do not fall in mortal sin those who call the Indians thieves and drunkards, because they do not take pride and honour, but on the contrary they brag of drunkenness, and little honour in theft ..."

p. 233: "Section VII. If the lawyers are under obligation to defend the cases of poor Indians and the physicians to cure them free?"

p. 227: [Brief of 1593 by Philip II]
"... I order you, that from now on you will punish with greater severity those Spaniards, who affront, offend, and ill treat the Indians, than these offences were committed against the Spaniards ..."

1678 edition, p. 303

p. 303: "Sixth Treatise. Of dreams. Prologue.
"It is very usual among the Indians to believe in dreams and to guess by them, which it is a kind of divination used commonly ...

p. 304: "Section I. If in some cases it is allowed to believe in dreams. [Bishop Peña reviews the opinions of Hippocrates and Galen on this subject].

p. 305: "Section II. If it [is] sinful to believe in dreams when it is understood that God probably sent them to warn about something?

p. 305: "Section III. If the Indians commit mortal sin every time they believe in dreams?

p. 307: "Seventh Treatise. Of drunkenness. Prologue.
"Drunkenness is such a common vice among the Indians, which it is very difficult to find one who having a drink available ... does not get drunk."

1678 edition, p. 418

p. 418: "Only Treatise. Of the Sacraments as a whole.
"Section I. If the Indians are fitted for the Sacraments? Useless doubt will appear to some, but it is founded upon the one many of the first discoveries of the Indies had, judging falsely and with imprudence that they [the Indians] are irrational, beasts incapable of reason, and in consequence unfitted for Baptism ...

"It was more extended was this grievous opinion in New Spain, judging them without prudence as beasts with human figure, and were treated like that, so much so that Frey Julian Garcés first bishop of Tlaxcala was forced to write a letter full of erudition and compassion to Paul III . . . which forced the Pope with a Brief and special Bull to define and declare that the Indians were rational men and fitted for the Catholic faith like the other nations of Europe and the rest of the world: *Indios ipsos, ut pote veros homines, non solum Christianae Fidei capaces existere decernimus et declaramus . . ."*

LUCAS FERNANDEZ DE PIEDRAHITA (1688)

He was of mixed blood and one of the best writers of the Colonial period. Lucas Fernandez de Piedrahita (1624–1688) was born in Santa Fé de Bogota and studied there at the College of San Bartolomé under the Jesuits, receiving a doctorate in Theology. After that he received holy orders and was priest of small Indian villages in Tierra Firme, the present area of Colombia, eventually becoming governor of the archbishopric. After appointment as Bishop of Santa Marta, Fernandez de Piedrahita spent six years in Spain, and upon return to Santa Marta he was taken prisoner by the pirates to the island of Providence where H. Morgan (1635–1688) ordered his release. Fernandez de Piedrahita was elevated in 1676 to the see of Panama where he died. He was the author of many literary works but his fame rests upon the *Historia general de las conquistas del Nuevo Reino de Granada* which was published the year of his death. This work, however, is only the first part and brings events up to 1563; the rest remained unknown. In the first chapters Fernandez de Piedrahita deals with customs of the Chibcha Indians whom he praises. He mentions the use of *Coca* (although falls into anthropological errors about its use), the ritual practice of human sacrifices with extraction of the heart, and some alleged Indian laws inconsistent with the observations of Cieza de León (1553).

1688 edition, pp. 20–21; I Part, Book I, Chapter III

". . . These *Xeques* [priests] . . . spent most of the night chewing *Hayo* which is the herb called *Coca* in Peru, with some leaves like *zumaque* . . . The juice of the *Hayo* has so much vigour and sustenance for the Indians that they do not feel thirst or hunger and supports during their work, which is the time when they use it most . . ."

1688 edition, pp. 22–23; I Part, Book I, Chapter IV

". . . the sacrifices they considered most agreeable to their gods were those of human blood; and among them held supreme the one carried out with a young man . . . (whom they call Mojas) . . . in reaching fifteen or sixteen years; at this age they took him out to sacrifice opening him alive, taking out his heart and the entrails while musicians were singing . . ."

Diego López de Cogolludo (1613–c. 1665) was born in Alcalá de Henares, where he entered the Franciscan Order at the Convent of S. Diego. He studied Philosophy and eventually became lecturer in Theology. In 1634 he went to Yucatan accompanying Fr. Pedro Enriques and moved to Guatemala during the visit of Fr. Luis de Vivar in 1637. López de Cogolludo was elected Provincial of the Franciscan Order in Yucatan in 1663, where he died. He was the author of an *Historia de Yucathan* published posthumously by Fr. Francisco Ayeta (1688) at Madrid. In this work he used material from Bishop Landa, and relied, in parts pertaining to Maya customs, upon original documents by Gaspar Antonio Xiu or Chi (1582). López de Cogolludo (1688 edition, pp. 108–109, Book II, Chapter XIV) refutes Las Casas' accusations of the Conquistador Montejo's cruelties in Yucatan during the first attempt at settlement in 1526. He also reports human sacrifices, anthropophagy, suicide, sodomy and oral confession among the Mayas.

1688 edition, p. 25; Book I, Chapter VII

"Shipwreck of Geronimo de Aguilar and other Spaniards ... fell into the hand of so cruel Cacique ... that he soon sacrificed Baldivia and other four with him, offering them to their idols and afterwards they ate them [the Spaniards] with great joy and feast ..."

1688 edition, p. 82; Book II, Chapter VII

"... the arrogance of this Indian was such, that being so badly wounded, to avoid being said he died at the hands of that Spaniard, he went away and in the presence of his own people he hanged himself with a liana ..."

1688 edition, p. 115; Book III, Chapter II

"... Two Spaniards moved away from the camp and the Indians ... took them with great hurry .. and sacrificed them to their idols, eating them afterwards as they used to do .. they were not satisfied and killed many of their boys, in sacrifice to their idols ... and ate them afterwards [in 1537] ..."

1688 edition, p. 177; Book IV, Chapter II

"Annexed to the building of the temple in some places there was another building where some maidens lived like nuns or the vestal virgins of the Romans ... If any of them violated the chastity while in there she was killed with arrows, although they could leave and get married, by licence of the high priest ..."

1688 edition, p. 188; Book IV, Chapter III

"... [the Mayas] bought from the peasants boys and girls for their sacrifices and according to the General Histories it seems they ate them. See what Gerónimo de Aguilar said, having stayed (as it has been reported here) eight years captive among these Indians . . . He says they were not inclined to the nefarious sin, but the opposite can be gathered from the sculptures of idols which Bernal Diaz said to have seen, at the beginning of his History . . ."

1688 edition, pp. 181–185; Book IV, Chapter IV

"Chapter IV. Of the crimes and penalties the Indians were punished and of their many superstitions.

"The native Indians of Yucatan did not arrest anyone for debt. But they did so for adultery, theft and other crimes . . . One of these cages was painted with different colours and kept inside the children who were sacrificed and those of more age, who were condemned to be killed by sacrifice. They punished the vices with great severity and there was not appeal to the sentence. The man or the woman who committed adultery received a death penalty . . . they say they very much abhorred this sin . . . Who raped a virgin or forced any woman received a death penalty . . . the same penalty had who killed another . . . The thief was made slave . . . They did not use oath, but instead they cursed those presumed to lie . . . Today they commit perjury easily . . . They did not use to beat the prisoners . . . [Quoted from the 1582 Account by Gaspar Antonio Xiu]

1688 edition, pp. 192–193; Book IV, Chapter VII

"Chapter VII. Of other rites of religion held by these Indians at the time of their gentility.

". . . The Indians of Yucatan practised vocal confession of their sins . . . They confessed some grave sins and told them to the priest or the physician, and the wife to the husband, and the latter to his wife. He who had been the minister of confession publicized the sins by telling them among the relatives, in order that all of them could ask God to forgive them, and thus they prayed privately . . . They sacrificed men, women and children with the same cruelty than in it [New Spain] although not in such a large number, because they were much less in number . . ."

AGUSTIN DE VETANCURT (1698)

Agustin de Vetancurt, Betancur or Betancourt (1620–1700) was born and died in the City of Mexico. He graduated as Bachelor of Arts in the University of Mexico, although he entered the Franciscan Order and followed studies of Theology in Puebla. Vetancourt mastered the Nahuatl language and published a Mexican manual (1672). He also taught Theology and Philosophy in his convent, and for over 40 years was chaplain of S. José Church. The *Teatro Mexicano* (1698) is one of the best sources of Indian history, which included the penalties for sodomy in use among the Mexican before their Conquest in 1519, and the ritual of confession in Peru taken from Acosta (1590).

1697 edition, II Part, p. 85. Chapter IX

"Second Part. Third Treatise. Chapter IX Of the Confession and Confessors used by the Indians.

"73. The Devil also wished to be honoured with the Confession, imitating the Father of lies a true Sacrament. In Peru was accepted that diseases and hardships came because of our sins, and therefore besides the sacrifices they had to appease in their belief the anger of the gods, they confessed vocally their sins and they had commissioned for this purpose minor and major confessors, who kept secret, and they considered a serious sacrilege to conceal any sin, which they found out by casting lots, or inspecting the entrails of certain animals and if they thought some had been concealed, they struck in the back with a stone and forced them to tell all, and gave penitences of sacrifices, the sins were external acts, thefts, homicides, and adulteries, to harm with potions, to speak evil of the Emperor, and to neglect the worship of their gods, and of these there were sins reserved for the higher confessors, those committed against cult and worship. The Inca confessed to the Sun, to be told to Viracocha who was their god, and afterwards they practised a washing to clean themselves of guilt called *opacuna*; when their Lord was ill all of them confessed to obtain his health, likewise when the wife and the children, the family confessed, and to these while they were having the washing were flogged with nettles by a deformed Indian; such as a hunchback, or crippled one, if the physicians or soothsayers declared that one was to die he confessed and all his family because they believed the disease was due to their faults attributed to the anger of the gods, and in the hope of health they sacrificed a son, and with this they thought that acquired their life by means of the sacrifice; if before the parents died a child died they were considered great sinners and tried to confess their sins; this happened in Peru according to Padre Acosta. In Mexico during the feast of their principal god Huitzilopochtli, and of Tezcatlipoca they confessed to the idols, considering a grave sacrilege to conceal any sin, they did this not because they thought were forsaking their glory, because they thought for sure they went to hell, but to avoid the anger of their idols and be deprived of wordly goods and to prevent their sins to be known and to fall into any infamy among men. In Venezuela as soon as they fell ill they had hope of cure with the remedy of vocal confession, which was done with the headman, or with her husband the wife and with his wife the husband . . ."

1698 edition, II Part, pp. 89–92

"Chapter XIII. Of the laws used by the Mexicans to govern in peace their republic . . .

"85. The Mexicans permitted women to earn a living with their bodies, although they did not have special places. Young men had before marriage their concubines and used to ask them to their mothers . . ."

"Chapter XIV. Laws of the Mexicans

"87. Those who had intercourse with his mother, sister, mother in law or step daughter, because the respect due to blood relations, and because it was a serious offence for a man to have intercourse with so close relatives, died by hanging, and if the woman had been willing both died with the same rope . . .

"90. The man who dressed like a woman, or the woman dressed like a man were hanged . . .

"91. Those who committed the nefarious sin, and the woman who had sexual pleasures, whom they called *Patlach incuba*, were hanged and they were very careful to avoid this sin; and if he was a priest was burnt to satisfy the gravity of the sin.

"107. Those young men who drank to much wine were sent to prison and there they were killed by blows; women who got drunk were stoned like adulteresses; those of noble hierarchy were removed from office and were ashamed in front of the people, their hair was cut and their home demolished. In Texoco the nobles were hanged and thrown into the river to get full of water the body which alive drunk so much wine; the peasant was sold [for slave] for several years, and at the third time he was hanged . . .

"110. The natives are lost and dissolute today in three faults which during their gentility were severely punished, because then knew to be frequent, they are adultery, drunkenness, and theft . . . It is a great pity that those things which were not tolerated as Gentiles, be tolerated as Christians. All of them are so inclined to drunkenness, that in order to get Pulque they invite, give away their own wife for lust, commit incests while drunk in order to say they are drunk being their excuse for their own guilt.

JOSÉ GUMILLA (1741)

José Gumilla (1686–1750) was born in Carcer, Valencia, and after early studies in Valencia he entered the Society of Jesus at Seville from where he went to South America as a missionary in 1705. In 1712 he was at the College of Cartagena de Indias, but in 1715 he went to study the Jíbaro language at Casiabo and tried in 1717 to enter Indian territory with several Spanish Soldiers, unsuccessfully repeating his attempt in 1722. In 1731 Gumilla started his explorations from Trinidad into the Orinoco river and established several missions including those of Meta and Casanare; he was then appointed director of the Jesuitic province in that area. After a short visit to Rome and Spain he returned to his province where he died. Gumilla's description of the hallucinogenic drug *Yupa* is excellent.

1741 edition, p. 45
   "Chapter V
p. 45: "The barbarous and wild Indian is a monster never seen, who has a
   head of ignorance, heart of ingratitude, chest of unreliability, shoulders
   of laziness, feet of fear; his abdomen for drinking and his inclination
   to drunkenness are to abyss without end."
   "Chapter XII
p. 117: "[The Otomaca Indians] the third and worse above all [drunken-
   ness] they have another foul way to get drunk through the nose, with
   certain evil powders called *Yupa* which entirely takes away from them
   their judgement, and furious, get hold the weapons, and if the women
   were not used to hold them and tie them down, they do cruel harm
   everyday: this is an enormous vice. They make these powders from some
   seeds called *Yupa*, but these only have the scent of strong tobacco:
   what they add by inspiration of the devil is what causes the drunkenness and the fury; after they have eaten some very large snails, which
   they find in the marshes, they put the shells in the fire, and reduce them
   to quick lime, whiter than snow itself; they mix this lime with the
   Yupa, putting the same amount of each ingredient, and after reducing
   the whole to very subtle powder, it results a mixture of a diabolic
   strength; so much so that touching with the tip of the finger those
   powders, the best accustomed to tobacco snuff, to whom by use does
   not suffer for it, just by approach it to the nose, without touching it,
   the finger which touched the *Yupa* he bursts in a storm of sneezing.
   The Saliva Indians and other nations I will deal with later, also use
   Yupa; but as they are peaceful, benign and cowardly people, they do
   not become furious as our Otomacos; though they have been and are
   formidable like the Caribs, because before the fight they got furious
   with the *Yupa*, hurting themselves and covered with blood and anger
   they went out to fight like rabid tigers".

   CORNELIUS DE PAUW (1768)
This Dutch historian (1739–1799), born in Amsterdam, received holy
orders in Gottingen and was sent by the Prince Bishop of Liége as
ambassador to Frederick II of Prussia. After retiring to Xanten, near
Clèverís, de Pauw wrote a number of philosophical studies on the Egyp-
tians, Chinese and the Greeks, but his most controversial work was the
Recherches philosophiques sur les Americains (1768–1769) reprinted and
translated several times. Besides the polemics in 1770 with J. A. Pernety
(1716–1801) de Pauw's thesis that the American Indians were physically
and intellectually inferior to the Europeans was passionately contested
by Clavigero. Among other vices de Pauw accused the Indians of gluttony,
drunkenness, ungratefulness and sodomy.

1768 edition, Vol. I, pp. 63–70
   ". . . but in America the civilized people did not have intercourse ever
   with women as soon as they suspected pregnancy and this is one of the

apparent reasons why so few deformed and crooked children were born, where multiplication have, more than one can think, and brutal incontinence.

"Far from attributing the continence of the Americans to reasons of virtue or religion, I cannot find other cause than their alienation for sex. This dislike has on the other hand produced other abuses.

"Sodomy was very much in vogue in the Islands, in Mexico, in Peru, and in all the New Continent, and this before the arrival of the Negroes who have been falsely accused of having transferred this corruption from one continent to the other . . ."

De Pauw continued with a description of certain sexual aberrations among American Indians and quoted a work by Martin Lister (1694) on venereal disease to show that syphilis resulted from the use of a poisonous insect on the sexual organ of the male during those aberrant practices. He also mentioned the episode of Vasco Nuñez de Balboa killing the king's brother in Quarequa.

1768 edition, Vol. I, p. 67

". . . Some authors, sold to Madrid's Court, had dared to write that the ancients in America had predicted that soon was going to arrive among them a foreign nation worse than the cannibals who were going to punish the Americans up to the hundreth generation, by God's commandment due to their sin against nature. But who cannot see that it is a stupid fallacy, imagined with boldness, to palliate the greatest injustice ever committed on the surface of the earth? I wish to say the Conquest of the New World by the Spaniards who massacred everything possible. *Ausi immane nefas, auroque potiti* [They risked this hideous crime, greedy for gold]. The Castilians were not certainly themselves entirely exempt of the weakness they reproached to the Indians, besides the Castilians were not competent judges in any sense, and with any right. It could have been better to persist in the opinion that the Americans were like monkeys, than to accept them as men, and to arrogate the frightful right to murder them in the name of God. This is without any doubt that to diminish the reward of the destroyers of Peru, that Garcilasso has maintained sodomy was punished by death before their arrival . . ."

Here de Pauw quotes Inca Garcilasso's text about the orders given by Capac-Yupanqui to his generals to destroy the sodomites and their villages.

1768 edition, Vol. I, pp. 68–69

"This text of fable by Garcilasso does not prove anything, but that indeed many peoples in America were inclined to this corruption that breaks the natural order and perverts animal instinct; because all this he mentions about penalties reserved for those found guilty, are without any doubt a great fiction. Was there in Peru only one village? Why have been demolished entire villages because of the faults of a citizen? Garcilasso has taken from Roman law the torture of fire he imagined and mentions so much, and which was ignored among the Peruvians. If in the Inca empire had the [sodomitic] men being burnt after the slightest evidence, this empire could have never survived ten years. Many years after the reign of the Inca Capac-Yupanqui, we find still another sovereign to renew the ancient laws against sodomy, they had not been able, despite their severity to stop the river of corruption."

MARIANO VEYTIA (c. 1775)

Mariano José Fernández de Echeverría y Veytia (1718–1779), as he should be known, was one of the few historians to study first-hand documents pertaining to the ancient history of the Toltecs and the Chichimecs who preceded the Aztec civilization. Veytia was born in Puebla, Mexico, and studied at the University of Mexico where he became Bachelor of Arts in 1733 and of Law in 1736. Despite his youth he sailed in 1737 for Spain with some legal commissions and held administrative appointments at Oña, his family homestead. From 1740 Veytia travelled extensively through Europe, Morocco and the Holy Land, returning to Madrid where he was host to Boturini, the Italian antiquarian whose collection of Mexican codices had been seized in Mexico. Veytia gained the support of Charles III the Spanish king who was very interested in American history. After the death of his first wife in Madrid, Veytia returned to Mexico and settled in Puebla to marry again; he had four children, one of them, Manuel, was executed by the Spaniards for his role during the Mexican fight for Independence. Veytia received the royal commission for inspecting the Jesuits' library and furthermore he had the opportunity of surveying several codices and documents which have not survived until today. This is why Veytia's *Historia antigua de Méjico*, published only in 1836, and in an easy and clear literary style with notes by F. Ortega, retains its importance. To make easy reading, the account of the Toltec fall in the 10th century A.D. has been simplified, but most of the facts are confirmed in the writings of Ixtlilxochitl and Sahagún. The reign of Topiltzin, the nature of the Tezcatlipoca cult, and the final destruction of Tula and Cholula after sexual debauchery can all be found in Veytia's writings.

1836 edition, Vol. I, p. 150

"Chapter XIII. Of the arrival of the Ulmec, Xicalanca and Zapotec nations to the Anahuac land, last destruction of the giants, which make them rulers of the land and found the city of Cholollan.

p. 152: "... This was not the worst, but lacking the giants women entirely, even before the arrival of these nations they were completely given without control to the sin of sodomy, and although these people had women, those barbarians did not like them no matter how much the men offered them and gave away their own wives and daughters to be free of that damage. They were so affronted with this and oppression they suffered that by decision of their chiefs and principal lords decided to finish once and for all with the giants. To this aim they prepared an abundant and splendid banquet to which all of them attended, and having eaten and drunk brutally, they were so inebriated that laid like dogs over the floor, they finished all of them in one day, being free from their slavery and lords of the land. The year that took place this event is indicated with the hieroglyph of the rabbit in the first number, which according to my computation was three thousand nine hundred and seventy nine of the world [A.D. 107].

p. 181: ". . . Quetzalcoatl taught to them [the sins] inspiring a great horror about them, not only to homicide, theft and the rest, which being forbidden by natural law are known by all nations, but also adultery, lies and lewdness."

1836 edition, Vol. I, p. 186

"Chapter XVIII. Of the other customs and rites found established in these countries when the Spaniards arrived in.

"It is not less notable the custom found established of confessing with the priest, declaring to them those things they considered sinful, and accepting the penitence imposed; and it was so severe the duty of the priests not to reveal the faults of those confessing, that if they broke this secret they were severely punished even by losing their lives. All the Indian historians agree about this custom and Herrera says (Decades 3, Book 4, Chapter 7, fol. 174, col. I and Chapter 12, fol. 216, col. 2) that the same was practised in Nicaragua and surely this custom in all its practice was not learnt by them from Greeks or Romans."

1836 edition, Vol. I, p. 239

"Chapter XXVI. Succeeds Ixtlilcuechahuac in the kingdom, in whose times died the wise man Hueman leaving the *Teamoxtli* written, and several prophecies; and having finished Ixtlilcuechahuac his time of ruling, his son Auetzin inherits the kingdom.

p. 243: "Hueman . . . declared to them . . . that . . . this kingdom of Tollan because a ruler who succeeded in it . . . will be very just and wise at the beginning of his rule, but afterwards falling into vices he would be evil and unhappy. That following his example his subjects would also give themselves to vices, and the time would come when the priests failing to respect due to the temples and the purity which must be kept in them, would rape women both virgins and married arriving to them to worship Tloque Nahuaque and to other inferior ministers of their own; and angry against them Tloque Nahuaque would punish them severely with lightning, hail, ice and locust, with famine, pestilence, and finally with the cruel lash of war which would cause an almost total destruction of their Kingdom."

1836 edition, Vol. I, p. 274

"Chapter XXXI. It starts with news of the beginning of Topiltzin reign, of his disorders, the fulfilment of Hueman's predictions, the plagues heaven punished with the whole kingdom and were presages of its destruction.

"... Four years ruled [Topiltzin] so happy and venturous that he could compete with the most fortunate of his predecessors, until ... the reins of his lust became loose, and not being satisfied with his own wife, multiplied his offences, with as many as his whim desired.

"To obtain with more safety his obscene offences, he decided to cover himself with the veil of religion and for this purpose he used two priests, who were of the most principal lords of his Court, so knowledgeable in the astronomical science and of so high a reputation among the people their prognostications, that ended by considering them divine. They were called one Tlatlauhqui and the other Tezcatlipuca, to whom they gave in later times cult and worship, placing them among their gods ...

p. 276: "Of these, therefore, he used to seduce and deceive all those women of any condition whatever to whom his blind passion led him, making them believe that it was the gods' pleasure to oblige the brutal whims of the king, and that they were far from committing an offence, but they were actions deserving praise for which they would receive deserved prices. Few or none resisted his persuasion, because of the high standing they held the wisdom and integrity of those malignant deceivers, who at the same time they flattered the king's passion, they gave themselves free rein to their lust, and following his and their example, everything was disorder and confusion; because shame being lost among men, and honour and modesty among women, they reached the profanity of the temples, being the priests the most abominable offenders; because not only they did not keep the chastity they had professed, but, going further into greater offences, they used force within their own temples with those who would not surrender willingly to their requests ..."

FRANCISCO XAVIER CLAVIGERO (1781)

Francisco Xavier Mariano Clavigero (1731–1787) was born in Veracruz and by his early contact with Indian servants he learnt the native languages Nahuatl, Otomí and Mixtec which were very useful in his historical work. In 1748 he entered the Society of Jesus where he became a distinguished scholar and even Prefect of S. Ildefonso College in Mexico. Years later Clavigero was able to study the excellent library of Mexican documents which C. Sigüenza y Gongora (1645–1700) had donated to the Jesuits' College of S. Pedro and S. Pablo in Mexico. After the expulsion of the Jesuits in 1767 Clavigero went to Italy, and, first in Ferrara and later in Bologna, wrote a *Historia Antigua de Mexico* published in an Italian translation at Cesena in 1779–1781, translated into English and also printed in Spanish (1826). Clavigero's text is preceded by a superb introduction of sources and terminated with several dissertations. In one of them, discussing the physical and moral qualities of the Mexican Indians, despite the fact that he was a *criollo*, son of Spanish parents, he defends the qualities of the native population and shoots down the arguments against them in the well known works of de Pauw and Robertson. Probably the most caustic remarks in Clavigero's text appeared on the subject of sodomy, and these serve to close the polemics on this subject by the historians of America during the Colonial period.

1780 edition, Vol. I, p. 119; Book L, Section XV

"They [the Mexicans] are now, and have ever been very moderate in eating, but their passion for strong liquors is carried to the greatest excess. Formerly they were kept within bounds by the severity of the laws; but now that these liquors are grown so common, and drunkenness is unpunished, one half of the people seem to have lost their senses; and this, together with the poor manner in which they live, exposed to all the baneful impressions of disease, and destitute of the means of correcting them, is undoubtedly the principal cause of the havoc which is made among them by epidemical disorders."

1780 edition, Vol. IV, pp. 196

"... There are four principal vices with which he [de Pauw] charges the Americans, gluttony, drunkenness, ingratitude, and paederasty... Drunkenness is the prevailing vice of those nations. We confess it sincerely in the first book of this history, explain its effects, and point out the cause of it; but we add also, that it did not prevail in the country of Anahuac before the Spaniards came there, on account of the great severity with which that vice was punished, though in the greater part of the countries of the old continent it is still uncorrected, and serves as an excuse for more heinous crimes. It is certain, from the inquiries made by authors into the civil government of the Mexicans, that there were several laws against drunkenness in Mexico as well as Texcuco, in Tlaxcala, and other states, which we have seen represented in their ancient paintings. The sixty-third painting of the collection made by Mendoza represents two youths of both sexes condemned to death for having intoxicated themselves, and at the same time an old man of seventy, whom the laws permit, on account of his age, to drink as much as he pleases. There are few states in the world whose sovereigns have shown greater zeal to prevent excesses of this kind."

1780 edition, Vol. IV, pp. 198–201

"But nothing of what de Pauw published against the Americans has been more injurious than in his affirmation that 'sodomy was very much in vogue in the [Caribbean] Islands, in Peru, in the kingdom of

Mexico, and in the whole New Continent.' I cannot see how after publishing such an horrid calumny de Pauw had the courage to say, as he did in his reply to D. Pernety, that all his work [the *Philosophical Researches*] breathes humanity. Can it be humanity injustly to defame all the nations of the New World with a vice so enormous and opprobrious to nature? Is it humanity to enrage, as he does, against the Inca Garcilasso because he defends the Peruvians against this charge? Even if there were serious authors who described this crime to all the people in America, there being many, as indeed there are authors also reliable who affirm all the contrary, de Pauw according to the laws of humanity ought to have abstained from so gross an accusation. How much more ought he to have avoided it when there is not a respectable writer on whose testimony he can support so universal an assertion. He may find, yes, some authors, as the Anonymous Conqueror [Lopez de] Gómara, and Herrera, who have accused some Americans of such a vice, or at the most some people of America; but where are we going to find a respectable historian who has dared to say that sodomy was in great vogue in the [Caribbean] Islands, Peru, Mexico and the whole New Continent?

"On the contrary, all the historians of Mexico say with one voice, that such a vice was extremely abominated by those nations, and make mention of the terrible penalties prescribed by the laws against it, as can be seen in [Lopez de] Gomara, Herrera, Torquemada, Vetancourt and others. The most illustrious [Bishop] Las Casas attested in 1542 in a memorial to Charles V that, having made diligent research in the Isles Hispaniola [Santo Domingo], Cuba, Jamaica, Puerto Rico, and the Lucayas, he found there was not memory of such vice among those nations. The same things he affirms of Peru, Yucatan, and all the countries of America in general, with exception of a place where it is said there are some guilty: 'but, not because of this—he adds—must we accuse to all that [New] World.' Who has authorized de Pauw to defame in a point so injurious the whole of the New World? Although the Americans were, as he believes, men without honour and without shame, the very same laws of humanity demand not to calumniate them. Such is the excess into which his ridiculous eagerness to depreciate America leads him, and such are the consequences of his perverse logic, that he frequently deduces universal conclusions from particular premises. If because those [Indians] of Panuco or any other people in America were infected with that vice, it is to be affirmed that sodomy was in great vogue in all the New World, the American might as well defame with similar accusation the whole Old Continent, because sodomy was in great vogue among some ancient people of Asia, and was very common among the Greeks and Romans. Besides it is not know that there is any nation at present in America contaminated with that vice, whereas we know by the statements of several writers, that certain Asiatic people have not abandoned that abomination, and that even in Europe, if what Locke and de Pauw say is true, it is common among the Turks, who make profession of hypocrisy, another vice more execrable of the same kind, and instead of being severely punished for it, they are held, by that nation, in the light of saints and all in competition offer them the highest marks of respect and veneration."

1780 edition, Vol. IV, p. 201

"Among the crimes charged to the Americans by M. de Pauw suicide is included. It is true that at the times of the Conquest many hanged themselves, or threw themselves down precipices or put an end to themselves by abstinence; but it is not the least wonderful that men who had become desperate from continual harassment and vexations, who thought their gods had abandoned, and the elements conspired against them, should do that which was frequent with the Romans, the Franks, and ancient Spaniards, the modern English, French and Japanese, for a slight motive . . ."

CHAPTER V

SPANISH TRADITIONAL MORALS

THE CHRISTIAN TRADITION

The Spanish morals during the Conquest and colonization of America were based on the Catholic dogma contained in the Ten Commandments. Although they basically were the Decalogue of the Jewish tradition, the Spaniards had accepted Saint Augustin's (354–430 A.D.) version which differs from the Mosaic one in several points. The first four Commandments were expressed in a different manner, but their context was so similar, that it did not entail major doctrinary divergences. The 5th "Thou shalt not kill" included not only homicide, but suicide and anthropophagy which were important subjects when dealing with American matters. The 6th, "Thou shalt not commit adultery", was issued to the Spaniards as "Thou shalt not fornicate"; this produced considerable controversy in Colonial America, because while they accepted that this commandment made sinful adultery and the sexual deviations such as incest, sodomy, and bestiality, a good many considered that normal sexual intercourse should be excluded from the sinful acts. The other Commandment important for consideration of Spanish morals in America was the 7th "Thou shalt not steal"; all the spoils of war, land distribution, and the riches of the Conquistadors were in jeopardy of being sinful, unless the issue of the Indian's irrationality was settled, or the Crown, based upon the Alexandrian Bulls of 1493, granted Conquistadors and colonizers sufficient legal evidence to make the Spanish actions in America morally right.

As a whole there were certain differences between Catholic morals observed by the Spaniards and those in the rest of Europe, not just resulting from the Lutheran Reformation with regard to divorce, but even between Spain and other Catholic nations like France or Italy, where infringements of the Commandments, particularly royal adulteries, were carried out with scandal and even notoriety. Spanish morals were far from stationary, being very much influenced by the Arabic culture and by historical events. Spain had left the mystic refuge of the medieval period to engage for centuries in a religious struggle. It was natural that after a period of national restraint under Isabella and Ferdinand, the Catholic Monarchs, Charles V (1500–1558) and Philip II (1527–1598), the Spanish power and wealth would lead to moral corruption, which reached its lowest point during the reign of Philip IV (1605–1665). The times of this monarch were the age of the *picaresca* or rogues' novel, when passions were brought out into the open, and all sort of excesses were exposed. The amazing paradox of those times, which was also reflected in Colonial America, was that in some instances the breakers of the moral laws were members of religious congregations or individuals under canonical vows called to maintain the moral order, and that made their errors all the more deplorable. The American chroniclers did not attempt to hush up these events; on the contrary, they made a point of reporting them in full, even when they involved members of the religious Orders. But in other instances the Spaniards in the New World seem to have been free from the blemishes to be found among the natives, or, in very exceptional circumstances, in the metropolis. The latter were indeed recorded in the diaries of earlier journalists who were always eager to write down the unusual or the scandalous.

THE CRIMES AGAINST HUMAN LIFE

The conquest of the American continent implied continuous warfare, a situation where homicide lost its meaning. The number of natives killed during the conquest and colonization was considerable and so was the number of Spaniards, as it has been indicated (Guerra, 1966). In his study on the Americans, de Pauw (1768) pointed out that, contrary to las Casas' "*Brief Relation*", the greater cause of death among the American Indians was disease, not homicide or genocide. This has been supported and clearly proved by medical evidence. Homicide in the Spanish tradition was removed from the stern connotation of ancient cultures. The *Fuero Juzgo* (Book VI, Title V, Law 11) stated that anyone who killed another person should be punished, but the law failed to indicate the penalty, and, owing to the great variety of customary laws in the different kingdoms and regions of Spain, the killer could get away with a fine. Moreover, the *Recopilacion de Leyes* (Book XII, Title II, Law 1) recognized that homicide was a felony, but in punishing the offender the law distinguished between those of noble birth and gentlemen, who were excluded from the death penalty and sent into exile, while the commoners were condemned to death. All this background of customary inequality in the Spanish law, the fact that generation after generation of Spaniards had been raised to hate and kill the infidel, without wilful homicide being considered immoral or sinful, makes it easy to realize that the killing of the American Indians during the conquest could not appear sinful to the conscience of the Spaniard. However, there are records of crimes against human life committed by the Conquistadors which cannot be ignored. Las Casas (1552) included a statement by Fr.

Marcos de Niza about the atrocities committed by Pizarro's expedition to Peru; these cannot be excused, although it is easy to prove that in many other instances, such as the events of Cholula during the conquest of Mexico by Cortés, las Casas was not telling the truth. The crimes were never silenced and Spain did not suffer the affront, neither was there any moral erosion in its rulers to condone those actions without punishment. Viceroys, Conquistadors and even Judges became subject to *Juicios de residencia* or inquiries, some high heads rolled, and many more people ended up behind bars. Cieza de León (1553), a fair historian, made a point of recording the end of those who abused the Indians.

1553 edition, folio 132. Chapter CXIX

"How mighty wonders have been clearly seen in the discovery of these Indies, how our Sovereign Lord God desires to watch over the Spaniards, and how he also chastises those who are cruel to the Indians.

"... Another thing must also be noted, which is, that those who carry the standard of the cross as their guide must not make their discoveries as tyrants for those who do so receive heavy chastisement. Of those who have been tyrants, few have died natural deaths, such for instance as those who compassed the death of Atahualpa. All these have perished miserably ... The marshal Don Jorge Robledo consented to allow great harm to be done to the Indians in the province of Pozo, and many to be killed with crossbows and dogs. And God permitted that he should be sentenced to death in the same place, and have for his tomb the bellies of the Indians. The comendador Hernán Rodriguez de Sosa and Baltasar de Ledesma died in the same way, and were also eaten by the Indians; they having themselves been very cruel to them. The Adelantado Belalcazar killed many Indians in Quito; and God permitted that he should be driven from his government by the Judge who came to try him, and that he should die at Cartagena on his way to Spain, poor and full of sorrow. Francisco García de Tobar, who was so much feared by the Indians by reason of the number he had killed, was himself killed and eaten by them. Let no one deceive himself with the belief that God has not punished those who were cruel to these Indians; for not one of them failed to receive chastisement in proportion of the offence ... "

Fate, we must remember, was not kind to the Conquistadors. A handful had their glory recorded in the pages of history, but most of those of equal merit left their bones bleaching in the deserts or rotting in the jungle even when they escaped the belly of the Indians. Spain was mother to a few, though step-mother to most of them, those who from Columbus to the last of that race of intrepid explorers went back to the mother land in chains, not with laurels.

There were very few instances in Spain's ancient history when suicide had been considered an act of courage, and even then historical analysis does not entirely support the accepted tradition. It is usually recorded with admiration that Cantabrians and Highlanders in Northern Spain preferred to kill themselves rather than become Roman prisoners; likewise the citizens of Saguntum in 218 B.C., allies to Rome, threw themselves into the flames instead of surrendering to Hannibal (247–182 B.C.). Again the defenders of Numantia after resisting siege after siege of Roman generals, died by their own hand in 134 B.C. rather than becoming slaves of Scipio Aemilianus (185–129 B.C.). Christian morals afterwards permeated the Spanish way of life and suicide was religiously and legally considered a felony. Saint Augustin (*De Civitate Dei*, Book 1, Chapter XX) pointed out that suicide was against the Fifth Commandment and Saint Thomas Aquinas (*Summa Theologicae* 2ª, 2ᵃᵉ, q 64, art V) expanded this idea, stating that suicide was a mortal sin against charity and the natural law. Suicides were excluded from holy burial grounds. Francisco de Vitoria in 1528 and 1536 analysed in his lectures *De homicidio* the moral aspects of suicide and since then his thesis has remained the accepted doctrine. The old Spanish laws of *Las Siete Partidas* (Part 7, title 8, law 10) considered it as homicide even to lend a weapon to another in order to commit suicide, and the *Recopilación de Leyes* (1581) in force during the conquest and colonization of America imposed the confiscation of property from a man or a woman committing suicide. Despite mutilation, torments and painful death which followed their capture, the Spanish conquistadors died fighting rather than resort to suicide.

Anthropophagy among Spaniards and other European nations was considered under two aspects: the habitual practice typical of the American Caribs and other primitive people, and the accidental, which sometimes was reported in long sieges or shipwrecks, where the only motivation was hunger. Fernandez de Oviedo (1535), when referring to the Spaniards in America, found horrible and immoral even accidental anthropophagy, though he mentioned a curious case of a shipwreck where the survivors accepted to serve as food for the others by lottery, a decision which fortunately was never implemented. The best known instance of anthropophagy among the Spanish conquistadors, which indeed las Casas did not fail to report in his *Apologetic History of the Indies*, to tarnish the Spaniards with the same faults as the natives, appeared in the *Narrative* of Nuñez Cabeza de Vaca (1542). It took place in November 1528 at the island of Mal Hado located at the mouth of the Mississippi river, when five members of the Narvaez expedition to Florida survived by eating their companions as they were dying. The last one alive when he was found had already consumed the last of his comrades to die. Fernandez de Oviedo related in full detail one of the most macabre stories ever to take place during the whole Spanish American history. It happened in 1536 during the expedition to Veragua in South America under the governor Felipe Gutierrez, when two Spanish soldiers after days of famine committed anthropophagy by eating a dead Indian, and afterwards, without shame, they killed the other Spanish soldiers who were sick and unable to carry on with the journey, and shared the flesh with other comrades.

1852 edition, Vol. 2 (3), p. 489; Book XXVIII, Chapter VI

"How some bad Christians (though I do not state they were Christians, despite they called themselves so) being famished they ate an Indian and killed two Spanish Christians, and ate them likewise, being helped in this evil by others, and the punishment they received.

"Following his journey the governor Felipe Gutierrez... with great suffering and extreme hunger, leaving behind many of their dead there was among them a Diego López Dávalos who being angry in the way with an Indian, drew his sword and killed him... Of those Christians travelling behind two of them arrived where the Indian was dead; they were certain Diego Gomez and Juan de Ampudia born in Ajofrin, who thinking they faced a good supper decided to spend the night there and celebrate the funeral of that Indian and bury him in their own bellies ... The fact is that to satisfy their hunger and need, they made a fire and satiated themselves with the flesh of that Indian, well or lightly roasted. Another day afterwards... those two who had the Indian for supper, killed a Christian called Hernando Dianes, born in Seville who was sick and in their company, and ate him these two evil men... and others up to the number of ten... Next day... that night the same two men Juan de Ampudia and Diego Gomez... killed another Spaniard who was sick called Alonso Gonzalez born in Ronda, and they and the other seven ate him. Those killers had disagreement about who among them should eat the brain, and one Juan de Ampudia, who was the worst and the most cynical of them and he ate them, and they had the same debate about the liver.

"... Juan de Guzman... discovered his felony... after having obtained pardon... the guilty were imprisoned, and spontaneously confessed their felonies... And after the trial, the High Justice ordered Juan de Ampudia and Diego Gomez to be burnt... and the other seven to be branded with a C of fire in the face for slaves..."

This Juan de Ampudia, so properly condemned to burning, must have been the same Juan de Ampudia denounced in the *Brief Relation* of 1552 by las Casas of having committed other depravities with the Indians of Tierra Firme. People like him were responsible for the abuses which were taken for granted to have occurred during the Spanish Conquest of America. On the other hand, we have another report of accidental anthropophagy in Tierra Firme, about the same year, by Cieza de León (1553) which offers the true attitude of the Spanish conquistadors to that practice even under the most severe conditions of hunger.

1553 edition, folio 18 verso, Chapter XVI

"Of the customs of the Caciques and Indians in the neighbourhood of the town of Anzerma...

"... The place on which the town of Anzerma is built is called by the natives Umbra... At this time twenty-five or thirty soldiers set out to procure, or, to speak more plainly, to rob whatever they could find, and near the great river they came upon some people who fled, for fear of being seen and taken prisoners by us. Here the soldiers found a great pot full of cooked meat, and they were so hungry that they thought of nothing but eating it, supposing it as the flesh of creatures called *cuis* [guinea pigs], because some came out of the pot. As soon as they had well eaten, one of them took out of the pot a hand with its fingers and nails, and they also found pieces of the feet and other parts of a man. When the Spaniards saw these things, they were troubled at having eaten of such flesh, and the sight of the fingers and hands caused them much sorrow . . ."

THE SEXUAL OFFENCES

There was indeed most free sexual intercourse between the Spaniards and the Indian women during the Conquest of America. Numerous accounts indicate that the Conquistadors in Mexico were offered women of noble origin and in Peru even the virgins for the cult of the Sun; a similar pattern occurred all over the New World. Some historians considered this a blessing since it resulted in the beginning of new nations, and they depict the Spaniards as stud breeders of a new race in the conquered lands. Fornication was persistently defended as excluded from the 6th Commandment, but in order to avoid it, providences were taken by the Spanish crown to allow wives to accompany their husbands in America, and, it should also be pointed out, to control women accompanying ecclesiastical persons. Indian wives or concubines, and extensive illegitimacy marked the start of the Colonial society. But, if in America the moral standards of the Spaniards regarding fornication were very low, they maintained the strictest observance against sodomy, and bestiality among the Spaniards was never recorded.

The severity of the biblical penalties for incest, where the Leviticus XX decreed the death penalty for those committing that offence, was not entirely incorporated into the Christian tradition. Ancient Spanish law defined this crime as being when intercourse took place between parties related up to the fourth degree, but the *Recopilación de Leyes* (1581 edition, Vol. II, Book VIII, title 20, law VII) only punished it with confiscation of half their property. Incest was very seldom found among the Spaniards in America, although there was a shameful case recorded by Calancha (1638) because it involved another Augustinian, Fr. Diego de Zarate Colchado, who had been in high office in the Peruvian province, and was an extreme disciplinarian. In 1594, after eight years in the Order, he left the community to live with his brother and sister. Their incest ended in a double homicide and the death of all parties.

1638 edition, pp. 916–922; Book IV, Chapter XXII

". . . [Fr. Diego de Zarate Colchado] left the Order . . . He had a brother priest, who was a missionary in a village near Lima; he had brought a sister with him because after the death of their parents she was without protection; and he [Fr. Diego] went to them and all lived together at the mission. The priest had the sister at home in order to find a position for her, she was good looking and the priest having her within reach and without fear of God, asked for her love, and she surrendered because she had not other to support her and her need was more powerful than the fear of God. They continued the incest, and being at home the other brother who had been a friar, he made love to the wretched one; and both brothers without knowing what the other was doing behaved in a sacrilegious way and lived in incest. They learnt she was pregnant, and between them (pretending to be furious about their honour) pressed her to discover who was responsible. Both brothers were afraid that she would confess their felony ... she answered that she had been solicited by a gentleman Juan de Iturrieta who after giving promise of marriage had enjoyed her two or three days before she left Lima ... They agree (oh iniquitous priests!) to kill Juan de Iturrieta, so innocent to that calumny, who had never spoken to her, not even seen her ... They arrived to Lima ... and in the hall of his home they stabbed his body and entrails ... and he died. They returned to the mission content of having killed the unhappy innocent, and told their sister: we have just punished the infamous man who robbed your virginity, he is already dead and well punished. The sad one, shouting said: ... that unhappy man was not responsible ... find out which one of you two is the owner of this pregnancy ... They left in confusion ... and both confessed to the other their incest, and without control agreed on the fratricide and went after the sister and killed her with a knife ... The two brothers after burying their sister ... went to Callao, where they found a ship leaving for Panama and at landing one of them jumped from the ship to the boat and fell into the sea, and while trying to get him out, the boat struck him, and there he died cursing without remedy; the other landed, fell ill to die, confessed the felonies and forced the Confessor to tell the justice the killing of Juan de Iturrieta ..."

The attitude of the Spaniards towards sodomy during the 16th century was deeply rooted in a customary law which had taken into consideration biological, religious and political aspects of its practice. The laws pertaining to sodomy in force during the conquest and colonization of the New World had been issued by King Ferdinand the Catholic (1452–1516) and Queen Isabella of Castille (1451–1504) at Medina del Campo on 22nd August 1497, and ratified by Charles V (1500–1558) and Philip II (1527–1598) of Spain. Very few people realize that sodomy under Spanish law was a most serious offence, second only to heresy and crimes against the person of the king. Those found guilty were burnt, and proof of their crime was easily accepted from testimonies or circumstantial evidence. The text of the law was indeed a most formidable deterrent against

sodomy and bestiality. Behind all this was the Spanish hate of Arab
morals, the finding of *bardajes* in Moslem areas, and to top that, stories
that among Arabs, pilgrimage to Mecca was not complete unless they
had intercourse with the camel!

1581 edition, Vol. II, folios 197 verso–198 verso; Book VIII, title XXI

"Of the nefarious sin. First law, How the nefarious crime against
nature must be punished.

"Because among the other sins and crimes offending Our Lord God
which are of special infamy on earth, is the crime committed against
the natural order, against which laws and regulations must be armed
for the punishment of this nefarious crime, not worthy to be named
which destroys the natural order and is punished by divine judgement,
by reason of which nobility is lost, the heart becomes cowardly and
leads to lack of strength in the faith, and it is hateful to God's devotion,
and degrades until it gives pestilence to man and other torments on
earth, and grows to give shame and affront to the people and nation
where it is tolerated, and it deserves the most severe penalties that can
be executed; and considering that the previous regulations and laws
established until now had and have ordered some penalties against
those who in that way corrupt the order of nature and are their
enemies, and because the penalties up to now in the statutes are not
sufficient to eradicate and completely punish such an abominable
offence, wishing in this to render account of Our Lord God and because unto us will fall the duty of repressing such cursed blemish and
error; and because in the laws issued up to now it is not sufficiently
provided what is convenient: we establish and order that any person,
no matter what may be his station, condition, hierarchy or dignity
who commits the nefarious crime against nature who is convicted on
such evidence as is sufficient in law to prove the crime of heresy or the
crime of *lèse majesté* shall be burnt in flames of fire, in the place, and
by the officer of the law to whom belongs the knowledge and punishment of such crime; and at the same time he shall lose for that fact and
reason without further proceedings all his property movable and im-
movable, which from thence forward we shall confiscate and shall
assign to our Chamber and Treasury as confiscated and applied. And in
order to further avoid such a crime, we order that if it happens that
such offence cannot be proved in perfect and completed manner, but
is proved and found in very near and contiguous acts to the conclusion
of such, in a way that the offender could finish this harmful error, he
shall be taken for the true performer of such an offence, to be judged
and sentenced to suffer the same penalty in the same way and manner
as a man who has committed the said offence with full perfection as
previously stated, and that proceedings can be started by petition of a
party, or any body, or by way of search, or by the judge's office: and
that in this crime and proceedings against the performer, and by way of

proof, whether interlocutory or final, and in order to proceed with torment and all the rest, we order that the method and procedure shall be observed which in law must be followed in such crimes and offences of heresy and *lèse majesté* but, that from the witnesses received during the proceedings of this crime. Copy and testimony of their names shall be taken and given and their statements and affidavits shall be made available to the accused, so he can put forward his rights: and we order that the children and descendants of the criminals by sentence, do not fall in infamy nor in any other blemish: but we order that those persons accused and punished for the commission of this crime committed before the publication of this law, and not after, shall be subject to the laws and regulations which existed before these our letters and those who were condemned in the said crime shall be judged and sentenced. And we order our officers of all our kingdoms and dominions to keep and execute with all diligence its provisions upon which we trust their consciences: and be obliged to give God account of everything which by them, or by their fault or negligence be left to punish, besides other penalties which we order to be given; and that they make especial oath to fulfil it at the time they were received with the letters".

During the conquest of America, despite the long sailing voyages and land journeys, only two instances of homosexual sodomy were recorded among the Conquistadors. One refers to three sailors under the German captain Nikolaus von Federmann (1501–1542) in the service of the Welsers, then bankers to Charles V, and the other of five Italian soldiers under Captain Alonso de Herrera during the conquest of Venezuela. Both episodes appeared in the *Conquistas de Tierra Firme* (1627) by Fr. Pedro Simon (1574–c. 1636) and are worth recording because they give a clear picture of the way sodomy was handled among the Spanish explorers.

1627 edition, p. 156; III Part, Chapter I

[Soldiers with Nikolaus von Federmann to the conquest of Tierra Firme, Venezuela]

"[In Cadiz] one [soldier] was infected with the abominable vice of sodomy, and returning to his sin with two others infected of the same, whom he already knew to be of the same fur, due to some quarrel between them, one was left dead, and the other two prisoners, and that is how the evil came to be known; because they confessed clearly both of them, that the disagreement had been about the exercise of the same abomination and nefarious sin; with that the three of them were burnt, and the rumour spread among the whole fleet that due to the sins of that sodomite, they had all suffered the storms and travails; and we do not have to be amazed at these suspicions because that sin is so abominable that it is the cause of these and greater punishments."

1627 edition, p. 219; III Part, Chapter XXIII

"... the Pilot gave notice to the Captain [Alonso de Herrera] that the nefarious sin was committed among certain trouble-makers in the camp; from this the Captain was greatly upset and after taking testimony from the Pilot with whom he sent the ship, he tried to examine the case with the proper witnesses. And having ascertained that there were five among whom the sin [of sodomy] was committed he received their confessions which they gave plainly, that it was indeed as they were charged and that all of them were Italians, among them one called Juan María born in Florence. This one promised to give the Captain a great sum of money to avoid being burnt and to be set free, and the rest of his companions asserted that he could give what he had promised and much more, because he was the successor and natural heir to a large estate belonging to his uncle; to that the Captain did not pay much attention, regarding all that as much less in importance than the punishment of the offence, with the due penalty, for it did not appear right to anybody to take with him people of that race in his army on account of interest, leaving open the opportunity for the infection of others, because from the abomination of the sin [sodomy] all can be feared, and thus he ordered all those implicated to be strangled and burnt, with general applause, as they all decided to act in that fashion ..."

The colonial archives of the Holy Office of the Inquisition fail to produce any significant records on sodomy. At Lima the study by Medina (1887) shows that during the period between 1569 and 1820, out of a total of 1474 prosecutions there were 40 cases dealing with the Sixth Commandment, mostly statements that fornication was not sinful and the like. But next to this can be found 109 cases of libidinous confessors soliciting love favours from their penitents. The text of the proclamation by the Lima Inquisition in 1630 against this sexual soliciting of the confessors indicated:

"... that many priest confessors ... dare to request their spiritual sons and daughters ... for obscene and dishonest acts, between them ..."

and this gives reason to believe that there were also certain homosexual offences. There was a notorious case of a Dominican friar at Lima in 1572, Fr. Francisco de la Cruz, imprisoned after acting as possessed by "divine powers", where the Inquisitors in 1575 stated that he had confessed to having committed the nefarious sin of sodomy with two friars of the same order, and furthermore that there were others in that convent practising sodomy. But the accounts of travellers during the colonial period, such as Frezier (1732) and Juan and Ulloa (1735–1746), indicate that the major problem for the Inquisition, as the records clearly proved, was loose morals and lewdness of a heterosexual nature even in those religious

12

11

PLATE III

FIG. 9. Mixtec representations of astrological influences on the body. *Codex Vaticanus*, B 3773, section 75.

FIG. 10. Mixtec representation of Tlatequani, goddess eater of filth at lower left. *Codex Vaticanus*, B 3773, section 79.

FIG. 11. Aztec representation of hallucinogenic mushrooms at lower right. *Codex Magliabecchi*, folio 78 (83).

FIG. 12. Aztec rebus writing for Ololiuhqui as coatl-xihuitl, a hallucinogenic drug. *Codex Magliabecchi*, folio 71 (83).

communities. We must bear in mind that the American Indians were excluded from the Inquisition and the power of the Holy Office had nothing to do with their sexual practices.

HABITUAL INEBRIATION

There were no hallucinatory drugs in Spain prior to the American discovery and opium was introduced into European medicine much later. Inebriation among Spaniards was only due to excessive drinking of wine from grapes or its distillates. It is well known that wine-producing countries usually have low statistics of violent intoxication although long-term effects of alcoholism may be higher. In Spain loss of judgement from inebriation was traditionally a condition granting attenuated responsibility in law, as it appears in the Leyes de Partida (law 6, title 11, part 7). This can be traced to Roman law, and was also found in Canonic law, where the state of intoxication removed the consciousness of responsibility. The action of inebriety was punishable, but the acts executed under intoxication were not considered felonies. Wine in the New World was a precious commodity entirely imported from Spain, because despite repeated efforts at acclimatization of grape vines American wine production was negligible. Minimal too was the consumption by the Spaniards of native drinks like pulque and chicha. Alcoholism among the Spaniards and also the Indians after colonization is related to another factor: spirits. Most references to rum production trace the beginning of distillation from sugar molasses to the British and French colonies in the West Indies at the middle of the 17th century. The pattern of colonial commerce between Britain and the New England colonies was actually based on a triangle whereby the West Coast of Africa provided the black slaves, who were transported to the West Indies and paid in sugar molasses. These in turn were taken to New England and paid for in rum, which was exported to Africa to purchase more slaves and to Britain to command large profits. Several millions of gallons of rum were distilled yearly in the British colonies in North America; in Boston alone during a year (1731), the records show that over seven million litres of rum were exported. But the sugar industry with its by-products of molasses and alcoholic beverages had a much earlier history. In fact Columbus in 1493 took the first sugar cane from the Canary Isles to Hispaniola and by 1516 Charles V received the first loaves of sugar from America. Hernan Cortés in 1523 had planted sugar cane in the garden of his Mexican home two years after the Conquest, and the studies by Sandoval (1951) and Barrett (1970) have shown that Cortés established sugar mills about 1528 at Tuxtla near Veracruz, about 1530 in Cuernavaca, and also at Oaxaca and Tehuantepec. They were too far inland to supply the export market of sugar to Spain, and this was mainly carried from Cuba. Sugar cane was also introduced later on in Peru and consumed by an internal market. The French in the Caribbean, particularly at Saint Domingue or Haiti, a colony which, it has been pointed out (Guerra, 1966), represented most of France's colonial commerce, also concentrated on sugar mills. However, the Spaniards exported from the American colonies to the metropolis precious metals, hides, sugar and drugs but never molasses or spirits. The production of sugar in continental Spanish America was consumed by the internal market and the molasses processed by alcoholic fermentation and distilled to obtain *aguardiente de caña, habanero,* rum and other spirits for local consumption. Molasses were of primary economic importance in the colonial mills because they were intended for the manufacture of distillates and its sale was estimated to cover the costs of running the whole sugar plantation. A perusal of colonial ordinances shows that from a very early date the sale of molasses to the Indians was forbidden, to avoid their manufacture of *aguardiente,* but the truth was that the native population always found ways of obtaining liquor, and colonial administrators and missionaries were unable to end the sale of spirits to the Indians by unscrupulous Spanish merchants.

Customary inebriation among the Colonial Spaniards is not described in the chronicles. The only mention appears in Huaman Poma (*c.* 1610), but even in his denunciation he did not accuse the Spaniards he hated so, but the mulattos and *mestizos* usually described by him as being in a state of intoxication.

SPANISH MORAL DECLINE

It has been a well accepted view that up to the end of Philip II's reign Spain had been perhaps a cruel, but also a pious nation. The Spaniards' virile behaviour during centuries of continuous wars, culminating with the expulsion of the Arabs from Iberian soil at the end of the 15th century, show they were a hard and sober people who also displayed their moral virtue in foreign lands to the extent that, for instance, their masculine style of dress was followed even in England. When Philip II of Spain reached London accompanied by a great number of Spanish knights, the Englishmen were reading the views of Anglerius (1555), an Italian observer, about their fashions and attire.

1555 edition, p. 112

"The Spanyards contemne effeminate plesures

". . . Also the most part of the Spanyardes, do laugh them to scorne which use to weare many stones; specially such as are common: Iudginge it to bee an effeminate thynge, and more meete for women then men. The noble men onely when they celebrate solemne marriages, or set forth any triumphes, weare cheynes of gold byset with precious stones, and use sayre apparell of sylke embrothered with golde intermixt with pearles and precious stones: And not at other tymes. They thynke is no lesse effeminate for men to smell of the sweete favours of Arabie: And iudge hym to be infected with sum kynde of fylthy lechery, in whom they smell the favour of muske or *Castoreum.*"

The inner feeling of religious moral rightness, the virile prowess indicated by sexual drives, and also the colossal adventures accomplished in America during the 16th century by Spaniards from every rank, was reflected in the braggadocio which has been associated until our own times with the Spanish character. It must be borne in mind that the traditional distaste for the Spanish arrogance among other Europeans and the American Indians was born with the hatred of things Spanish in the 16th century, when Spain was the most feared and the most powerful nation in the world. This political connotation tainted sodomy and bestiality in the eyes of the Spaniards with an alien nature very similar to that already described by medical historians in the case of syphilis; the Spaniards called it the French disease, the French the Neapolitan malady, the Germans the Spanish scabies and the rest *bubas* from the Indies, and so every nation cursed its neighbour or enemy with the provenance of the venereal disease. Likewise the Spaniards refused to acknowledge among themselves the existence of sodomy and blamed the foreigners for its importation.

But the 17th century witnessed the decline of the political, economical and military power of Spain and the erosion of its moral values. Perhaps the most candid view of the Spaniards immediately after the 16th century may be obtained from Francisco Gomez de Quevedo (1580–1645) who depicted in the crudest fashion the daily life of Spain in that period. His adventures at the Royal Court or among the common people, in Spain and abroad, with the Church or with ruffians, display with unique literary quality the nature of Spanish morals, and their attitude, for instance, to sodomy. Probably as a result of his quarrels in Italy following amorous experiences, he blamed the Italians, particularly the Genoese, for the practice of sodomy even with their wives and in the *Premática de las Cotorreras* (1609) Quevedo included the following fictitious ordinance:

"... And we order that those [women] who have a Genoese for a lover may have a Spaniard as another, without jealousy of the first, because each of them works in a different area ..."

However, years afterwards Quevedo was not so sure about it, perhaps after the ambiguous affairs of his enemy, the notorious Duke of Villamediana (1580–1622), who was sometimes involved with royal ladies, sometimes in homosexual scandals, giving the impression that sodomy and decadence had reached the Spanish Court. Quevedo then wrote in the *Sueño de la Muerte* (1622) or *Vision of Death* the following lines:

"... Honoured were the Spaniards when they could call the foreigners sodomites and drunkards ... Then [in Spain] there was no sodomite other than [the expression] *oxte* which was always said *oxte puto*! [begone queer] all of them [the Spaniards] were inclined to women ..."

The loose morals during the reign of Philip IV have been studied by Deleito y Peñuela (1948) by extracting the news about criminal offences from a number of diaries and letters reporting these events. Gonzalez Palencia (1942) has edited the *Noticias de Madrid* 1621–1627 and Rodríguez Villa (1886) the *Nuevas de Madrid* 1636–1637; there are also the *Cartas* by some fathers of the Company of Jesus 1634–1648; the *Avisos históricos* for 1640–1647 by José Pellicer de Ossau y Tovar (1602–1679), which were published by Valladares de Sotomayor in volumes 31 to 33 of the *Semanario Erudito* (1790) and finally the *Avisos* for 1654–1658 by Jerómino de Barrionuevo (1587–1671) edited by Paz Melia (1893). If the 16th-century Spain is at her best, even in morals, the 17th century show the Spaniards at their worst, particularly in morals. Deleito y Peñuela (1948) by computing all the moral offences faithfully reported in the *Avisos* by Barrionuevo for 1654–1658 gave the following statistics of Madrid for those five years: 4 parricides, 11 poisoning, 8 suicides, 21 thefts—6 of the thieves were priests—3 incests, 6 cases of sodomy, and 1 of bestiality. It must be kept in mind that Barrionuevo was a priest, and like Pellicer, and the Jesuits, who systematically reported these events, they were accurate and reliable sources. Of the six cases of homosexual sodomites recorded, two of them were Italians, and it appears that those accused of that felony sought refuge in the residence of the ambassador of the Republic of Venice. In other group cases the servants of the Duke of Villamediana, one of them a mulatto, appeared prominently. The first news about homosexuals appeared in the *Avisos* in the following manner:

"December 1622. Six young men were burnt on account of committing the nefarious sin. The first was Mendocilla a bufon. The second a servant of the Duke of Villamediana chambers. The third was a young mulatto slave. The fourth another servant of Villamediana. The last one was Don Gaspar de Terrazas page of the Duke of Alba. It was an execution that made considerable noise in the Court."

"March 1626. The 18th Don Diego Gaytan de Vargas, Solicitor in the Royal Courts for Salamanca, was subjected to torment in prison, because he was accused of the nefarious sin ... The 21st two young men were burnt, one of them had indicted Don Diego Gaytan ... who denied it shouting in the streets when he was taken to be burnt. The whole court felt pity."

The year before Quevedo's death, shortly after he left prison, Pellicer recorded in his *Avisos históricos*, the first case of heterosexual sodomy between husband and wife:

"15th November 1644. The wife of a mechanic accused her husband before the officer of this town that he committed the nefarious sin with her, and he is in prison.

"29th November 1644. Last Friday the man whose wife accused him of committing the nefarious sin with her was burnt. And she remained in prison because she is pregnant."

The law was not against homosexuality itself, but against sodomy in any form, on moral, biological and religious grounds. The ultimate in sexual depravity was also reported once in Spain, and is to be found in the *Avisos* by Barrionuevo.

"July 1659.... A farmer married to a young woman very nice looking, while spreading manure with a small she-ass from the field to his orchard, fell in love with his beast and had intercourse with it at noon. He was seen and fled. He was captured near the bulls in Guadalajara ... Friday the lover of his she-ass was burnt in Alcala, and the same day arrived news that another man who lie with his sow was arrested in the mountains. All that while there are women around three for a farthing."

Before passing judgement on the Spaniard in the New World on the eve of the Discovery every one of their critics must first read some of their narratives, and among them the accounts of Cabeza de Vaca (1542), Cieza de León (1553) and Díaz del Castillo (1632) are compulsory. Those narratives, honest, plain and vivid, tell better than any document the moral character and the stamina of a group of men who incorporated a continent within the moral world of Western civilization.

Although the reading of cases of moral failures among the Spaniards in the New World might lead us to accept the distorted view of cruel, greedy, and lustful men as depicted by ill-intentioned historians, it is fitted to appraise the morals of the Spaniards in America with the lines of one of their worst enemies. He was Sir Walter Raleigh (1552–1618), the founder of the Virginia Colony in 1584, who was in the attacks on Cadiz in 1596 and on Fayal in 1597, and who was also the settler of Guiana in 1615; writing in the *History of the World* (1614) he had this to say about those men:

1614 edition, II Part, p. 367; Book V, Chapter I, Section X

"Here I cannot forbear to commend the patient virtues of the Spaniards; we seldom or never find that any nation hath endured so many misadventures and miseries as the Spaniards have done in their Indian discoveries; yet persisting in their enterprizes with an invincible constancy, they have annexed to their kingdoms so many goodly provinces, as bury the remembrance of the dangers past. Tempests and shipwrecks, famines, overthrows, mutinies, heat and cold, pestilence and all manners of diseases, both old and new, together with extreme poverty and want of all things needful, have been the enemies wherewith every one of their most noble discoverers, at one time or other, hath encountered. Many years have passed over their heads, in the search of not so many leagues, yea, more than one or two have spent their labours, their wealth and their lives, in search of a golden kingdom, without getting further notice of it than they had at their first setting forth. All which notwithstanding, the third, fourth, and fifth undertakers have not been disheartened. Surely they are worthily rewarded with those treasuries and paradises which they enjoy; and well they deserve to hold them quietly, if they hinder not the like virtues in others, which perhaps will not be found."

CHAPTER VI

THE COLONIAL ACCULTURATION

THE PSYCHOLOGICAL CONQUEST

The transfer of the Christian civilization into the New World and the taming of the pre-Columbian mind was entirely dependent on the logistics of the Spanish Conquest, which have never been explained in simple military terms. The superiority of steel over obsidian and wooden weapons, or the role of the horse and gunpowder were far from decisive elements. The firing power of 16th century arms was very limited or scarcely superior in range to bow and arrow, besides being slower to handle. The horses were indeed feared, but were soon attacked and destroyed by the Indians. On the other hand, every campaign invariably ended in single-handed combat where the advantage of weapons became reduced to a minimum. Therefore, the Conquest of America meant in the end not only the survival of the Spaniards in adverse environmental conditions, but the fight of man against man, endurance against endurance, and above all mind against mind. The Spanish campaigns of the Conquest fail to conform to any rational logistical analysis of our own time: in the first place the Conquistadors had to control a continent extending for over 40 million km². Secondly the climatological and environmental conditions were so hostile to individuals of temperate climates, that even today with accurate intelligence reports, adequate food and medical supplies, and better means of transportation, it is impossible to repeat the journey of Cortés from Mexico to the Hibueras, or the itinerary of Belacazar in Tierra Firme. Third to be considered was the pre-Columbian enemy, with a population at the time of the Discovery never ascertained, but estimated at about 20 million, or even as high as 100 million. Whatever the figure they were subdued by a handful of men, because the number of Spaniards actually engaged in the decisive battles which accomplished the Conquest of the New World were in all less than two thousand men.

The Conquest of Mexico was launched in 1519 with 600 men and 16 horses, and by the time Hernán Cortés first entered Mexico city there were 400 men left, 150 of whom died in the withdrawal from Mexico city during the "Night of Sorrow". Counting those joining from Velazquez's party, at the crucial battle of Otumba and the siege of Mexico city, which ended the resistance of the Aztec army under Cuauhtemoc, the men under Cortés' banners never exceeded 1000 soldiers. In the conquest of Yucatan the first entry by Francisco de Montejo the elder in 1527 with nearly 400 men had to withdraw in 1535, resorting to the degrading stratagem of escaping under the cover of the night, leaving behind a hungry dog to toll the alarm bell. When Francisco de Montejo the younger landed back at Champotón in 1537 his party survived the first assault by returning to the ships, but losing in one night 150 men of the expedition. Their honour hurt by the insults from the beach and the memories of the dog tolling the bell, they left the protection of the sea to join in battle again with the Mayan army, which was defeated never to recover again. The conquest of Tierra Firme by Gonzalo Jimenez de Quesada in 1536 was achieved by only 166 men and 59 horses who were able to subjugate the Chibcha Indians and control one of the most rugged areas of South America. The conquest of Peru by Francisco Pizarro in 1532 was also carried out by 166 men, who in the boldest action of American history captured the Inca ruler Atahualpa at Caxamarca in the face of his army numbering about 30,000 men. Finally the conquest of the inland areas of South America was crowned in 1542 by Alvar Nuñez Cabeza de Vaca when with 198 men and 12 horses he destroyed an army of over 4000 Guaycurúes. These Indians had been considered invincible until then, to the point that the Guaraní Indians allied to the Spaniards refused to attack the Guaycurú camp at the final assault. Travelling nowadays from Alaska to Tierra del Fuego the question that keeps recurring in our thoughts as we travel over deserts, mountains, jungles, rivers and savanas is: how could the Conquest have ever been accomplished by such small groups of men, and in the face of such considerable odds?

History relishes in telling us the refined education received by the great captains of the classical antiquity, but Cortés or Pizarro never had the benefits that fell upon Caesar or Alexander; in fact, most of the Conquistadors were peasants, swineherds, or at their best, drop-outs from school. It has been mentioned that historical events during the Conquest changed as a result of certain acts of courage: for instance, the burning of the ships by Cortés in 1519 to make impossible the withdrawal from Mexico; or by men like the "Thirteen of Fame" who crossed the line drawn in 1532 by Pizarro's sword on the sand of the isle of Gallo, deciding to go into Peru rather than return to herd pigs. These were mere incidents projecting the mental processes in the mind of resolute though almost illiterate men, whose behaviour proves the paradox about the great intelligence of the illiterate Spanish mind. It is only by accepting the incalculable role of the mind in human endeavour that the outcome of those five decisive campaigns during the Spanish conquest of America can be explained, because, examined by the standards of military capability, they seem sheer lunacy.

Some Conquistadors have been graced by historians with shrewd political genius. They were able—like Cortés with the Tlaxcaltecs—to obtain allegiances which led to the Indians' mutual destruction. This indeed occurred in a number of instances, and many natives died side by side with Spaniards subjugating other tribes during the Conquest. That could give some grounds to the dictum that the "Conquest of America was done by the Indians ... and the Independence of Spanish America by the Spaniards" as many leaders of the 1810–1821 wars of Independence were Spanish liberals. Technical superiority in the art of war can also explain certain Spanish gains during the Conquest. In turn, the military training given by an early Spanish captive to some Mayan chiefs—so they could overcome certain neighbouring tribes—afterwards made the conquest of Yucatan by the Montejos the bloodiest and most difficult campaign of the American Conquest.

The role of the pre-Columbian mind has also been investigated for an explanation of its psychological conquest. The fall of the Aztecs and the Mayas has been attributed to a mental submission to the prophetic return of Quetzalcoatl or Kukulkan fulfilled by the arrival of the bearded Spaniards, in the same way that the Incas fell because the Spaniards were considered to be the expected Viracocha. This is, however, a fallacy because the Conquest was war, death and destruction, and centuries after the great collision of Indians versus Spaniards we can still count the corpses in their ranks. The Conquest of America was possible because the pre-Columbian mind immediately became captive to the Spanish mind, which was guided by loftier ideals, operated by stronger motivations, and nourished by cultural values of a classical tradition which had produced a more rational human being. And in that process religion played the dominant role, because the instructions to the Conquistadors from the Popes, monarchs and captains always began as those received by Cortés in 1519: "... Bear in mind from the beginning that the first aim of your expedition is to serve God and spread the Christian faith ..."

The pre-Columbian civilizations were deeply committed to religion, to the point that the life of the individual from birth to death was ruled by rituals, the more elaborate as the civilization became better developed. Some of them, like the Aztecs, seem to have lived for nothing else but religious practices. Because of this religious intertwining within the life of pre-Columbian societies, the re-shaping of the Indian mind fell entirely upon the Catholic institutions charged to carry out the declared evangelic aim of the Spanish Conquest. Most pre-Columbian religions were based on polytheism with gods which could easily be superimposed upon the pantheon of ancient Greece or Rome, and even on the Catholic theogony. It has been pointed out (Guerra, 1969) that the Aztec religion, which incorporated the gods of vanquished tribes, was particularly prone to an easy syncretism with the Catholic church. Besides the similarity of a god creator, an obscure trinity, and other manifestations of the male principle, the ancestral mother appeared in the pre-Columbian mind as a domineering influence—*Teteoinam* among the Aztecs, *Ixchel* of the Mayas, or *Mamacocha* for the Incas—and was easily superimposed in the native mind by the image of the Virgin Mary, mother of God. Her most celebrated manifestation, Our Lady of Guadalupe in Mexico, had her shrines built upon the temples of *Teteoinam* the mother of gods, and she was always called *Tonatzin*, Our Lady. Likewise the baroque list of patron saints in the Catholic church substituted the multiple familiar *tlalocs* and *conopas*, which were the smaller gods of ancient Mexico and Peru.

Another factor which made the Catholic church a readily operational institution among the American Indians after the Conquest was the institutionalized nature of the priestly hierarchies in pre-Columbian societies. Priesthood was as powerful among them as in the Old World, and had a similar structure. There were high priests or popes, and lower priests ranking in hierarchy from equivalents of bishops down to sextons. All of them displayed similar dignity, were considered sober, honest and chaste and were held in great esteem. Annexed to the temples there were congregations of men and women bound to religious service and chastity, which hardly differed from the nuns and friars of the Catholic church.

There was, finally, a most important similarity between the sacraments of the Catholic dogma and those of the pre-Columbian religions, particularly the Aztec, at least in their rituals. They both had Baptism, Confirmation, Penance, Communion, Holy Orders and Matrimony, and only the Extreme Unction could be excluded as doubtful. The admission of the Indians into the Catholic Church was done by Baptism, and in Asia the practice had been to baptize first and follow with catechism. This procedure was used generally in America until the synod of 1555 which forbade the baptism of adults who had been insufficiently instructed. The ritual of the baptismal water fitted into the pre-Columbian psychology with its concept of sin as a kind of material soiling. There can be little doubt that confession, as part of the Catholic ritual of penance, was the sacrament more eagerly sought by the pre-Columbian mind. The accounts by Motolinia (1541), Mendieta (1596), Torquemada (1615) and many others show that the missionaries were overwhelmed by crowds seeking confession, which followed them wherever they went. And when the Indian minds were unable to communicate their guilt to the priests because of language barriers, they resorted to pictographic techniques and arrived at confession with painted representations of their sins on wood or *amatl* paper. However, this acceptance of confession by the pre-Columbian mind was indeed remote from the penance of the Catholic dogma involved in the remission of sin, repentance and acknowledgment. Restitution, however, seems to have taken place, at least in some instances mentioned by Torquemada (1615). The sacrament of matrimony led to considerable trouble when applied to pre-Columbian civilizations where concubinage and polygamy had been customary.

Veracruz devoted one of his earliest works, the *Speculum conjugiorum,* Mexico (1556), to discuss the grounds for repeated annulments, which for practical purposes gave Indian Catholic marriages a very insecure nature. The idea of only one wife was received by some chiefs (according to Ricard, 1933) as a miracle which enabled them to get rid of old and burdensome wives. But more frequently it was the opposite case of men having to decide which one of their wives was to be kept, or of men changing wives simply by following the religious rules to the letter. Annulments were easily made either by admitting consanguinity, or better by declaring that prior to their Catholic marriage they had been in concubinage with another woman. The Catholic marriage was then dissolved and the man could marry his mistress. He could also reverse the procedure and annul his marriage to the concubine, by declaring to the priest that he had lied, immediately obtaining annulment of the second marriage and returning to his first one. In a few instances the Catholic church made extreme compromises in an effort to reconcile pre-Columbian customs with Colonial needs. One case in point were the marriages allowed in 1558 to the Inca Sairi Tupac in Cuzco after his submission to the Peruvian Viceroy. He was married first to his first cousin the daughter of the Inca Huascar, and afterwards to his niece Cusi Huarcay the granddaughter of Huascar; incest had to be tolerated on political grounds.

The establishment of the Catholic religion in the Spanish American dominions was a formidable task which can be followed in the excellent accounts left in the chronicles of the religious orders in America. A few priests accompanied the early campaigns, but the evangelical work during the first century after the conquest fell almost entirely upon the Mendicant Orders. The first to arrive in Mexico were the Franciscan friars in 1524, the Augustinians in 1533, and the Dominicans in 1536; the Jesuits did not arrive in Mexico until 1576. Half a century after the conquest of Mexico the Franciscans had 80 convents and 380 friars, the Dominicans 40 convents and 210 friars and the Augustinians also 40 convents and 212 friars. Every one of the missionaries was first trained in the historical and ethnographical background of the area and went into a thorough linguistic training which enabled them to spread the gospel among the Indians. The high character of the early missionaries—humble, chaste and pious—who lived in love and charity, considerably enhanced the acceptance of the new faith. Accounts of the arrival of the first Franciscans in Mexico in 1524, known as the "Twelve Apostles" because of their number and exemplary behaviour, tells how much the Indians marvelled at the sight of their feared victors, like Hernán Cortés and the Conquistadors, as they dismounted from their horses to kneel down and kiss the hands of those poorly garbed and barefooted friars. The early support given by the Spaniards to these holy men and the good disposition of the Indians during the early stages (according to Braden, 1930) account for the initial success of the religious indoctrination. Braden

also believes that the indifference of later settlers, the ill-treatment of
the Indians, the lower moral character of the priests afterwards and even
the conflicts between the clergy and the monastic orders progressively
discredited the standing of the Catholic faith in the mind of the Indians.

THE EVOLUTION OF SEXUAL DRIVES

Despite Lopez de Gomara's (1552) candid statement, the Spanish conquest
did not eradicate the practice of sodomy among the Indian population,
although their sexual behaviour began to adapt itself within the new
morals of Western culture and the commandments of the Roman Catholic
faith. Sodomy among the Spaniards and creoles was socially negligible
and can only be traced within male communities such as convents and
prisons subjected to extreme sexual repression.

For an analysis of the American Indian sexual practices after the Conquest, sources other than the records of the Inquisition must be studied.
It has been pointed out (Guerra, 1970) that the *Manuals of Confession*
prepared by the Catholic missionaries in American Indian languages
form a segment of religious literature of extraordinary importance. In
fact they deserve to be considered as the earliest tools for American
anthropology and psychotherapy. Their careful analysis confirms the
contrast in patterns of sexual aberration between the high civilizations of
Middle America and those of South America.

The *Confessionario mayor, en lengua Mexicana y Castellana* (1565) by
Alonso de Molina (1514–1585) is the earliest bilingual confessionary in
Nahuatl and Spanish to bring up the problem of sodomy in America.
Molina was a Franciscan friar who arrived in Mexico as a child and grew
up among the native boys, mastering their language. He later produced
the finest Mexican dictionaries. His large *Confessionary*, like that by Fr.
Juan Baptista some years later, mentioned sodomy between man and
woman and lesbian acts between women.

1565 edition, folios 32–35

"Questions concerning the Sixth Commandment of God.
... And if it is a woman at confessions, ask her ...
... Did you sin with another woman, committing the sin against
nature? ...
"Questions for the male ...
... By chance, you and the legitimate wife you have, have you both
avoided the procreation of children, because you are poor and in need
or because of some quarrel or for some other reason? ...
"Questions for the female ...
... When you were with your custom [menstruation] did you ask your
husband to have relation and intercourse with you; did you do it
improperly? Was the intercourse he had with you in the ordained
vessel for generation or elsewhere? How many times did you commit
this sin?

"Questions for the male . . .

. . . when your wife was with custom [menstruation] did you have intercourse with her? And at the time you both joined was it with lewdness and not in the proper vessel? And by chance did you execute any other lecherous things and filthy pleasure, which are not mentioned here; remember all of them to confess and declare all."

The *Confessionario en lengua Mexicana y Castellana* (1599) by Fr. Juan Baptista (1555–1613) is not only interesting for its text, but for the author's background. He was a second generation creole born in Mexico, and when he entered the Franciscan order became a pupil of Fr. Bernardino de Sahagún, the father of Mexican anthropology; Baptista was in turn the teacher of the great historian of Indian nations Fr. Juan de Torquemada. In Baptista's *Confessionary* homosexual offences between males are suggested in the questioning, but not in a clear and positive form.

1599 edition, folios 48 verso–51

"Questions pertaining to the Sixth Commandment (for the male).

. . . By chance, with yourself have you done anything improper or dirty: or with another man?

. . . When you approach your wife, do you keep the natural order or did you by chance approach her from behind, or did you by chance, have use in that act other improper practices unworthy to be named here? . . .

"Questions for women.

. . . Have you by chance committed the nefarious sin with another woman?"

The *Camino al cielo* (1611) by the Dominican friar Martin de León (fl. 1611) is interesting because of its detailed and systematic study of the syncretism between Mexican and Spanish hagiology and its bilingual confessionary. There is no mention of sodomy between males, but León points out that lesbian acts between young women were very frequent in Mexico.

1611 edition, folios 115–116 verso

"Sixth Commandment . . .

Question, When you approached your wife or some of your wenches, being drunk or not did you have access to her from behind outside the normal and usual vessel?

. . .

To young girls and single girls, and this is very common.

Question. Have you lain sometimes one above the other, playing like man and woman as a joke and touching in some part?"

The *Confessionario Mayor y Menor en lengua Mexicana* (1634) by Bartolomé de Alva (fl. 1634) contains a similar text in Nahuatl and Spanish and gives the first clear mention of sodomy between men, and also of bestiality.

1634 edition, folios 22–25

"Questions pertaining to the Sixth Commandment

. . . By chance when you were drunk, losing your senses, did you fall into the abominable sin of sodomy having to do with another [man]. [Answer] Yes, father or No.

. . . Or have you committed the sin against nature, executing this act with some animal? [Answer] Yes, father or No.

"Questions for women alone.

. . . Did you have sexual intercourse with another woman like yourself, or she with you. [Answer] Yes or No.

When your husband had excess with you, being drunk, was it by the normal vessel or did he execute the nefarious sin, changing the part and you did not avoid it. [Answer] Yes, father or No."

Following the *Miscelanea espiritual en el Idioma Zapoteco* by Cristobal de Aguero published in Mexico (1666) there is a *Confessionario en Zapoteco* by the same author and this is of great interest. Aguero was born in San Luis de la Paz, Michoacan (fl. 1666) and entered the Dominican Order at Oaxaca's convent in 1618. A graduate in Theology, he was for over 40 years a missionary among the Zapotec Indians and was very learned in their language. His *Confessionary* shows clearly the sexual obligations of marriage, the questioning on sodomy, lesbian practices, and even bestiality.

1666 edition, pp. 32–37

"Confessionary in the same Zapotec language.

p. 32: Priest: Have you sinned with another man and committed the nefarious sin?

Penitent: No Father, I only sinned in that way with my wife, having copula with her in the rear vessel.

Priest: Son, that is a most grave sin in front of God and of men, do not do it again, because His Divine Justice will be angry and will punish you and your wife.

Penitent: Sometimes certain women use to accuse themselves of lying with others, having relations like if they were men and say:

Priest: How many times have you done that?

Penitent: Four or five.

Priest: Have you committed any sin of bestiality?

Penitent: No Father . . .

p. 36: Priest: Have you denied the [sexual] debit to your wife, have you resisted her, and rejected her when she wanted you?

p. 37: Penitent: Truly Father, I have done it in two or three occasions; because I was angry with my wife, and was jealous of her, due to suspicions I have of another man, and I also do not pay the debit, because I have been ill.

Priest: Son, it was not a sin not to pay the conjugal debit if you have been ill, but to deny it because of anger or jealousy, and suspicions yes, because by reason of the marriage bond, you do not belong to yourself but to your wife ...."

The *Manual de administrar los Santos Sacramentos* by Fr. Angel Serra, first published in Mexico (1697) and reprinted there (1731), is also very important. Serra (fl. 1697) was a native of Michoacan who after entering the Franciscan Order was missionary among the Tarascan Indians of Charapan and afterwards custodian of the Querétaro Convent. His *Manual* written in Spanish, Latin, and Tarascan languages is one of the most detailed documents for the confession of the natives and includes not only the usual questions about lust, fornication, incest, sodomy and bestiality, but also enquires about suicidal compulsion.

1731 edition, folios 111–136

f. 112: "Question. Are you a married woman, or a widow, or a virgin, or have you lost your virginity?
    Q. How many times?
    Q. Many? ...
    Q. Did you want anybody? ...
    Q. Are you relatives?
    Q. In what degree are you relatives? ...
    Q. Have you been drunk losing your senses? ...

f. 115: Q. Have you desired to be dead [because of being] lazy, or because of some travail you were in or you had? ...
    Q. Have you sinned with a woman? ...

f. 116: Q. Were they your relatives? ...
    Q. Did you commit sin with some woman using both parts? ...
    Q. Did you commit sin with your sister? ...
    Q. Have you kissed any woman?
    Q. Was she your mother, the one who gave you birth? ...

f. 117: Q. Have you committed sodomy?
    To the consenting one they call [*cuecetze*].
    Q. Have you touched the lower parts of a man with pleasure wishing to commit a sin?
    Q. Have you committed sin with any beast?
    Q. Have you committed sin with a woman while she was lying down like an animal on four feet, or you put her like that wanting to sin with her?

f. 118: Q. Have you sinned with your sister? ...
To a woman you ask ...
    Q. And how many men have sinned with you? ...
    Q. And was your Father, the one who begat you? ...

f. 120: Q. And was your elder brother?
    Q. And was your younger brother? ...
    Q. And have you sinned with another woman like if you were man and woman?"

There is also the *Confessionario de Indios* (1761) in Nahuatl and Spanish by the priest Carlos C. Velazquez de Cardenas y León (fl. 1761) who was very knowledgeable about the customs in the valley of Mexico. Since he used a progressive numerical system to familiarize the confessor with quantities, Velazquez's *Confessionary* gives the impression of colossal sexual prowess on the part of the Mexican Indians. He is, incidentally, one of the first authors to bring out the Oedipus and the Jocasta complexes by including the problem of sexual desire towards the mother, as Serra did before him (1697).

1761 edition, pp. 9–12

"6th Commandment . . .

". . . I wished to sin with my mother, and had bad thoughts with many women, they cannot be counted, I cannot tell how many times; sixty-six times . . .

. . . To these men I taught and made known what it is not honest; seventy times . . .

. . . I changed from my correct position, because I reached my wife from behind; seventy-two times . . ."

These quantities, however, have no significance; they are merely examples of how to answer the questions and the same will be found for thieving, murder and so on.

Of considerable importance for the study of sodomy among the South American Indians, particularly in the ancient Inca territory under Spanish rule, are the discussions of the III Provincial Council at Lima in 1583 where the Jesuit José Acosta (1540–1600) played a leading role. It can be accepted that he was the author of the Catholic Doctrines, Confessionaries and Sermonaries published at Lima by the *Concilium* between 1584 and 1585. He discussed these matters in *De procuranda Indorum salute* . . . (1588) although he obtained well deserved fame with his *Historia natural y moral de las Indias* (1590). Acosta only arrived in Peru in 1571 but he was very learned in Indian cultures and was the consultant theologian of the Lima Council. The *Catechism* approved by the Provincial Council of Lima in 1583, with text in Spanish, Quechua, and Aymará has an interesting section.

1584 edition, folio 62

". . . Question. Who break the Sixth [Commandment], which is, Not to fornicate?

"Answer. He who commits hideousness with the wife of another man, or with an unmarried woman and much more if it is with another man, or with a beast. And also who enjoys dishonest words or contacts with himself or another. And such depravities are punished by God with eternal fire in another life, and many times in this present, with serious diseases of body and soul."

14

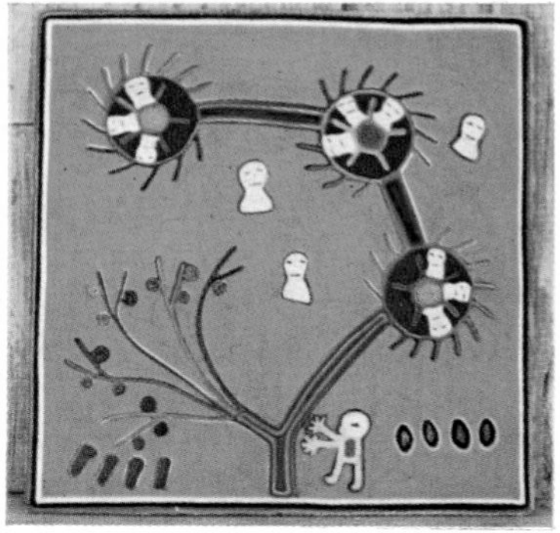

16

13

15

PLATE IV

Fig. 13. Huichol nearika representing the journey of the soul. D. Montgomery, 1970.
Fig. 14. Huichol nearika portraying the abode of the soul. D. Montgomery, 1970.
Fig. 15. Huichol nearika symbolizing a road of sexual taboos. D. Montgomery, 1970.
Fig. 16. Huichol nearika with symbols of sexual aberrations. D. Montgomery, 1970.

The *Confessionario para los Curas de Indios, con la instruccion contra sus ritos* approved by the Provincial Council at Lima in 1583 and published in Spanish, Quechua and Aymara in 1585, gives good detail and indeed questions sodomy and bestiality.

1585 edition, folios 11–13

"Sixth Commandment. Do not fornicate.
[Question] 21. Have you committed the nefarious sin with another person?
[Question] 22. Have you committed bestiality with some animal? (To women these questions must be adapted to their persons. And none of the above questions may be asked except that expected to be done by the person under confession. In Quechua and Aymara language we must adapt in this commandment the words pertaining to male and to female)..."

The Catholic approach to the Indian problem of sodomy in the ancient Inca area culminated with the detailed instructions approved during the III Provincial Council of Lima of 1583, for the Sermons of the *Tercero Cathecismo y exposicion de la Doctrina Christiana* printed in 1585. It was also trilingual—Spanish, Quechua and Aymara—and incorporated all the pagan beliefs of the Incas concerning sin and disease, mixed with strange ideas about mental and bodily ailments. This catechism is of paramount importance for the understanding of the transfer of sexual beliefs between Indian and European culture.

1585 edition, folios 147 verso–154 verso

"Sermon XXIIII. Of the Sixth Commandment. In which it is taught how much adultery angers God and how he punishes it, and also how fornication with an unmarried woman, even on a single occasion is a deadly sin, and of the other manners of lewdness because of which God punishes the Indian nation...
...God punishes also this sin with diseases; what do you think is the *Bubas* malady but punishment for this sin?...
"...Above all these sins is the sin we call nefarious and sodomy, which is for man to sin with man, or with woman not in the natural way, and even above all these, to sin with beasts, such as ewes, bitches, or mares, which is the greatest abomination. If there is anyone among you who commits sodomy sinning with another man, or with a boy, or with a beast, let them be known that because of that fire and brimstone fell from heaven and burnt the fine cities of Sodom and Gomorrah and left them in ashes. Let it be known that they carry the death penalty under the just laws of our Spanish kings. Let it be known that because of this the Holy Scriptures say that God destroys kingdoms and nations. Let it be known that the reason why God has allowed that you the Indians should be so afflicted and vexed by other nations is because of this vice [sodomy] that your ancestors had, and many among you still

have. And let it be known that I tell you from God's command that if you do not reform all your nations will perish, and God will finish you, and will eradicate you from the earth. This is why my beloved brothers cry your great sins, and ask mercy of Jesus Christ, that I turn to tell you that God will finish you, and he is already doing so if you do not reform. Take away drunkenness and feasts which are the sowing ground of these abominable vices, remove the boys and men from your beds, do not sleep mixed up like pigs, but each one of you by himself, do not sing or say dirty words, do not entice your flesh with your hands because this is also a sin and deserving death and hell . . ."

Shortly after the III Lima Council Fr. Luis Jerónimo de Oré (1554–1629) a Franciscan friar in Lima published a *Symbolo Catholico Indiano* (1598) in the three languages—Spanish, Quechua and Aymara—where he also calls the attention of the Confessors to questions of sodomy among the Indians.

1598 edition, folio 184 verso

"Sixth Commandment. Do not fornicate . . .
[Question] 7. Have you committed the nefarious sin or (the sin) of bestiality with another person or with any animal?"

One of the most extraordinary features of sodomy during the colonial period in Spanish America was the printing of special prayers for delivery from the sexual aberration. These were *Novenas* offered to Saint Boniface, Martyr "efficacious to obtain from God the separation of those needy who have fallen into the misery of the deadly sin of the dishonourable vice." The riddle behind the publication of this sodomitic prayer has been an irritating and elusive search for many long years, because it lacked any European ancestry and had appeared only in Mexico. The first printed Novena to Saint Boniface was issued in 1732 and was recorded by Medina (1907–1912) under No. 3238, but it is so rare that Medina learnt of it from the announcement in the *Gazeta de Mexico* No. 53 for April 1732; the only surviving copy is in the author's collection. The Novena to Saint Boniface was reprinted, always at Mexico, in 1785 (Medina No. 7599), in 1817 (Medina No. 11308), in 1821 (not in Medina) also in the author's collection, and several times after the end of the colonial period. They are small 16° booklets (8 × 5 cm) made of 16 leaves, printed on linen paper, with a woodcut of Saint Boniface on the verso of the title page. The puzzle of an Anglo-Saxon missionary being the patron saint of homosexuals in Mexico was too daring to remain unchallenged. Although there are over twenty Saint Bonifaces in the Roman Patrology it was soon possible to focus the search on Saint Boniface Martyr, Bishop of Mainz (680–755) whose feast is celebrated on 5th June. He was born in England and is also known as Winfrid. There are references in his life to the usual temptations of the flesh during his youth, but no reference to sodomy. On the contrary he was the apostle of Germany and spread the

Christian faith among the Frisians and Hessians and in Thuringia. Like Columba before him, Boniface found the Frankish kingdoms with most corrupt morals, and they also had viciously contaminated bishops and clerics to the point that a reading of his reports immediately establishes a parallel with the sexual behaviour of the American Indians, as depicted in the Spanish chronicles: the same pagan sacrifices, the same idols, and the same lewdness. Of course, Boniface writes of Sodom and Gomorrah and in his letter to King Aethelbald of Mercia in the year 746 (Tangl letter 73) accused him of raping nuns, and of all sorts of sexual offences. There is one letter from Pope Gregory II to Boniface in the year 732 (Tangl letter 28) which holds the key to Saint Boniface's position as patron saint of sodomy. In that letter Pope Gregory II replied to Boniface concerning a priest who had committed the nefarious crime of sodomy, and had been absolved of the sin by the Pope in confession. The account is rather lengthy and detailed because the priest under Boniface's episcopal jurisdiction relapsed several times and claimed repeated forgiveness. Accounts of this could be found in the *Epistolae S. Bonifacii Martyriis* printed frequently in the 17th century. The author of the Novena to Saint Boniface was the priest José Manuel García del Valle y Araujo (fl. 1730), first chaplain of the *Hospital de la Limpia Concepción y Jesus Nazareno* in Mexico City founded by Cortés for the cure of syphilis, who died as chaplain of the Convent of S. Lorenzo. He wrote several prayers and had a deep knowledge of Patrology. The Novena to Saint Boniface was dedicated and the printing paid for by José Bernardo de Hogal, a Treasury Officer from Andalusia who arrived in Mexico in 1720, opened a printing shop in 1721 and died in 1741. He was married and had a son José Antonio de Hogal. Another printer, Juan Bautista Arizpe, was still using the types of the Hogal shop a century later, and reprinted Saint Boniface's Novena for sodomites using in 1821 the same woodcut of Saint Boniface which had been carved in 1731.

THE TRENDS IN INEBRIATION

The use of native drugs producing hallucinations and the consumption of alcoholic beverages by the American Indians were profoundly affected by the process of acculturation. In most cases they can easily be analysed in terms of pre-Columbian patterns, but for two instances: the surge of alcoholism in the former Aztec area, and the spread of addiction to *coca* in the ancient Inca dominion. The Spaniards were completely ignorant about the hallucinogenic drugs and looked upon their use with fear. Francisco Ximenez (1560–c. 1620), a Dominican friar who edited Hernandez's Mexican Materia Medica (1615), when referring to the *ololiuhqui*, a plant reputed to induce lewdness and visions, wrote:

"It would be better not to say at this point where it grows, because it matters little that we shall not write here of this herb, and not even that the Spaniards should know of it . . ."

It has already been shown (Guerra and Olivera, 1953) that in the Mexican area practically all the known hallucinogenic drugs were in use, particularly the mushrooms *teonanactal* (*Psylocibes mexicanorum*) and other species, the cactus *peyotl* (*Lophophora williamsii*), the vine *ololiuhqui* (*Rivea corymbosa*), and the herb *toloache* (*Datura stramonium*), all of which are extremely active upon mental processes. In the Caribbean the use of the snuff of *cohoba* (*Amadenanthera peregrina*) continued, but soon disappeared with the depopulation of the Antilles, although it firmly remained in the South American coastal areas. Inland in the continent the Indians preserved the use of a vine, *yage* or *ayahuasca* (*Banisteria caapi*) and above all the leaves of the tree *coca* (*Erythroxylon coca*).

Owing to the use of these *Phantastica* drugs in religious ceremonies associated with pre-Columbian rituals the Holy Office of the Inquisition became active in eradicating the practice, and in 1616 the Mexican Inquisition issued a proclamation instituting severe penalties for the users:

1616 edition, folio 2

"We the Inquisitors against the heretic perversity and apostasy in the city of Mexico ... that many people ... take certain drinks made of herbs and roots with which they lose and confound their senses, and the illusions and fantastic representations they have, judge and proclaim afterwards as revelation, or true notice of things to come ... Mexico, 8th May, 1616."

A perusal of the Inquisitorial proceedings on witchcraft after 1600, the date when a renaissance in pre-Columbian practices seemed to be taking place among the Indian population in Spanish America, shows a considerable increase in witchcraft prosecutions where hallucinogenic drugs had played an important role; Aguirre Beltran (1963) has offered many examples from the records of the Mexican Inquisition and similar trends are noticeable in the contemporary works by Ruiz de Alarcon among the Mexicans (1629), Arriaga for the Incas (1621), Sanchez de Anguilar in respect of the Mayas (1613), Balsalobre (1656) for the Zapotecs and several others. The missionary work was fairly successful in sending into hiding the use of hallucinogenic drugs, at least in the cities, but the Indians still retained the secret knowledge of their virtues and usage in rural areas. However, the *coca* was a different case, and early sources are apparently in conflict about pre-Columbian addiction to it (cocaism). The chewing of *coca* leaves was described by early chroniclers of the Conquest in Tierra Firme and in all the northern area of South America, but the historians of the Inca period seem to indicate that *coca* leaves were only used among the Incas by the ruler and the high dignitaries of his government. In conflict with these records colonial writers were in no doubt that cocaism kept the Indian population going during the three centuries of Colonial administration. Among many reports describing the use of *coca* leaves before the Incas' dominion, during the Inca hegemony, and the hesitant attitude of the Spanish officials after the Conquest— whether to suppress the cultivation and use of *coca* or to use its market as a source of revenue—that by Santillan (1563) is the most interesting.

1968 edition, p. 144

"115. There is in that kingdom (Peru) another type of gain which is the worst of all and most harmful to the Indians, that is the *coca*, which is a herb like *zuzamal*. The Indians use to have it in the mouth while they work or walk, or do any other job, and this is the oldest habit among them, even before the Incas subjugated them. They consider it very precious and of great support and sustenance, because they say that swallowing it they do not feel hunger, thirst or fatigue ... The Inca had then coca *chacaras* [orchards] and to cultivate them he put *mitimaes* [forced labour] to whom they call *camayos*, who cured and collected the *coca* for the Inca and some lords in small amounts, because not everybody reached it. And as it was a precious thing among them, due to that imagination, all of them began to use it after the Spaniards entered in the land ... which has costed and costs now infinite number of Indian lives ... some in government tried to surpress the *coca* ..."

In pre-Columbian times there was a great diversity of intoxicating drinks obtained by alcoholic fermentation of fruits, roots, or grains; practically every civilization or tribe had its own particular drink. Two of them had particular significance owing to the extent of its consumption: the *pulque* in Mexico and the *chicha* in Peru.

The *pulque* was called *octli* by the Aztecs and *balché* by the Maya, and its use according to the legend of Queen Xochitl could be traced until shortly before the fall of Tula (*c.* A.D. 1057). It was obtained by the alcoholic fermentation of *aguamiel*, a sweet sap collected at the centre of the excavated *metl* or *maguey* (Agave mexicana), and the final product was a whitish beverage with an alcoholic content between 6 and 10%. The *maguey* was a plant of many uses growing profusely in the Mexican high plateau, where it was easier to find *pulque* than water; this ecological fact, the reports of extended consumption of *pulque* in the periphery of the Aztec area during the Conquest, and the surge of inebriation among the Mexican Indians after the Conquest, seem to agree with some records of taxation under Moctezuma II. He, for instance, received as tribute, just the village of Aoxocopan and two other nearby localities 2512 vessels of *aguamiel* every 88 days, i.e. 62,500 litres a year. However, in the Codices Mendoza (*c.* 1548) and Magliabecchi (*c.* 1565), and in the reports by Sahagún (*c.* 1565) and other historians, it is maintained that the consumption of *pulque* among the Aztecs was very much controlled, and it was used only during the execution of heavy work, at feasts, or as medicine; inebriation was only tolerated among old people over 50 years of age and severely punished, usually by death, in other persons. The Mayas also held inebriation as a social disgrace. After the Conquest every source agrees that alcoholism became the most damaging feature in the behaviour of the Mexican Indians. This vice was aggravated by the free household production of *pulque* all over Mexico, and the introduction of alcoholic distillation capable of producing liquors with much higher alcoholic content—over 50%—from the native *maguey*, and also from sugar molasses. Colonial officials and the Catholic Church were also concerned with certain drugs and roots which were added to *pulque* during the fermentation process, and which were alleged to enhance inebriation. Several studies were made, including one by the University of Mexico (1690), and Viceroy after Viceroy tried without success to control the production, distribution and sale of *pulque* and spirits. Something was gained in the use of molasses for *rum* and similar drinks under the control of creoles, but the native Indians began to use the core of *maguey* as the starting fluid of alcoholic fermentation, distilling it in earthware vessels to produce the *mexcal* or *tequila*, with an extremely high alcoholic content. This new technological advance contributed to the spread of alcoholism as a social vice, and the by-products of poorly operated distilleries tending more frequently to have systemic toxic effects upon the central nervous system among the natives. Wine imported from Spain remained an expensive article. The best report on this problem appears in the work by Mendieta (1596), which was also quoted by others, including Torquemada (1615).

1870 edition, pp. 138–140; Book II, Chapter XXX

"Of how the Indians used wine before and after the Conquest and the pity felt when they were intoxicated.

"After this New Spain was conquered then all over the Indians began to drink wine and get drunk, both men and women, principal people and peasants, which seems as if the devil hurt of losing these people after the preaching of the Gospel, tried to make them fall in this vice, so they leave to be true Christians. And this happened easily with the great changes taking place after the Spaniards took over this land, and the native lords and ancient judges were intimidated without the authority they previously had in their offices. And because of this it was taken as an universal licence for everybody to drink until they fell down, and each one went after his lust, which never happened at the time of their heathenism. On the contrary these natives condemned inebriation as a great evil and cursed it like it is done among our Spaniards, and punished it with great severity. The use they made of wine in ancient times was with licence of their lords or judges, who only granted it to old men and women over fifty years of age more or less, saying that after that age the blood was getting cold and wine was a remedy to warm up and sleep. And these [older people] drank two or three small cups, or four at the most, and with it they could not get drunk, because in order to get drunk with their wine they had to drink much larger amounts. But with that [wine] of Castile with a little is enough, and all of them men and women like it. At weddings and festivities and other gatherings they could drink at length. The physicians gave their medicines in a cup of wine. It was a very common thing to give after delivery of a child some wine in the first days, not for pleasure, but as something needed. The peasants and workers when they carried wood from the mountains, or when they brought large stones, then some drank more, others less, to get strength and encouragement in their work. Among the Indians there were many who detested wine and did not like to taste either in sickness or in health. The lords and headmen, and the warriors had as a point of honour not to drink wine; their drink was cocoa (which is a dried fruit like almonds they also use as currency, and it is drunk ground and mixed with water) and other beverages made out of ground seeds. And although they were inclined to this vice of drunkenness, they did not drink the wine as freely as nowadays; not out of virtue, but for fear of punishment. The penalty given to drunkards and even to those who started to feel the heat of the wine, singing or shouting was to shave their hair publicly in the square, and then they went to pull down their house, indicating that those behaving like that, were not worth of having a house in the village, not to be among the neighbours, because they made themselves beasts losing their reason and judgement, so they should live in the field like beasts, and they were deprived of every honourable office in the republic. Now the [Indian] governors, mayors and aldermen in the villages, are those with more facilities and power to get drunk every day, because nobody can prevent it, but they get the wine in exchange for labour force. And like this, they cannot reprimand and punish others ..."

In South America pre-Columbian tradition and the chronicles agree that inebriation was a regular feature among the male population. The *chicha* was manufactured daily at home by pouring hot water on ground maize (*Zea mais*) or by a more elaborate process—used by the *ucllas* or virgins to prepare the *chicha* for the Inca rulers—by first chewing the ground corn; in the latter technique the ptyalin in the saliva initiated the degradation of carbohydrates in the grain. After two days' fermentation, boiling and straining, a drink of low alcoholic content was obtained. Years after the Conquest distillation was also introduced into Peru and applied to molasses and wine from local grapes of southern Peru; this distillate from wine is called *pisco*. Cieza de León (1553) had already pointed out that both Chibchas and Incas could hardly talk without having in their hands a *chicha* cup. This trend continued or even increased, despite colonial measures, during the Spanish administration and the reports by Peña y Montenegro (1668) and other writers indicate that the alcoholism of the America Indians was the worst and most extended vice during the colonial period.

Mendieta's honesty cannot be doubted, neither can the reports by other authors about the stiff penalties for inebriation among the Aztecs; but the truth of the matter is that alcoholism indeed existed on a large scale among them, as we can see by reading Sahagún's (c. 1565) long list of the gods of wine, the vivid description of the different types of inebriation among the Aztecs and the reasons for their drinking. What happened after the Conquest was that the Aztecs' penalties for inebriation disappeared and alcoholism became universal.

1938 edition, Vol. I, pp. 51–52; Book I, Chapter XXII

"Chapter XXII. It deals about the god Tezcatzóncatl, who is one of the gods of the wine.

"The wine or *pulque* of this land was always considered evil, due to the bad effects it produces, because some of the drunkards were killed in falls, others hanged themselves, others threw themselves into the water and drowned, others killed another being drunk; and all these effects were attributed to the god of the wine, and not to the drunkard; and they even believed something else, that if somebody spoke evil of this wine or grumbled about it, he was going to suffer some disaster; the same about any drunkard because if someone gossiped about him or insult him, even if the drunkard did a thousand knaveries, they said he was going to be punished, because they said those things were not done by the drunkard, but the god, or better said, the devil in the wine, who was this Tezcatzóncatl, or someone of the others. This Tezcatzóncatl was a relative or brother of the other gods of the wine, ...

'From what it has been said before it is clearly understood that they did not considered sinful whatever they did being drunk, even if they were most grave sins; and it is thought with sound basis that they got drunk to do what they had in mind and not to be blamed for it and be punished ..."

1938 edition, Vol. I, pp. 313–315; Book IV, Chapter V

"Chapter V. Of the different kinds of drunkards.

"They said that the wine is called *centzontotochtin* meaning '400 rabbits' because there are many types of drunkenness. To some drunkard by reason of the constellation under which they were born wine was not damaging or contrary; as soon as they get drunk they fall asleep or become pensive; sitting down and withdrawn, they do not make any trouble or say anything; and other drunkards begin to cry in silence and sob, and tears fall from their eyes, like water springs; and other drunkards soon begin to sing, and they do not want to talk or to listen to jokes, but they only find relief in singing; and other drunkards do not sing, but soon start to talk, and talk to themselves, and to insult others and tell offensive things to others; and talk big of themselves, saying that they are of the most important, honest, and show contempt for others and say offensive words, and get up, and move their head saying they are rich and reprimand others for being poor, and praise themselves, proud and arrogant in their words, they speak loud and rough, moving their legs and kicking; and when they are in their senses they are as if mute and are afraid of everybody and are timid and excuse themselves saying 'I was drunk' and 'I don't know what I said, I was taken by the wine'. And other drunkards suspect the worst, are suspicious, and of bad condition and twist things around, and say false things about their wives, saying that they are bad women, and get angry quickly with anybody talking to their wife, etc.; and if anybody talks, he thinks are gossiping about him; and if anybody laughs, he thinks he is laughing of him, and thus he quarrels with everybody without motive or reason. They do this because they are disturbed by the wine. And if it is woman the one who gets drunk, she soon falls seated on the floor, and legs folded, and sometimes stretches the legs on the floor; and if she is very drunk her hair is all entangled, and she lies there with the hair in a mess, asleep, all the hair in disorder, etc. ... They also had feast for the gods of the wine and ... drank wine from that large earthen jar, because some day they would be captives of their enemies, or they would take captives their enemies in battle; and they went on, enjoying themselves, drinking wine, and the wine was never exhausted because the winekeepers put more wine each time ... and not only did this the innkeepers during the feast, but every day, because such was the custom of the innkeepers"

We obtain a similar picture from South America from Ulloa's report:

Antonio de Ulloa (1716–1795) was one of the great Spanish scientists of the 18th century. Born in Seville, he studied at the Naval Academy in Cadiz and, at only 19, Ulloa was commissioned with Jorge Juan to join the expedition of La Condamine in 1736 to measure one arc of meridian near Quito. At the return of this mission he fell prisoner of the British from 1745 to 1747, but because of his academic merit was then elected to the Royal Society of London. Ulloa occupied very high offices in the Colonial administration of America, at the mercury mines of Huancavélica, Peru, as Governor of Louisiana and Florida, ending his career as Admiral of the Spanish Fleet. With Jorge Juan he published the results of their expedition to South America in 1735–1746, and also other works: his *Secret Instructions about America* were also eventually published. In his *Noticias Americanas* (1772) Ulloa gave an honest but crude description of the extent of alcoholism among the Peruvian natives explaining that after the *chicha* the Indians favoured the use of *aguardiente*, obtained by distillation of local wines at Ica, Pisco and Huasca. His account, based on first-hand observations, presents the true pattern of inebriation and its economic effects upon the labour force in the Colonial period. Ulloa furthermore shows that native mothers were responsible for giving *chicha* to their children and making them addicts from childhood.

1772 edition, pp. 316–320; Chapter XVII

13. "It is universal among these people, the inclination to drunkenness, and they prefer for this purpose the strongest liquors. Those of Peru used *chicha* down to a few years ago, when due to the industry of the landowners of some estates in the lower lands, where vineyards are grown, mainly in the Valleys of Ica, Pisco and Huasca, *aguardiente* has been introduced resulting in the visible annihilation of the Indians. The same inclination has been found among the different Indian nations populating North America from Florida, Mississippi up to the territories further North, where the British of New England on one hand, and the French of Louisiana and Canada on the other have accustomed the Indians to these spirits which have led to their extermination, as it has been found to have diminished noticeably each Indian nation.

14. "The strong tendency they have preserved towards laziness and idleness makes them to fall into extremes in the use of inebriating drinks; they feel so strongly attracted to them, that they break any barriers, and take any risks to satisfy this unbridled passion. In Louisiana has been seen, not just once, the most trusted Indian, and apparently the most reasonable, to kill his master treacherously when going hunting or travelling, just to steal a small flask of *aguardiente*, spirits, which he had noticed, and wait for the attack until his master was asleep, drink the *aguardiente* and leave the empty flask a few steps from the corpse. In the highlands of Peru we frequently find at dawn dead people in the streets, as a result of inebriation, because when they lose consciousness they fall asleep and the ice freezes them. These painful and repeated examples do not intimidate them, neither the continuous advice trying to persuade them to abstain or to take some precaution to avoid the danger. In Quito it was a custom for the Indian women not to drink and to keep company to the husbands to take care of them when the men were unable to stand up because of drunkenness. In Peru the women drink like the men, they get drunk like them and they cannot help each other. What is most singular about this is that the mothers entice their children to drink from the time of nursing, giving them the same drinks and before the children have understanding they become accustomed to inebriation.

15. "It happens with the Indians in this vice what is usual with the rest, that when they start to drink there is not end to it, and keep drinking until they fall down and lose their senses; and if we try to take them away, beside they strongly resist it, they go back to it called by the frenzy of passion. In this, those from one part or the other are true brothers, without distances between countries making much difference. In Huancavélica, due to the large number of Indians

arriving to work the mines, in Potosi, and in other large mines, this problem is very grave; the custom there is to pay them on Sunday the salary of the week, to those who are not *Mitayos* [labour force from other areas] and to these to pay down only half and give them the rest when they complete the *Mita* [contracted time of labour]. This payment is completed about 4 to 5 in the afternoon for the miners, and amounts in Huancavélica to about 10.000 pesos; of these about 4.000 pesos are drunk in *aguardiente* during the rest of the afternoon and the night; from this it results that there is little work done until Monday night because the Indians are unfit for work, and have no money left for the expenses of the week, and pay until the next Sunday the little food they eat during the week. There are Indians who can drink in those short hours up to 7 pesos, which is about twelve to thirteen bottles without showing any signs of immediate damage after inebriation, which shows their resistance. The *chicha* inebriates them after very large quantities, but it did not produce the damages caused by *aguardiente* which should be forbidden like *poison*, considering the need to preserve those people, whose fall in numbers will mean the decline of these kingdoms as they are engaged in all sorts of heavy works, mining, cultivation of land, care of cattle, and others.

16. "If inebriation is damaging to the Indians because it decreases their number, and their need to maintain these kingdoms, it is also damaging for the disasters produced among them, quarrels, arguments, ending in tragedies, fortunately not too extreme because they are not allowed to carry weapons; but blood runs because they hurt each other with stones, clubs, and sometimes with knives. In this way on Sunday which should be kept with the highest reverence and fear of God. The towns are full of people unconscious, others with broken skulls, others hurt all over, and similar results of their lunacy, until tired they fall on the streets to temper with sleep the fury of the spirits.

17. "The deaths caused by the Indians in the North [America] of Whites and Negroes or other Indian nations, even while in peace-time, have not other origin than inebriation. Under intoxication they become infuriated, are inclined to cause harm, and they do not respect or fear anything. Even those who provide the drink must take precautions against their frenzy; this is somehow the way their wars begin among those nations. Because they have the custom of repaying the affront with a similar punishment, the head of the killer will appease the harm to the offended . . . In the commerce and dealings these Indian nations have with the Europeans the main item is *aguardiente* . . ."

THE NEW MEANING OF LIFE

The commitment of the Catholic Church to the spiritual and physical health of the American Indian was a natural development in the practice of the theological virtues—faith, hope and charity—and this made religion the most important cultural factor in the evolution of medicine in Spanish America. The respect and care for human life was, therefore, incorporated with the religious idea of human redemption, and should have influenced the pre-Columbian outlook on life. The rationality of the American Indian, furthermore, embodied the dignity of the individual and implied a basic equality between the sexes, which was intended to lift the relegated status of the woman in pre-Columbian societies. The results of acculturation in these respects were disappointing and nothing expresses the situation better than the story told by Gumilla (1741) in quoting the answer given by an Indian woman to recriminations for allowing her newly born girl to die:

1741 edition, p. 347–349; Part II, Chapter VII

"... I wish, my Father, I wish that when my mother delivered me she had loved me enough and had had pity on me, to free me from so many toils I have suffered until today and I will have to suffer until I die. If my mother had buried me as soon as I was born, I had died, but without feeling death, and in that way I had escaped the death that must come and I had avoided travails more bitter than death. Who knows how many others will I suffer before I die? You, Father, meditate well on the labours a poor Indian woman endures among the Indians: They come with us to the field with their bow and arrows in hand, nothing else; we go with a basket of tools in the back, a child in the breast and another on the basket; they go to shoot a bird or a fish, and we dig and toil in the plot; they come back home in the evening without any load, and us, beside the burden of our children, have to carry the roots to eat, and corn to make their drink; in reaching home they leave to talk with their friends, and we have to get wood, bring water and cook their dinner; after supper they go to sleep, but we have to keep most of the night grinding corn to make their chicha; And where it ends our care? They drink *chicha*, they get drunk and out of their senses they give us blows, grab us by the hair, drag us and step on us. Oh my Father! I wish my mother had buried me as soon as she delivered me! You know well that we have good reason to complain, because everything I said you see it everyday; but our greatest sorrow is something you cannot realize, because you cannot experience it. Do you know, Father, what death is for the poor Indian woman who serves her husband like slave sweating in the field and without sleep at home, that at the end of 20 years, he takes another woman, a girl without judgement? He loves her and even when she beats and punishes our children we cannot speak, because he does not care for us or love us any longer; the girl must order us around and treat us like her servants, and if we talk she makes us to shut up with the stick. How can this be endured? An Indian mother cannot do anything better for a newly born girl than to spare her from these travails, to take her away from this slavery worse than death. I wish, I tell you again, my Father, that my mother had given me a token of her love by burying me as soon as I was born: with that my heart did not have to feel so, nor my eyes so much to cry for . . ."

Suicide continued to be a nightmare for the missionaries because the Indians did not seem to have basically changed their inclination to self-destruction despite the punishment of eternal damnation preached by the Catholic Church for those attempting to take their own lives. The reports during the colonial period are all similar: Landa (1570), and years later Sanchez de Aguilar (1613), indicated how easily the Mayas committed suicide, particularly if they fell ill. Arriaga (1621) mentioned that the Incas frequently hanged themselves after feasts, drinking bouts or just to avoid labour. Even from remote places the observers always gave the same accounts; Rodrigo Ponce de León, writing in 1579 from El Tocuyo, Venezuela, said:

1962 edition, p. 152

"[The Indians] in saying: I wish to die and that the heart aches, they let themselves die. And others, both men and women, they hang themselves for little reason . . ."

Indoctrination was unable to prevent the practices of self-mutilation characterizing the rituals of pre-Columbian religions which found new outlets in the Catholic Church. Long pilgrimages were made under conditions of genuine physical torture, and the Indians arrived to worship at the Shrines of Christ, the Virgin Mary, or the Saints, with bleeding sores on their knees. Exhibitions of self-inflicted wounds which covered the penants with blood became regular features of the Spanish American religious festivities. In the colonial cities, the religious and civil authorities were able to stamp out human sacrifices, but in rural areas they continued to be executed for many years under the eyes of the officials, sometimes by their most trusted native leaders. Tozzer (1941) in his notes to Landa's *Relación de las cosas de Yucatán* (1570) reports the findings of an inquest in 1562 at Mérida, Yucatán, concerning sacrifices executed by members of a powerful Maya family. Because of the illness of Juan Cocom, a descendant from the rulers of Mayapan, and himself formerly *Ah-Kin* or priest of Sotuta, a sacrifice of children was carried out, and months later two more boys were killed by extracting the heart, afterwards throwing their bodies into the *cenote* or sacred well. Bishop Landa's inquest in 1562 also revealed that Juan Cocom and his brother Lorenzo, both baptized, had sacrificed three boys into the *cenote* of Chichen Itzá, and that Lorenzo, who was the *Halac Uinic* or headman of Sotuta, had crucified two girls, and after extracting their hearts, he had thrown their bodies into the *cenote* according to the ancient pre-Columbian ritual. When Lorenzo Cocom was found guilty he hanged himself in the traditional manner of pre-Columbian suicide. Examples like these can be found all through the Colonial period and the deep-rooted emotional significance of the sacrifice by extraction of the heart, not only in the former Aztec and Maya areas, but in the Chibcha as well, are clearly manifested by their existence even today. Acosta Saignes (1950) has reported sacrifices by extraction of the heart executed by Motilones Indians on white explorers as recently as 1947. Vicarious sacrifices of animals by extracting their hearts, and the offerings of *pulque*, or *chicha* and other presents to the Catholic images prolonged the pre-Columbian rites, and so did many dances and ceremonies.

During the Conquest there were several instances in the campaigns of Mexico, Nueva Granada and the Guaranís narrated by Cieza de León (1553) and Cabeza de Vaca (1555) when the Indians allied to the Spaniards committed anthropophagy by eating the bodies of their enemies. Motolinía (1542) mentioned that anthropophagy kept taking place many years after the Conquest of Mexico in circumstances the Spaniards could hardly prevent.

1969 edition, p. 20; Chapter 11

   "... After the Spaniards waged the war, and Mexico was won and the land was pacified, the Indians friendly to the Spaniards many times ate those [Indians] they killed, because not in every instance the Spaniards could forbid it, and sometimes because of the need they had of the Indians, they tolerated it, although they hate it ..."

Even the pre-Columbian practice of capturing prisoners and eating them after fattening at the celebration of certain pagan festivities kept occurring in certain areas far into the Colonial period, the victims being in most cases Spaniards. Fr. Alonso Ponce, a missionary among the Maya Indians in the Lacandon area, gave in 1588 an account of these events, which was quoted by Fr. Antonio de Ciudad Real (1827).

1872 edition, pp. 57–58

   "... That year 1586, some of these [Lacandon Indians] set out for the mainland with their arms which are bow and arrows and they passed one night in a farm of a Spaniard, a man of Chiapas and having killed a negro who defended himself, they carried as captives nineteen persons, young and old, and placed them on their island where they were fed and fattened as if they were pigs in order to offer them one by one for sacrifice to the demon in their feasts and rituals ..."

As Cervantes de Salazar (1562) put it, a display of violence and cruelty seemed to mark the behaviour of the natives. Parties or festivities which began in the most friendly manner usually ended in homicides even within close family circles, and it would be difficult to single out events or to quote references, because they permeated the daily life of the Indians everywhere in the Continent. The *mitotes* or Indian feasts became synonyms of joyful gatherings developing into quarrels and having a tragic end.

CHAPTER VII

THE PRE-COLUMBIAN INHERITANCE

THE ARCHAEOLOGICAL EVIDENCE

The testimony of the chroniclers on pre-Columbian behaviour has often been claimed to be biased, and this has been shown to be the case in many instances; but the information provided by the archaeological specimens can always be trusted as genuine, accurate and unbiased. It is of limited use when referring to psychothropic drugs, for instance hallucinogenic mushrooms, and gives little help in the interpretation of the human attitude towards life and death, but it does have considerable value in the assessment of sexual aberrations.

Fernandez de Oviedo (1535) described a sodomitic jewel in gold, about 150 g in weight, destroyed by him at Santa Marta, and although no other sodomitic jewel has been recorded, there are still in existence certain gold and alloy jewels with erotic motifs, such as the Peruvian *Orejón* [big ears] at the Museum of Ethnography, Geneva. The Anonymous Conquistador (1519) and Díaz del Castillo (1632) described sodomitic statues and other stone works observed during their early expeditions into Mexico, which in part found later archaeological confirmation in the Maya area. Pictographic or hieroglyphic representations in the great Mexican and Mayan codices failed to depict sexual aberrations, although it has been pointed out (Guerra, 1967) that in the Codex Magliabecchi are depicted various hallucinogenic drugs, the use of *pulque,* and sacrificial rituals. The latter are also frequently found in other pre-Columbian codices. As in other civilizations, clay is the material which has provided not only qualitative, but also quantitative data for the study of the sexual aberrations occurring in pre-Columbian America. Middle America was free from sodomitic representations, and in our limited experience, even erotic pottery in the Maya and in the Mexican area is exceedingly rare. But, on the other hand, South America was rich in domestic ware portraying sexual aberrations in practically all the classic Peruvian civilizations, from the Virú in the Formative era to the Chimú in the Imperial era, which preceded the Inca conquest. The specimens began to appear about

500 B.C. in some Virú finds, they continued from the first century A.D. with the beautiful white and red ware of the Mochica period, and from about A.D. 700 with the more severe Nazca pieces, ending after A.D. 1200 with the dark grey clays of the Chimú period. The most common articles of pottery were drinking vessels of the spout-and-bridge type 15–30 cm in height.

Repositories allowing quantitative data on pre-Columbian sexual aberrations include the Rafael Larco Herrera private museum at Lima—which represents by far the largest collection—the National Museum, Lima, the Museum of the Banco Nacional Quito, and in the United States of America the specimens at the Art Institute, Chicago, are particularly interesting. Some of them have been examined by me personally (1957–1970), but for a quantitative survey it is more convenient to refer this analysis to already published material, such as the monograph by Larco Hoyle (1965) whose specimens can readily be assessed. Most of the illustrations in Larco Hoyle's monograph belong to pieces from the private collection made by his father, the late Rafael Larco Herrera (1872–1956), a Peruvian economist and archaeologist who gathered a great part of that ware from the tenants of his large sugar estates at El Chiclín near Trujillo in northern Peru, an area where the Virú, the Mochica and the Chimú civilizations flourished between A.D. 100 and 1200. This pottery represents remnants of huge numbers of *huacas* which survived the systematic destruction by missionaries, particularly that carried out early in the 17th century. The archaeological specimens reproduced by Larco Hoyle (1965) fall within the following categories: 24% erotic representations of the human penis; 4% erotic vessels representing the human vulva; 11% representations of normal coitus; 5% figures showing male masturbation; 31% heterosexual sodomy or anal coitus between man and woman; 3% homosexual sodomy between men; 1% homosexual relations between women; 14% oral copulation or *fellatio*; 6% bestiality or coitus between human and animal. The erotic representations of the penis (24%) which, by the way, has only been examined once by me in pottery of western Mexico, mostly consist of drinking vessels. The user is forced to drink from the penis, every time executing the action of *fellatio* or oral copulation, and to make it unavoidable some vessels have perforated holes all around the other opening used for filling up the vessel. If the user tries to drink from that end avoiding the penis, the liquid—water or *chicha*—will emerge through the holes and pour out all over, wetting the person drinking, without reaching his mouth. In some erotic vessels the drinking opening represents a woman's vulva (3%) and the user has to execute the action of *cunnilingus* for drinking. There are two vessels with two openings, one at the end of a neck shaped as a penis, the other at the base of the penis reproducing a human vulva; this vessel gave the user the choice between drinking through *fellatio* or *cunnilingus*. In another vessel shaped as a woman and with a double bottom, the fluid enters the woman's body through the vulva. When the upper part is emptied the

FIG. 18. Chimú drinking vessel with heterosexual sodomy. British Museum, London.

FIG. 17. Mochica drinking vessel with heterosexual sodomy. Art Institute of Chicago.

Fig. 19. Mochica drinking vessel with heterosexual sodomy. Art Institute of Chicago.

Fig. 20. Chimú drinking vessel with homosexual sodomy. British Museum, London.

Fig. 21. Maya god of death, Ah Puch, outlined from *Codex Dresden*, section 11.

Fig. 22. Maya goddess of suicide, Ixtab, outlined from *Codex Dresden*, section 53.

Fig. 24. Inca physicians for dreams by F. Huamán Poma, 1610, p. 179.

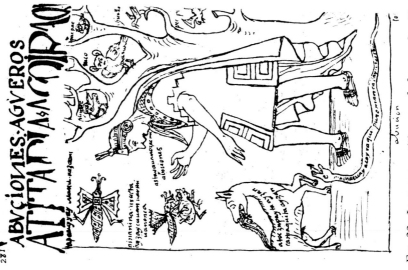

Fig. 23. Inca superstitions and dreams by F. Huamán Poma, 1610, p. 281.

remaining liquid can only be drunk if the user rubs the vulva with the tongue and executes actual *cunnilingus*. The specimens of normal coitus (11%) represent copulation in a lying down position with the male on top (7%), and others with both partners in a sitting position (4%). In one of the specimens a cylindrical instrument protrudes from the woman's vulva which cannot be considered a case of gynaecological malformation or descending vagina, but must be an artefact to reduce the size of the vagina aimed at constricting the male penis, or increasing its friction. Masturbation (5%) appears in the specimens executed by the man himself or by a woman; in one of the specimens she appears to be a mature woman while the male is clearly a boy; in another instance the woman masturbates a representation of death. One mutilated group shows a most realistic digital stimulation of the vagina in a woman by a castrated man, although the active party could also be described as a woman engaged in a Lesbian practice. Sodomy, represented as anal coitus between man and woman (31%), constitutes the most frequent aberration; and in 14% of the specimens the woman is facing downwards on all fours with the man behind in a kneeling or squatting position. In 12% of the cases both partners are performing coitus against nature in a reclining sideways position. In two of these cases the anal coitus is being performed while the woman is suckling a baby, or has a baby by her side and she appears with a passive and dispassionate face. Homosexual sodomy (3%) is clearly portrayed in two specimens; in another the sex of the passive partner could be left in doubt. The active man is kneeling or squatting while the passive sodomite is facing downwards; in another case the active sodomite stands behind the passive partner. Oral copulation or *fellatio* (14%) is the second largest type of aberration represented and the man is clearly portrayed introducing a larger than nature penis into the mouth of his partner. In 8% of the cases the man is in a reclining position, in 3% he is sitting down and in another 3% he is standing. The partners of the men are clearly women kneeling or in reclining positions (12%), but in two cases the partner could be identified as another man. In one group it is not clear whether the man is introducing his penis into the mouth of an animal or a human being. There are no representations of *cunnilingus* where friction of the woman's vulva is performed by the tongue of her partner, but there are 4 specimens where man and woman are engaged in sexual stimulation of the erotic areas of the mouth and the tongue of the man protrudes lasciviously to caress the woman's lips. The curious thing is that the man in three of the four cases shows mutilation of nose and lips. There are finally the specimens reproducing acts of bestiality (6%); one of them shows a man having sexual intercourse with a large mammal, the others are of women having intercourse with animals. In one case the male copulating with the woman is a jaguar; in another a dog and the woman has opened her thighs wide, offering her vulva to the animal; the rest are of women engaged in sexual intercourse with cormorants, and in one of them the bird can be clearly seen to be impregnating the woman with seminal fluid.

Most Peruvian historians have recorded that the pre-Columbian cultures used to bury their dead with household ware of daily use—jewellery, clothing, also food and drink, and even servants or wives. This funeral custom was far from unique, because at approximately similar dates it can also be found in China. This comparative examination is important in explaining the true nature of the pottery portraying sexual aberrations in the Peruvian *huacas*. The *Ming-chi*, or Chinese spirit objects buried with the deceased, provided after-death facsimiles of all the things he loved or was inclined towards, so that his spirit could be provided for in a permanent way. Those funeral ceramics—horses, musicians, *lokapalas* or guards, and the like—reached their most elaborate perfection during the T'ang Dynasty, A.D. 618–906, which corresponds with the summit of the Mochica civilization. It is reasonable to accept that the pottery depicting sexual aberrations in the Peruvian *huacas* reflects the customs and living practices of the Mochica and the Chimú civilizations. The interpretations advanced by Larco Hoyle (1965), that they are moralizing specimens, does not seem to agree with the facts, particularly when he states that the pottery showing sodomy, where the man has the nose and lips mutilated and in some instances is even castrated, indicated the punishment for sexual offenders. The archaeologists have regrettably missed the accounts of Gutierrez de Santa Clara (1580) and Valera (1590) which reported that nose and lip mutilations, and in some cases castration, were ritualistic operations undergone by the priests who took care of the *ucllas*, or virgins at the temple of the Sun. This fact also leaves without support the idea that nose and lip mutilation, frequently found in effigies of normal pottery, were the sequels of *uta* or cutaneous leishmaniasis. Evidence has also been presented from several chronicles indicating that in some cases these priests were punished because of homosexual sodomy, and more frequently because they had heterosexual intercourse with the virgins in the temples. Sodomy could be committed with them without loss of virginity which was of paramount importance in their office as maids of the Sun.

There is one fact made brutally clear by the archaelogical evidence, which was never reported in the chronicles; the sexual aberrations of pre-Columbian cultures in Peru were not restricted to homosexual sodomy, but included every type of erotic variation. If, for instance, Larco Hoyle's monograph (1965) could be accepted as a random population and the number of cases (100+) as sufficiently representative of the ancient Peruvian civilizations, normal coitus appears among them as a very neglected sexual custom when compared to sodomy or *fellatio*. Nothing can be found among the archaeological specimens of Middle America comparable in sexual perversion to ancient Peru; the closest resemblance to the amatory Mochica groups is perhaps seen in certain Maya figurines occurring from the third to the ninth century at Jaima—whistles with an effigy of an old priest caressing a maid. The celebrated erotic sculptures outside the temples of Khajuraho, India, carved between A.D. 950 and 1050, later Japanese erotica or the sensual mosaics and paintings of Rome in our own era, seem like naïve Victorian illustrations when compared with the Mochica pottery. This ware, manufactured during a span of over 1000 years by successive civilizations of pre-Columbian Peru, confirms the practice of every possible type of sexual aberration to an extent never recorded in the history of civilization.

In Middle America the archaeological evidence is a silent witness denouncing cruel funeral rites involving human sacrifices. The memories of the *huetzompan* or skull pyramid in ancient Tenochtitlian, now Mexico City, where tens of thousands of skulls from victims were counted, find confirmatory evidence in the religious capital of Teotihuacan, and in the archaeological excavations at Azcapotzalco, Xolalpan and other sites. Hundreds of burials have been found with the skeleton of the deceased in a sitting position surrounded by pottery vessels and clay idols; this is also the way funeral scenes were depicted in some Mexican codices, showing the deceased tied up into a bundle and in a squatting position. In the archaeological sites, around the skeletons of the deceased can be found shallow dishes cut from the top of skulls, or large cooking bowls containing remnants of sacrificial banquets celebrating the farewell funeral party. Vaillant (1941) has described the upper parts of the legs and hips as the most succulent portions for festive consumption, a fact also recorded in several codices, particularly the Codex Magliabecchi.

THE RECORD AGAINST RATIONALITY

While archaeological finds have revealed many pre-Columbian sexual aberrations of a kind never mentioned in the chronicles, these were indeed discussed for over three centuries as the main issues upon which theologians have reasoned the rationality of the American Indian ever since the discovery of the New World. A brief recollection of the main behavioural blemishes alleged to have affected the pre-Columbian mind, as they were examined by Vitoria (1537), and the evidence gathered in the long but necessary anthology of primary sources, will provide a much clearer assessment of the problem.

ANTHROPOPHAGY

The earliest author to report that the American Indians ate human flesh was Alvarez Chanca (1494) referring to the Caribs, from whom cannibalism took its name, and this was followed by the account of Anghiera (1511). The extent of anthropophagy in South America was recorded by Ortiz (1525) and Fernandez de Oviedo (1526) for the northern coast, and Cieza de León (1552), Benzoni (1565), Escobar (1567) and Lopez de Velasco (1574) for the Chibcha area down to the Inca territory, which seems to have been free of this depravity. Deep inland, cannibalism among the Tupí-Guaraní was initially described by Nobrega (1552) and Cabeza de Vaca (1555), followed by other writers. In the Aztec area Cortés (1522) was the first to mention anthropophagy, followed by Motolinia (1541), Lopez de Gómara (1552), Sahagún (1565), who like Motolinia produced a detailed calendar of ritual cannibalism, depicted in the Codex Magliabecchi (1565), besides further records by Diaz del Castillo (1568), Lopez Medel (1569), Herrera (1601) and many more. The Maya area had few records of anthropophagy but for those of Landa (1570), Coronel (1588), Herrera (1601) and Lopez Cogolludo (1688).

HUMAN SACRIFICES

The sacrifices of human beings as part of religious ceremonies, followed or not by cannibalism, were very frequently reported. Among the Aztecs these sacrifices were described by Cortés (1522), Motolinia (1541), Lopez de Gómara (1552), Sahagún (1565), Durán (1581) and many more, giving in some instances detailed descriptions of their cruelty. Among the Maya sacrifices were reported by Landa (1570) and Lopez Cogulludo (1688). The Inca, however, were less inclined to religious human sacrifices, although they were described by Bandera (1557), Polo (1559) and a few others. For the Chibcha area the best description of ritual sacrifices was given by Fernandez de Piedrahita (1688).

SUICIDE

Customary suicide by poisoning with *yuca* sap was reported by Fernandez de Oviedo (1526); and Lopez de Gómara (1552) and Benzoni (1565) described the frequency of suicide by self-inflicted wounds in South America. Landa (1570) was the first to mention the religious basis of suicide by hanging among the Mayas, also recorded by Sanchez de Aguilar (1639) and Lopez de Cogolludo (1688). The suicide among the Chibcha by hanging from the hair appears in Benzoni's account (1565). Arriaga (1621) described in detail the suicide by hanging among the Incas.

DRUG ADDICTION

The earliest report on drugs producing hallucinations came from Columbus (1493) referring to the snuff *cohoba*, afterwards also described by Pané (1496) and Anghiera (1511); it was confused by Fernandez de Oviedo (1526) with tobacco, but rightly identified by Las Casas (1542), Lopez de Gómara (1552), Gumilla (1741) and others. The use of *coca* was first mentioned by Vespucci (1505), followed by Fernandez de Oviedo (1535) and many Peruvian historians, with excellent accounts by Acosta (1590), Oliva (1631), Cobo (1642) and Fernandez de Piedrahita (1688). In Mexico there were many drugs affecting behaviour and producing hallucinations— *teonanacatl, peyotl, ololiuhqui, toloache*—described in the Codex Magliabecchi (1565), and by Sahagún (1565), Muñoz Camargo (1576), Hernandez (1577), Durán (1581), Cárdenas (1591) and Ruiz de Alarcón (1629).

ALCOHOLISM

The existence of alcoholism as a social vice among the Aztecs was denied by all sources, but alcoholic inebriation from *octli* or *pulque* was prevalent in the periphery of the Mexican area according to the Anonymous Conquistador (1520), Castañeda (1565) and others. The problem of pre-Columbian alcoholism among the Aztecs is still an unsolved question because of the consistent reports of customary inebriation since the brief of Queen Isabel (1529), the accounts by Motolinia (1541), Lopez de Gómara (1552), Ruiz de Alarcón (1629) and even Clavigero (1779). In the Chibcha and the Inca areas, where *chicha* was consumed, all the sources (Ortiz, 1525; Cieza de León, 1553; Benzoni, 1565; Peña, 1668, and the rest) confirmed extensive alcoholism during the pre-Columbian period.

SODOMY

Homosexual sodomy in the Caribbean was reported by Alvarez Chanca (1494), Fernandez de Oviedo (1526), whose writings set the problem in the continental context, and was debated by las Casas (1542). In the Aztec area it was recorded by the Anonymous Conquistador (1520), Cortés (1522), Cabeza de Vaca (1542), Codex Quauhtinchan (1545), Lopez de Gómara (1552), Codex Chimalpopoca (1558), Cervantes de Salazar (1562), Castañeda (1565), Sahagún (1565), Díaz del Castillo (1568), Lopez Medel (1569), Alva Ixtlilxochitl (1605) and Torquemada (1615). Several writers denied it and mentioned penalties for those committing sodomy; these include Zorita (1575), Muñoz Camargo (1576), Vetancurt (1698) and Clavigero (1779). The earliest report on sodomy among the Maya was made by las Casas (1542), and it was recorded by Lopez de Cogolludo (1688), but denied by Landa (1570). The accounts of homosexual sodomy in Darien, the Chibcha area and the territory under Inca dominion were much more consistent and began with Anghiera (1516), Ortiz (1525) Fernandez de Oviedo (1526), Lopez de Gómara (1552), Cieza de León (1553), Zárate (1555), Lopez de Velasco (1572), Gutierrez de Santa Clara (1580), García (1607), Garcilasso (1609), Lizárraga (1611), Santa Cruz (1613), Ramos (1621), Salinas (1630), Oliva (1631), Calancha (1638), Montesinos (1644), Peña (1668) and de Pauw (1768). Heterosexual sodomy was well described by Fernandez de Oviedo (1526) and Lopez de Gómara (1552). The reports of sodomy by Fernandez de Oviedo (1526), Cabeza de Vaca (1542), even by las Casas (1542), and those by Lopez de Gómara (1552), Herrera (1601) and Torquemada (1615) have special relevance because they mention the existence of *bardajes*.

BESTIALITY

Sexual relations between human beings and animals were first reported by Cieza de León (1553) in ancient Peru, and discussed at length at the Lima Concilium 1583; afterwards they are mentioned not only in the Manuals of Confession for South American Indians, but in those for Central America as well.

INCEST

The problems of incestuous concubinage and marriage was initially discussed by Vitoria (1537), arising from oral reports from missionaries. Incest was mainly reported in South America and was described by Cieza de León (1553), Benzoni (1565), Escobar (1567), Toledo (1570), and dealt with at the Lima Concilium (1583). Of course Garcilasso (1609), like Herrera (1601), explained the dynastic incest of the Inca rulers on religious grounds. But incestuous intercourse was frequently found among the Chibcha and also reported by Vasconcellos (1663) among the Tupí. It was not widespread among the Mexicans and the Mayas, although it was described in the Codex Chimalpopoca (1558), by Castañeda (1565) and by several writers of the Colonial period, including Vetancurt (1698).

ADULTERY

Without exception all pre-Columbian civilizations regarded the wife's adultery as a most serious offence. The Chibcha and the Inca, according to Cieza de León (1553), cared little for prenuptial virginity, although this did not seem to be the case among the Aztecs. However, once the marriage took place the infidelity of the wife was punished by death.

PROSTITUTION

This appears to be a marginal problem among the sexual drives in pre-Columbian America, but it did not fail to be reported in the chronicles. Lopez de Gómara (1552) first mentioned public whores in Nicaragua who charged ten cocoa beans for their services. Castañeda (1565) described the ceremony used in Culiacan for those women initiated into the "oldest profession". Sahagún (1565) left an excellent description of the prostitutes in ancient Mexico, and years later Vetancurt (1698) mentioned their status. Herrera (1601) gathered the earliest reports on prostitution from Central America, and both Valera (1590) and Huaman (1610) recorded that they were accepted among the Incas as a necessary evil and permitted to attend feasts and drinking bouts. Lopez de Gómara (1552) also mentioned the existence of brothels of *putos* or sodomites in Darien and in Pánuco, where previously the Anonymous Conquistador (1520) had reported extensive sodomy.

A FINAL ASSESSMENT

In reaching a historical judgement on the pre-Columbian mind care has been taken to analyse texts that are devoid of corruption, presenting in their original versions the ideas of the authors, and to point out whether they narrated the truth as they saw it or whether their chronicles were biased. Some accounts were written as the spiritual world of the Indian was unfolding during the Conquest; in other cases the narratives are dated well into the Colonial period, but nevertheless their observation are pristine as those of the Discovery because they referred to native communities unaffected by alien cultural trends. Some key issues about abnormal behaviour were bitterly contested, but beneath the controversy the existence of aberration became apparent. A comprehensive analysis of the testimonies regarding behavioural patterns in pre-Columbian America indicates that:

(a) *Human sacrifices* were carried out among the Aztecs, the Mayas, the Chibcha and minor civilizations mostly in religious ceremonies, but they were very limited among the Incas.

(b) *Anthropophagy* was customary among the Caribs, the Chibchas, the Tupís, the Guaranís, and other groups; it had religious connotations among the Mayas, and reached its summit among the Aztecs; it does not seem to have existed among the Incas.

(c) *Suicide* was very common in the Antilles and among the South American civilizations, particularly the Incas, it was less recorded among the Aztecs, but very frequent and with deep religious roots among the Mayas.

(d) *Drug addiction:* to snuffs was common in the Antilles and northern South America; to coca chewing in the Chibcha and the Inca area; the Mayas were less inclined to drugs, and the Aztecs used a variety of hallucinogenic drugs in association with religious practices.

(e) *Alcoholism* of *chicha* was deeply established in all civilizations of South America, particularly Chibchas and Incas. The Aztecs imposed strict control on inebriation, but alcoholism of *octli* in the marginal Mexican civilizations and *balché* among the Mayas was common.

(f) *Incest* was frequent in the Chibcha area, less among the Incas, the Mayas and the Aztecs, and customary to a certain degree among the Tupí, Guaraní, and other groups.

(g) *Homosexual sodomy* occurred all over America with a high incidence; the passive sodomite *bardaje* was institutionalized in the Antilles, and among the Aztecs, the Mayas, the Chibchas and the Incas.

(h) *Heterosexual sodomy* was frequent in the Antilles, and among the Incas, but less frequently observed in Central America.

(i) *Bestiality* and other sexual aberrations were frequent among the Incas, but not recorded among the Aztecs or Mayas.

The overall perspective of pre-Columbian aberrant behaviour, as judged by Old World standards, justified the charges of irrationality brought against the American Indian on legal, religious and biological grounds.

THE EVILS OF ACCULTURATION

There are no human societies that are fundamentally good, but neither is any of them fundamentally bad, as Levi-Strauss (1961) has pointed out, because, it might be added, our judgement about them can change according to the side from which we make the observation. The Spaniards might have considered many pre-Columbian trends as aberrant, but the Aztecs in turn could find aberrant the Spanish trend towards usury, and similar charges could be made by the Incas in respect of theft and

idleness which were abhorred in their society. Nevertheless, it would be
difficult to contest that any of the pre-Columbian civilizations was more
humane, or better developed than the Christian civilization introduced
into America by the Spaniards. However, it could be argued that the
transfer of a more advanced or even a more humane culture into a less
advanced civilization, such as the pre-Columbian societies, did not bring
about in the New World higher moral standards, better individuals, or
happier communities. Concerned about a similar problem, Soustelle
(1967) has complained about the vanishing way of life of the Lacandon
Indians, who, let us remember, practised cannibalism far into the Colonial
period. It would hardly be expected that the Spaniards after the Discovery, or nations today trying to conquer jungles and deserts should
halt their progress in order to preserve aboriginal groups in their primitive
condition for the benefit of the ethnologist. However, the process of
acculturation of the pre-Columbian mind offers sobering lessons which
in part justify the apprehensions of the ethnologists. Several Conquistadors and missionaries—accepted as honest and intelligent observers—
began to notice that the eradication from the pre-Columbian mind of the
blemishes considered by the Spaniards to be aberrations, progressively
led to the moral collapse of the American Indian. The observers were
candid enough to blame themselves—the Spaniards—for providing the
examples of moral corruption which the American natives eagerly followed; but the true psychological reasons for the behavioural changes in
the Indians had much deeper and more tortuous roots. A selection of
references from diverse areas and at different times will illustrate the
situation. Mendieta (1596), following the advance of the Christian indoctrination in Mexico, had this to say about the acculturation of the Aztecs:

1870 edition, p. 501; Book IV, Chapter XXXIII

"Chapter XXXIII. Of the many damages caused to the Christianity of
the Indians by the frequent intercourse with the Spaniards.

"So many inconveniences have followed, and damages grown among
the Indians in the way of their Christianity, by being mixed with the
Spaniards, that I do not know who could suffice to give an account...
The Indians were weak and sinners (as we all are), but they had a
manner of hypocrisy or prudence, which they did not want to be held
for such, either for fear, or shame, or for whatever reason they only
knew. And because of this, when they committed some evil or sin, they
never trusted anybody they knew, neither friend, nor even their father,
as it is usually said. And now they have learnt, not only to sin without
fear and shame, but to join into gangs...for their bad deeds...the
Indian, if he robbed, he was a petty thief (I meant after being Christian,
because in their heathenism very few dare to steal); but afterwards,
they have dared with the example of the Spaniards and those other
people they are becoming as good thiefs as they can be found...One
of the worst evils done by the company the Spaniards keep with the

Indians is with the wine, because they being inclined to drink it, it is a sort of lure and procurer for the Spaniards to do anything they want with their persons and properties ... If we deal with the bad habits of words and the vices of language, it is true that one of the things the Indians lacked was this, that they did not know what it was to swear, or to curse, or to send to the devil, and as among the old Christians and particularly among women, goes this language so dissolute, they are being contaminated, which is a pity to hear it ..."

In Tierra Firme, scarcely a generation after the Conquest, Fernandez de Oviedo (1851 edition, Book XXV, Chapter XXII) narrated an anecdote about the Bishop of Coro, Rodrigo de Bastidas (1460–1526), from which the words quoted from the Indian seem to have been repeated afterwards again and again. When Bishop Bastidas reprimanded an Indian for his lewdness, and for being a liar asking him: "Tell me, you scoundrel, why do you do these things?" The Indian with great composure calmly replied: "Don't you see Sir, that I am becoming a Christian?" Zorita (1575) recalled that the Mexican Indians severely punished liars and they even split the lip of a person given to falsehood. When he asked the Indians why were they lying so frequently, they replied that they had learned it from the Spaniards. As there was no longer any punishment for it, and they feared the Spaniards, (Zorita continues to say), they always tried to say the thing that would please and not the truth. In Yucatán Chi (1582), after mentioning the deterioration of social behaviour among the Mayas, reminded Bishop Landa that before the introduction of Christianity they all faithfully kept their word, but after they were taught the meaning of an oath, the Indians perjured themselves despite the preaching and the menace of hell. Remesal (1619) referring also to the Maya and the Zapotec Indians presented a similar view of the results of acculturation:

1619 edition, p. 302; Book VI, Chapter VII

"... Because they did not lose any of their ancient vices, particularly lust, but they acquired some of those from the Christians as well, which they did not consider faults, and he who before baptism did not rob, swear, kill, lie or take away women, if he did such things after baptism, he said: I am becoming a bit Christian ..."

Ricard (1933) has noticed that Sahagún—considered to be the most reliable witness of the evangelization of New Spain—pronounced a severe judgement which amounted to a condemnation of the acculturation process, because he doubted that idolatry had been eradicated, and he believed that after half a century of intensive missionary work pagan practices and beliefs kept re-appearing and multiplying in secret. Motolinía held similar views, although Valadés (1579) refuted the opinion that the acceptance of the Christian way of life by the Mexican Indians was no more genuine than that of the *Moriscos* of Granada. Even before the close of the Colonial period, European travellers began to point out that the Christian acculturation of the pre-Columbian mind with all its moral and spiritual values had failed to reach the necessary depth to produce a change in behavioural patterns, and this idea gained general acceptance by the middle of the 19th century. Alexander von Humboldt (1769–1859) writing (1811) after his visit to Mexico made very harsh judgements about the Indian population, and predicted the cruelty of social and religious struggles to come.

1811 edition, Vol. I, p. 409–411; Book II, Chapter VI

"... the introduction of Christianity had no other effect upon the Indians of Mexico than to substitute new ceremonies, symbols of a gentle and humane religion, for the rites of a sanguinary cult ...

"It is not a dogma; but only a ceremonial that has left its place for another ..."

1811 edition, Vol. I, pp. 413–414; Book II, Chapter VI

"I know of no race of men who appear more destitute of imagination [than the Indians of Mexico]. When an Indian attains a certain degree of civilization he displays a great facility of apprehension, a judicious mind, a natural logic and a particular disposition to subtilize or seize the finest differences in the comparison of objects. He reasons coolly and orderly, but he never manifests that versatility of imagination, that glow of sentiment, and that creative and animating art which charac-terize the nations of the South of Europe and several tribes of African negroes ...

"The families [of Indians] who enjoy the hereditary rights of *cacicasgo* [administrative power] far from protecting the tributary caste of Indians, more frequently abuse their power and influence ... they not only delight in becoming the instruments of the oppressions of the whites, but they also make use of their power and authority to exort small sums for their own advantage ...

"These very stupid, indolent Indians who suffer themselves patiently to be lashed at the church doors appear cunning, active, impetuous, and cruel, whenever they act in a body in popular disturbances ..."

It took some years after the 1821 independence from Spain for the new Spanish American nations to open their lands to foreign observers. Some of these were Protestant missionaries who were too keen to find as many faults in the work of the Catholic church as in the native religions. One of the earliest travellers was Charles Joseph Latrobe (1801–1895), later British governor of Australia, who after his visit to Mexico questioned (1836) its cultural and religious changes:

1836 edition, pp. 164–167

"And this is Christianity? ... The detestable character of the ignorant idolatry in exercise among the ancient race needs no demonstration; yet at the present day, with the exception of the single item of human sacrifice as a part of the religious system, it may well be asked, by what has it been supplanted—fewer and more dignified divinities? less disgusting ignorance? purer rites? a less degrading superstition? a better system of morality?—who will dare to assert it? As to the charge of the inhuman rites and the bloody festivals of the later generations of the Aztecs, the magnitude of which, as asserted by the Roman Catholic historians, is almost incredible, no one offers to palliate them... A change of names—a change of form and garb for the idols—new symbols—altered ceremonials—another race of priests—so much and no more has been effected for the Indians.

"The change was easily made. The ancient superstition abounded with facts, feasts and penances; so did the new. The whole system of the aboriginal hierarchy bears a striking resemblance to that which took place under the domination of Spain. Even the monk found that his vocation excited no surprise; the existence of regular orders of celibates of both sexes whose lives were devoted to the service of certain amongst their gods, seems indisputable.

"With the Indians, Teotl the unknown God 'He by whom we live', as he was termed, he whom they never represented in idol form is still the supreme being under the name of God. They continued to adore the god Quetzalcoatl, the feathered serpent, under the name of St. Thomas. It is indifferent to them whether the spirit is called the devil or Tlacatecolotl. They retain their superstitions, their talismans, their charms, and as they were priest-led under the old system, so they are kept in adherence to the church of Rome by the continual bustle of festivals and ceremonials and processions of the church. But, as to change of heart and purpose, a knowledge of the true God as a spirit who is worshipped in spirit and in truth; a sense of their degraded and fallen state as men and an acquaintance with the truth of the gospel; its application to their individual state and its influence upon their lives and characters, they are as blind and as ignorant as their forefathers..."

The German naturalist Carl C. Sartorius (1796–1872), who also travelled through Mexico during the middle of the 19th century, searched with the eyes of the ethnologist into the meaning of Catholic ceremonies among the Mexican Indians and repeated in his book (1855) what earlier Colonial writers, such as Acosta (1590), León (1611) and Torquemada (1615) had made quite clear. Sartorius mentioned in particular the persistence of the ritual of human sacrifice behind the feasts of Corpus Christi and the All Saints and All Souls.

1859 edition, pp. 160–164

"... that which is most singular and a relic of ancient times, which the Christian priests have permitted to be continued as a harmless amusement, is the sacrifice of sylvan beasts which the Indians offer to the divinity as their ancestors offered to Quetzalcoatl and to Tlaloc...

"This innocent gratification may well be conceded to the child of nature. The Indian generally, and more particularly, the inhabitants of ancient Anahuac, exhibit in their lives many traces of the primeval nature worship of the Toltecs, to whom subsequent generations owed this civilization and religion. Mountains and springs, he still conceives as tenanted by tutelary genii; the goddess of the clouds still draws her nets over the sky to fertilize the earth... His love for flowers... was not taught by the Spaniards, nor is it accidental; but since many centuries interwoven with his life, and derived from another race than that of the Aztecs with their bloody rites... Another festival which is kept by the whole people, but which is of peculiar significance for the Indians, is that of All Saints and All Souls... with the Mexicans the festivals of All Souls received a national colouring, dating from the aborigines, but gradually adopted by the mestizos and even by the creoles... The ancient Aztecs held an annual festival in honour of the dead and offered the departed dead, sacrifices. The Christian priests suffered these rites to be combined with those of All Souls and thus the heathen, probably Toltec custom has maintained itself until the present day..."

The comments made by Edward B. Tylor (1832–1917), the British archaeologist whose book on Mexico (1861) has rightly been considered the foundation stone of modern American archaeology, have particular significance because Tylor was an excellent observer with a deep respect for facts.

1861 edition, pp. 289–290

"... As it is, I cannot ascertain that Christianity has produced any improvement in the Mexican people. They no longer sacrifice and eat their enemies, it is true, but against this we must debit them with a great increase of dishonesty and general immorality which pretty well square the account...

"Practically, there is not much difference between the old heathenism and the new Christianity. We may put dogmas out of the question. They hear them and believe them devoutly and do not understand them in the least. They had just received the Immaculate Conception, as they had received many mysteries before it; and were not a little delighted to have a new occasion for decorating themselves and their churches with flowers, marching in processions, dancing, beating drums and letting off rockets as their custom is. The real essence of both religions is the same to them. They had gods, to whom they built temples and in whose honour they gave offerings, maintained priests, danced, walked in processions—much as they do now, that their divinities might be favourable to them and give them good crops and success in their enterprises. This is pretty much what their present Christianity consists of. As a moral influence, working upon the character of the people, it seems scarcely to have had the slightest effects, except, as I said, in causing them to leave off human sacrifices which were probably not an original feature of their worship, but were introduced comparatively at a late time . . ."

A Catholic priest, Joseph H. McCarty (1830–1897), who travelled extensively throughout Mexico and devoted some time to comparative studies of the ancient American religions, refused to accept a positive balance from the centuries of missionary work in Mexico. Writing after his travels (1886) he even reported human sacrifices at Puebla on St. Michael's day.

1886 edition, pp. 229–230

". . . The Mexican is not a Catholic. He is a Christian simply because he has been baptized. I speak here of the masses and not of the numerous exceptions which are to be found in all classes of Society. I affirm that Mexico is not a Catholic country, because the majority carry ignorance of religion to the point of having no worship but that of form. Their worship is materialistic beyond any doubt. It does not know what it is to adore God in Spirit . . .

"It is vain to look for good fruits from this hybrid tree, which makes of the Mexican religion a singular collection of lifeless devotions, of haughty ignorance, of unhealthy superstitions and of horrible vices. It would take volumes to recount the idolatrous superstitions of the Indians which are still left in existence . . ."

A perusal of the 19th and early 20th century travel books on Spanish America, some of which have been quoted by Braden (1930) reveal the same story: every author believed that the pre-Columbian mind was manifest everywhere in the people's behaviour and that the ancient patterns have never been erased. The books referring to Mexico were outstanding because of its more highly developed ancient civilizations and because the Indian stock of its people had left a profound mark on the social and political history of Spanish America. Probably the most vicious book about Mexico, which scholars fail to mention, was written (1922) by Wallace Thompson (1883–1936), a North American editor from the Middle West, who during his stay in Mexico was very much influenced by the ideas of the "scientific" remnants from the era of Porfirio Diaz's government. Thompson's book imputes the vilest concepts of human behaviour to the Mexican Indians:

1922 edition, pp. 4–8

". . . Millions of Mexicans, mixed blood and Indian, remained red, and red they are to this day . . . and today behind the flimsy curtain of their Spanish language and religion . . . that Indian culture . . . is perhaps the most sinister threat against the civilization of the white man which exists in the world today. Its strength is in its inertia . . . Brothers indeed we may be before Heaven, but the Indian differs from the white man in qualities more fundamental than the mere variation in ideas and in the ages of their cultures. White and red were, and today still are, further apart than any, even yellow and black, in the processes of their thoughts and in the ideals of what is worth living for and what is worth dying for. Our search here plunges into the untracked jungle of Indian and Mexican psychology. The Mexico of today is root and stem of this ancient jungle . . . The Indians . . . of the Mexican people are in many ways more Indian than the reservation tribes of the United States . . . they remain much the same peoples as they were when the Spaniards came . . .

p. 49: "The missionary priests . . . in their zeal for conversion transmitted virtually every pagan deity into a Christian saint . . .

p. 153: "The sex instinct . . . is the outstanding example of the Mexican's devotion of all his intellectual forces . . . no people, probably, have ever devoted so much intellectual concentration to the ends of sex as the average and typical Mexican . . ."

The curious thing about Thompson's book is that the author also acknowledges the existence of great fundamental virtues in these wretched Indians:

1922 edition, p. 156

". . . One phase only of true love persists, the family instinct . . . a mighty and a hopeful factor in Mexico . . . In the lower classes, the family ties are virtually all on the maternal line (p. 188). There is, however, a very definite love of home itself in the Mexican . . ."

And in the final pages, Thompson is the first to recognize the strong links of family and kinship, and the devotion of the Mexican to his small bit of territory.

Almost five centuries have elapsed since the great experiment of acculturation of the pre-Columbian mind began, and according to the testimonies surveyed some aberrant trends have disappeared entirely, adopting new forms under the new Christian culture, while others are yet extant. The alleged aberrations were found in pre-Columbian civilizations such as the Aztec and the Inca which had established their hegemony for not more than two centuries; we are, therefore, forced to admit that Mochicas, Toltecs, Mayas, Aztecs and Incas either inherited and adopted aberrant patterns of behaviour, or developed their civilizations by introducing or re-shaping them. The archaeological evidence examined, at least for sexual perversions, shows that in northern Peru these aberrations were well established before the hegemony of the Incas, and in the opinion of early historians the rise of the Inca military power was mainly aimed at the destruction of sodomy and sexual debauchery in the

Chimú civilization. Rowe (1948) has pointed out that the Incas tried vainly to stamp it out by liquidating whole families and tribes.

The statistics of the Inca method of acculturation for the Chimús, who we must remember had inherited the cultural traditions of the Mochicas, can be implemented by data provided by Cieza de León (1553). The Incas made compulsory their Quechua language and their system of political administration, but historians have failed to see that this in fact converted the whole Inca area of subjugated nations into an immense concentration camp, with the transfer by force of great masses of population, uprooting them from their own ecological environment, and imposing conditions of labour where the worker only retained one third of his produce. The data that may be quoted here in connection with the acculturation of sexual drives by the Incas is that of Cieza de León (1553): he reports that in the Chimú area after the campaign against sodomy, fifteen women were left for each man; this means that 93% of the Chimú male population was exterminated by the Incas on that count. Despite this method of instant solution of sodomy, the problem subsisted and was repeatedly mentioned after the Conquest. Both the Chimú and the Mochica areas, where sexual aberrations developed, are valley cultures marginal to a river surrounded by desert zones, where a balance between population levels and food production had to be kept. Bearing this in mind, one may draw, in respect of the sexual perversions there, a parallel with Greece; Guyon (1934), like Haire, reminds us that the ancient Greeks lived in small states with a limited food supply which approved and tolerated sexual pleasure as an end in itself without reference to procreation, and therefore homosexual and heterosexual sodomy were prevalent. The Jews, on the contrary, were a small nation with great racial ambitions in need of a large army, and therefore their religious and social ideas were directed to that aim. It is difficult to accept sexual practices as directed by political motivation; probably the biological factor behind past and present heterosexual sodomy is as much a contraceptive device of nature, as a procedure to obtain a prolongation of orgasm by the greater constriction by the anal sphincter in cases where the vagina is dilated as result of parturition.

Personal communications of psychiatric reports on sodomy, incest and other sexual deviations seem to indicate a higher incidence in Spanish America than in Spain, but any statement on this subject would be unsound without proper statistics. The open discussion of the problem has only been possible after the momentous study by A. C. Kinsey (1894–1956) uncovering the extent of homosexuality in the United States of America (1948 and 1953) and the report of the Wolfenden Committee (1957) showing current readjustment in sexual morals in Great Britain on medical and legal grounds. The idea that the incidence of homosexuality is historically and culturally uniform, and the considerable magnitude of the problem, have given support to the suggestion that homosexuality is a genetic aberration. However, Ellis (1963) has indicated that although certain genetic factors may contribute indirectly, anthropological surveys do not offer supporting physical proof, and this cultural approach lacks objective and confirmatory evidence of a scientific nature. Nevertheless, the cultural and historical incidence of homosexuality cannot be disregarded, because as West (1968) has pointed out, if to most contemporary cultures homosexual indulgence appears abnormal or immoral it must be remembered that many primitive and some classical cultures have taken different attitudes. Biblical, Greek and Roman literature is indeed full of instances of institutionalized sodomy, and recent studies on surviving marginal American tribes also confirm this view.

Goldman (1963), surveying the present practices of the Cubeo in the north-west Amazon, indicates that they are very strict in preventing premarital heterosexual relations, but permit adolescent homosexuality. In his detailed and far-reaching studies on the Mohave Indians of North America, Devereux (1937) shows that they have institutionalized homosexuality. The *alyhas* are Mohave youths who live and dress as women and are permitted to set up house with a "husband". They are industrious and have quite a respectable position in the community. Apparently among the Mohave Indians there is also a recognized class of exclusively homosexual women. Benedict (1935) found institutionalized sodomy among the Zuñi Indians of North America with *bardajes* having a definite position in their social structure and living useful lives. This attitude towards homosexuality among contemporary aboriginal American Indians, still preserving ancient cultural characteristics, agrees with the findings of Ford and Beach (1952) on patterns of sexual behaviour; they found that in 49 out of 76 primitive societies (i.e. 64%) sodomy was considered a normal and acceptable practice. These and other similar studies have suggested recently to Sonenschein (1966) the need for approaching homosexuality as a subject of anthropological inquiry. But now that the taboo of sodomy has been broken and the subject has become medically respectable it seems more appropriate for it to fall within the province of medical historians who by the nature of their professional training are well qualified to assess both the sources and the findings.

Bestiality, or so-called animal sodomy, was another problem the Incas tried to stamp out in their area, where the sexual isolation of shepherds with herds of large ruminants provided the necessary conditions, never found in Middle America among the Aztecs and the Mayas. It was represented in ancient pottery and mentioned by the chroniclers. Contemporary folklore indicates that bestiality still exists in South America and stories of female ruminants jealous of the sexual favours of their masters, or how they attend to their voice and calls, like the mutual accusations of bestiality between shepherds, are not uncommon.

The problem of inebriation under the process of Aztec acculturation may on the other hand be examined through a limited number of historical sources. Apparently *octli* or *pulque* from maguey began to be manufactured by the Toltecs in about the tenth century, precisely at the time

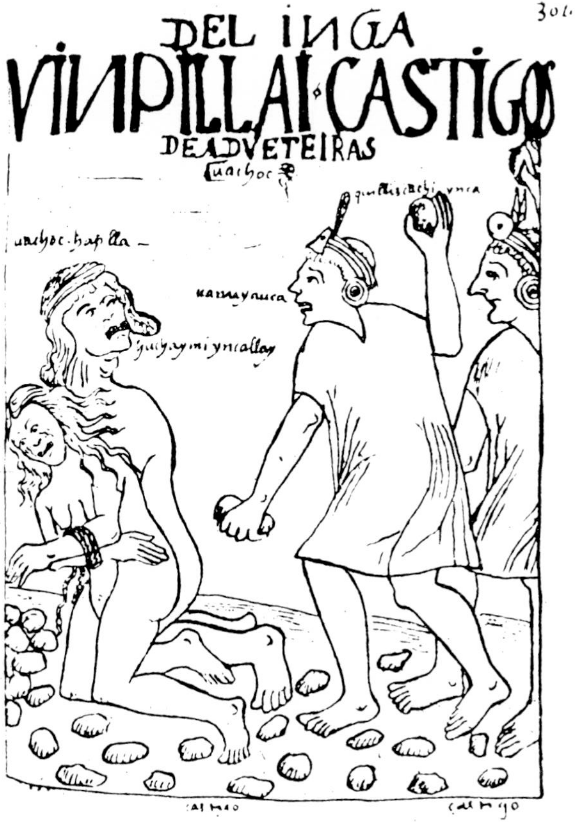

FIG. 25. Inca punishment for adultery by F. Huamán Poma, 1610, p. 306.

FIG. 26. Inca epilepsy by F. Huamán Poma, 1610, p. 128.

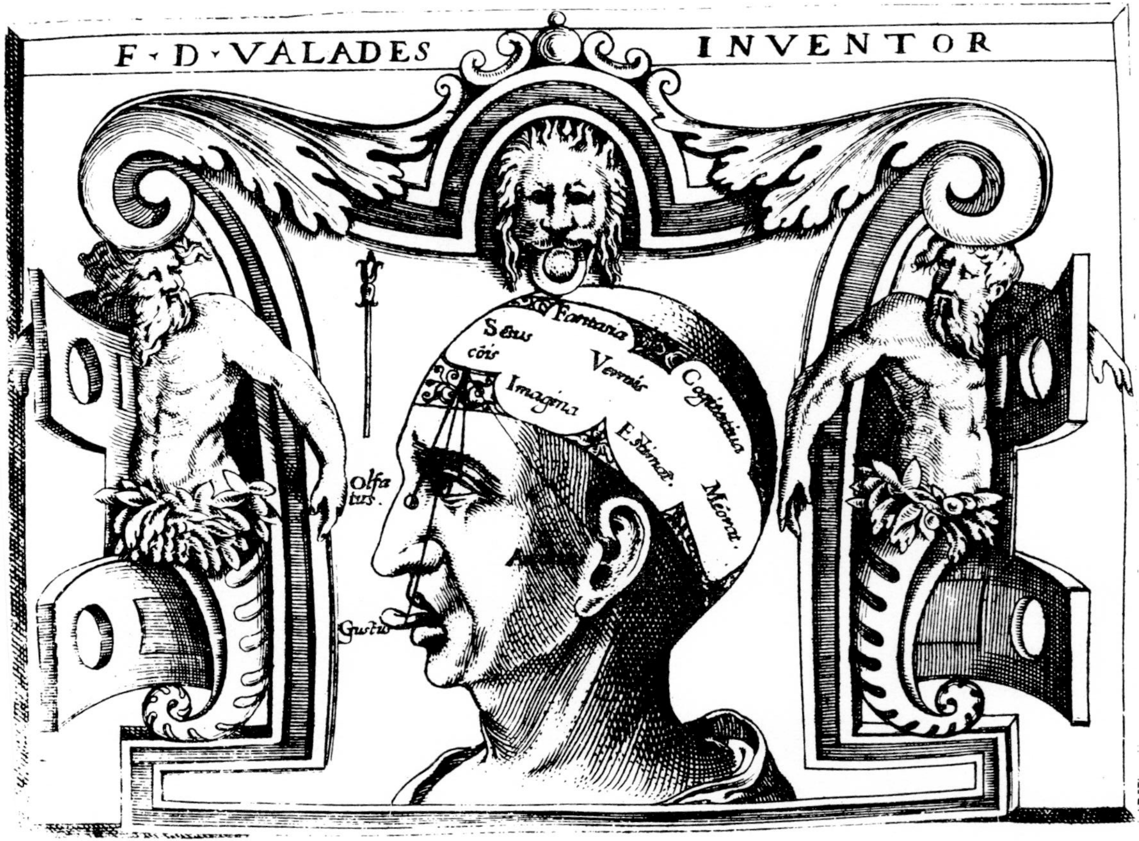

FIG. 27. Conception of higher cerebral processes by D. Valadés, *Rhetorica Christiana*, 1570, p. 88.

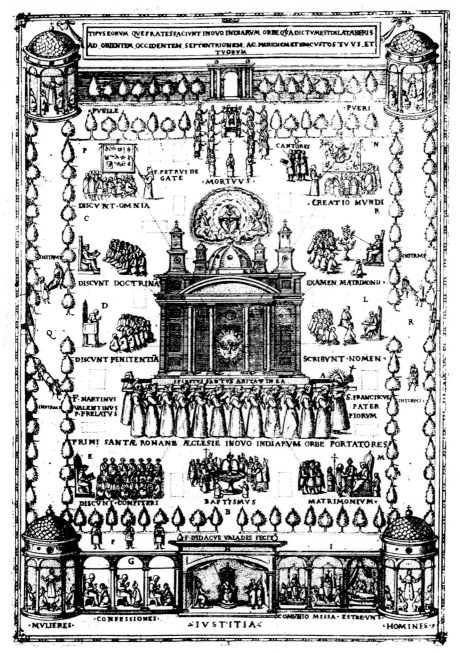

Fig. 28. Missionary work of the Catholic Church in America by D. Valadés, *Rhetorica Christiana*, 1570, p. 207.

Fig. 29. Pictographic representation of sins and confession by D. Valadés, *Rhetorica Christiana*, 1570, p. 216.

of the Aztec arrival on Mexico's high plateau, and it was indeed used by them and all the Mexican civilizations including the Mayas. Sources have been quoted consistently stating that inebriation was severely punished among the Aztecs, even by death; despite this social condemnation alcoholism was and still is the greatest social problem in Spanish America, and current literature in this respect is too large to single out one area. The studies by Ruiz Moreno (1939) on the Jesuit's campaigns against alcoholism among the Guaraníes during the Colonial period will suffice.

The acculturation of crimes against human life among the Aztecs also appears to have a short history. Human sacrifices seem to have been initiated after their contact with the Toltec civilization and several contemporary anthropologists believe that they were taken by the Aztecs from the Toltecs. Soustelle (1967) maintains that the increase in bloody rituals among the Aztecs grows paradoxically with what he considers a mellowing of their customs. What does seem clear is that Aztec anthropophagy kept expanding after the famine of the year 1450 when the Aztecs gained more political and military power. They made a practice of the *xochiyaoyotl* or flowering war—expeditions into neighbouring territories, particularly the Otomí area, to capture prisoners for the human sacrifices in their religious ceremonies, invariably ending in banquets of human flesh. As for suicide, it can be easily deduced from Sahagún (1565), Landa (1570) and Arriaga (1621) that although it was intimately connected with inebriation, it also had deep religious roots.

One great cultural feature in the aberrations of the pre-Columbian mind is the attitude to life and death manifested even today by the cruelty of living and the contempt for death in Spanish America. The problem is rooted entirely in pre-Columbian religious concepts because the ancient American civilizations have no meaning for eternal damnation, or hell, and the consequences of this lack of moral deterrent had to be compensated in customary law with extreme severity in the punishment of transgressors. This basic fact gives a particular significance to the acculturation of the Christian religion into pre-Columbian thinking. Sins carried, whether known or ignored by the community, the punishment in hell after death. This was the main deterrent in the new moral law implanted after the Conquest, because of the serious limitations in the implementation of positive law during the Colonial period.

Christian acculturation of the pre-Columbian mind, despite criticisms about the methods used under the Spanish colonization and the survival of certain aberrant trends in the character of the Spanish-American people, succeeded up to the point which could be expected in three centuries of indoctrination. This success was not due to the material gains received from a more advanced society, but sprang from the religious aim which, with all its faults, was the paramount reason of the Conquest and colonization of Spanish America. Today we give the name of Spanish Americans to the people south of the Rio Grande, because they represent the blending of two cultures, but we cannot find their equivalents in any other colonizations in the rest of the world. They are not Anglo-Hindus but half-castes in India, and not Franco-Arabs but mulattoes in Africa. As for the American Indians north of the Rio Grande, they have disappeared for practical purposes or they have become ethnographic curiosities.

ABORIGINAL PSYCHOTHERAPY

There is a certain universality in human psychology of which Zilboorg (1941) advises we should never cease to be aware: the problem of illness awakens in man, wherever and whoever he may happen to be, specific reactions which are responsible for many similarities among people from different cultures and at quite distant historical stages. In respect of the mind we also find that similar emotional states concerning survival, sex or power produce, regardless of time and place, similar deeply-seated psychological reactions and imagery. Likewise all men show natural outlets for therapeutic forces which only in the past half century have begun to be properly understood. The heavy pathological burden of the pre-Columbian mind manifested its self-curative powers in dreams, symbols and myths which were complemented by means of a very well integrated psychological catharsis which has been discussed elsewhere (Guerra, 1970).

The chronicles repeatedly pointed out that pre-Columbian civilizations held a profound belief in dreams to the extent, reported by Cabeza de Vaca (1542), that the Indians did not hesitate to kill their own children if the interpretation of their dreams so required. Sahagún (1565) mentioned the story of Huemac acting as a procurer for his own daughter who dreamed of receiving sexual gratification from Tezcaltlipoca, and discussed the meaning of dreams among the Aztecs. Huaman (1610) described certain types of Inca physicians who specialized in the interpretation of dreams, and Peña Montenegro (1668) devoted a treatise of his work to discuss how much truth there was in the Indians' belief in dreams, comparing their ideas with those found in Hippocrates and Galen. All these pre-Columbian outlets which were of great therapeutic value have found complete justification in contemporary psychiatry. The work of both Freud (1949) and Jung (1958) indicate that dreams project unconscious contents into consciousness, revealing astonishingly specific solutions to spiritual conflicts which appear insoluble to the rational mind. It is in this light that the colloquial expressions in Spanish America of a woman declaring to her love that she dreamed of him, or similar phrases, have to be interpreted, because these experiences represent in current psychiatric practice the persistence of ancestral trends.

Another pre-Columbian curative force was manifested in symbols because the aboriginal civilizations, unable to crystallize their ideas in writing, resorted to symbolism. The Mayas were perhaps more ideographic, and their glyphs more abstract, because they had developed hieroglyphic writing; but the Aztecs used pictographic representations, ideograms, and for certain names resorted to phonems or rebus writing. Danzel (1938) believes that in Peru only the Nazca civilization showed any resemblance of symbolism, although with decorative tendencies. Certain Maya medical hieroglyphs have been studied (Guerra, 1964), discussing the meaning of *cimi* death, and also the Aztec symbolism and rebus writing which led to the deciphering of the hallucinogenic drugs in the Codex Magliabecchi (Guerra, 1967). But the symbolism of ethical problems in the Mexican codices is very wide and complex. Danzel (1938) pointed out that the idea of sin was represented as a dog urinating; the sinner, or filthy one, appeared as a human figure with a mass of faeces on his back; the ball of faeces, being a symbol of spiritual darkness, had open eyes; the goddess of lustful things, Tlazoltéotl, to whom the Aztecs confessed, was also known under the name of Tlaelquani, which means eater of filth; death was symbolized by skull and bones, meaning not only physical death but also the spiritual one; the snake was connected with the penis and the orgasm; the lizard in the back of the human figure has been associated with moral suffering and pain. Several archaeologists have found sexual symbolism in the ring of the ball game played by the Aztecs and the Mayas. It is only by knowing this pre-Columbian symbolism that we can understand certain contemporary expressions still used in Spanish America, such as a pregnant woman being in that condition, because, as the Indians say, she was bitten by the snake, meaning the penis, and other similar expressions. The value of symbols has been fully appreciated by Jung (1958) who believes they represent the inexpressible in an unsurpassable way, and that they play a most important role in the psychiatric patient's life by stating his problems in their deepest terms and pointing a way towards a solution.

Although to apply Jung's ideas to the symbolic analysis of Mexican codices would be beyond the limits of this work, a certain understanding might be gained by surveying the first section of the Codex Magliabecchi where a number of Aztec symbols, equivalent to the traditional coat of arms of European nobility, can be studied. Fortunately much of the pre-Columbian symbolism of power, sexual, and survival drives has been preserved until our own time in the techniques of *nearika*, or wool blankets painted with beeswax colours by the Huichol Indians of Tepic, Mexico, who have been well studied by Lumholtz (1900). A number of *nearika* painted by an Huichol shaman have been recently examined by N. Lewis and D. Montgomery (1970) and they indeed confirm in their symbolism the external life problems encountered by the collective unconscious. Most of the representations refer to sexual guilt or sexual problems, food and survival experiences, and were obtained under *peyotl* or mezcaline inebriation (see Plate IV). Figure 13 shows the journey of the soul to the abode of dead with its record of the sexual life; four penis representations for the man at the left and four vaginas for the woman at the right. The souls of the dead appear in the tree as torso figures and

will join the newly arrived souls in a dance. Figure 14: the tree abode of
the souls flung there by the new arrival and the torso of the dead souls
surrounded by the sexual organs, penis at the left and vaginas at the
right. Figure 15: the path to be followed by the soul to reach the abode
of dead. At the left the way of those who broke the sexual taboos with
a black dog watching, a crow refusing to eat the soul, an opossum whose
meat is forbidden, a worm meaning the earliest sexual experience, and a
pool of water. At the right the way for the virtuous souls with purifying
fire, thorn for penance, pool of hot water, and a flower. Figure 16: The
soul of those who committed sexual aberrations in the corral of angry
mules, meaning they had intercourse with non-Huichol people, such as
Spaniards, mestizos or animals; the mule is sterile and double-barrelled
portraying sexual perversions.

The myth is another immense field of psychiatric research in the therapeutic trends of the collective unconscious. All pre-Columbian human
life was based on religion and all religion was based on mythical representation. Díaz Infante (1963) has made a psychoanalytical study of the
Quetzalcoatl myth, but, as has already been pointed out in this work,
we can find every one of the myths of classical Greece which are currently
used in psychiatry, in the history of pre-Columbian civilizations. Ehrenwald (1960), for instance, has surveyed the legend of Quetzalcoatl's return
and used some archetypes of the pre-Columbian history and the Conquest
of Mexico to explain the relationship between Cortés and his loves, particularly *Malinche*. Current psychiatric practice in Spanish America is
continuously confronted with adulterous or polygamous sexual experiences well described, as has been quoted by Ruiz de Alarcón (1629). This
social condition of *casa grande y casas chicas* or main house and little
houses, to describe the family home of a married man and the residences
of his mistresses, evolves from the multiple wives in pre-Columbian
societies, which were also very much accepted during the Colonial period.
Even Mme. Calderón de la Barca (1843) had respect for this situation,
and she mentioned Mexican ladies in high society who prior to marriage
had had progeny by a man other than the husband. What is interesting
in Ehrenwald's (1960) work is his analysis of the sado-masochistic
concept of life in Mexico, which he rightly traces to the practices of self-
mortification and human sacrifices of the Aztec religion. He concludes
there can be little doubt that these religious practices had a profound
influence upon the formation of the Aztec character; and, it can be added,
upon the cruel nature of life in Mexico and the rest of Spanish America.

Jung (1958) has studied in detail some of the most important symbolic
rituals of pre-Columbian religions, drawing a parallel with similar ones
in the Catholic religion; but he recognizes that it is precarious to draw
conclusions from our modern mentality about the primitive state of mind.
Among the parallels to the transformation mystery, he recalls that the
Catholic Mass contains allusions to the prefiguration in the Old Testament
and thus indirectly to ancient sacrificial symbolism in general. To him it

FIG. 30. Pictographic representation of the soul, sin and hell by D. Valadés, *Rhetorica Christiana*, 1570, p. 217.

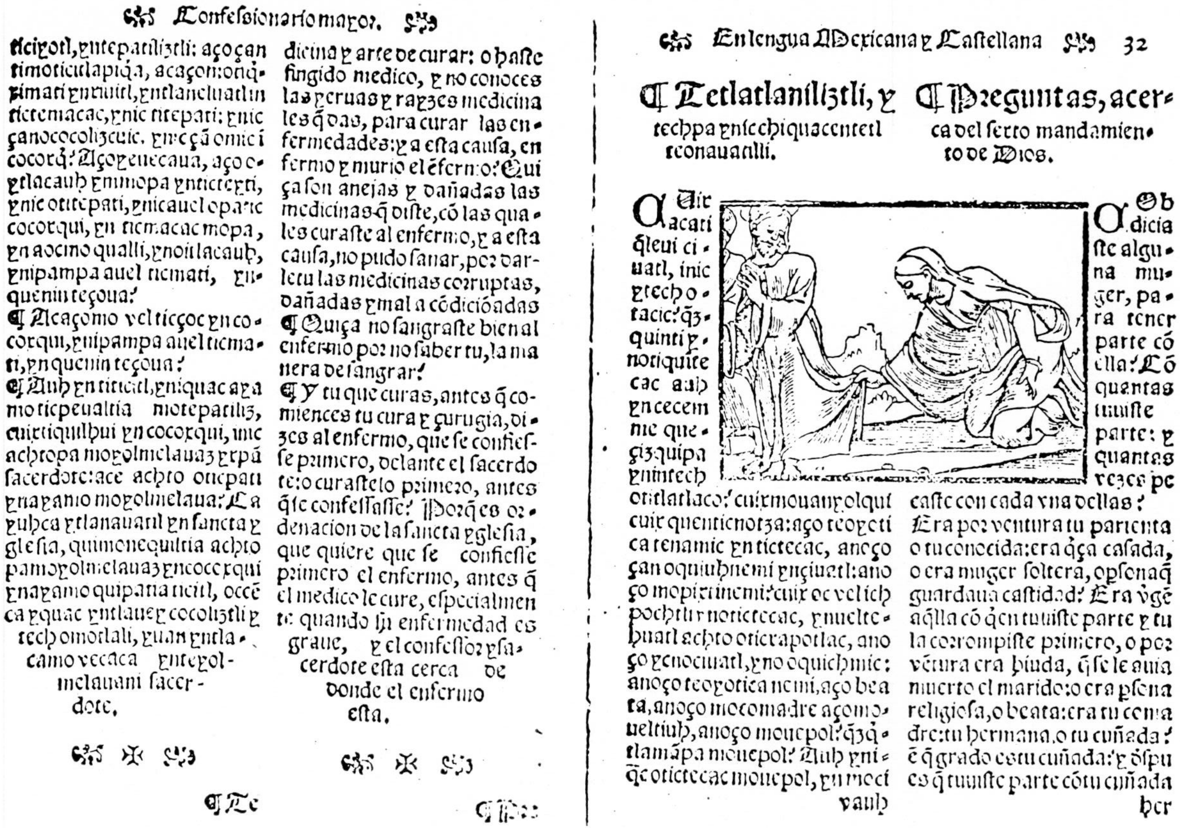

¶ Tetlatlaniliztli, y Preguntas, acerca del sexto mandamiento tode Dios.
techpa ynitechpiquaccuetl ticonauaztli.

FIG. 31. A. de Molina: sexual matters in the Mexican–Spanish Confessionary, 1565, folio 32.

R.

P. Inic intechpa titlatlacoz ceme cihua, cuix teixpa impñoticaclac, anoço tetech oti mocuuh inicmitzlanochiliz que, anoço quinozazque.

R. Si viere q̃ algunos muy carnal preguiole si. R.

P. Cuix q̃mamian otimoma chiuh inic momatica tiquix tia motlacaxinachyo, inic ticahuiltia? R.

P. In icuac yuh ticchihuaya cuix aca cihuatl tiquilna micticateca, ichpochtli, anoço cahuilli noço tenamiç? R.

P. In icuac titlantcateca in monamic anoço ceme mome cahua cuix queman motla huaçacopa itech otieic in y cuidapampa in ynemanahui ampa anoço in icuac tiyol qui?

R.

P. Cuix quemanian otictzin colhua-hui momanic in i cua itechtaci, jnic ticchihua in aclihualoni, cuilo yotl?

¶ Este modo para con la muger propria, aunque no es pe cado mortal, algunas vezes suele er ocasion de mayor mal en particular estando borrachos, como yo è topado mu chos, y así es bien reñirselo, y reprehenderselo, y advier te el confessor que todas sus vezes que el indio dixere o. nictzincolhui onictzincolhuazhui in. monamic, scuidapa pa ytech ondcic, titixnamictoque, tolos son malos con munes y para satis facerlo bien le diga, cuixoncan inic ci

P. Para pecarõ alguna de. las mugeres entranas publi. camente en su casa, ò tomas te algunas terceras que te la llamasen y las hablasen?

R.

P. Alguna vez as tenido al guna polucion y derramado tu simente con tus manos to candote?

R.

P. Quando haziase sto tenias por objeto y pensauas en al guna muger casada donzella ò soltera?

R.

P. Quando llegauas à tu mu ger ò a alguna de tus mance bas estando borracho ò no lo estando tuuiste acceso à ella por detras fuera del va so comuny ordinario? R.

P. Alguna vez as tenido ac ceso a tu muger poniendola de barriga ò con otros mo dos malos, con q ayas hecho algun pecado mayor? R.

cihuatl in yuh oticchiuh. Hizifte esto por el baso comun y ordinario que lue, noç se declara muy bien.

A ellas solas, quando fueren muy carnales.

P. Cuix otimonepilchichiuh in icuac mocel tucochi, aço iç ço occentlamantli yca icti mociluayoluia, ic tiquilna miqui oquichtli?

R.

P. Cuix quemmanian timoq qizolhuia in icuac titeci, ti moyoyoma, anoço in icuac ca ni tehuatica inic quiça in mocihuayre?

R.

P. Cuix omnnopilachluiq in ancihuatotontin aço quê manian quinmonccehhuiq ycannahuiltia, in quhqui o. quichyotica anquichiuha?

R.

¶ A todos ellos y a ellas.

P. Cuix aço cihuatl noço o quichtliotica luilti, oticca. manallui, oticziriquilui ni nacaye, anoço çhuatl mote copa omitztlaquitzquili, à noço ycochizpan otictlamat toquili, inic oquiz motlaca xinachyo?

P. Antenido contus dedos ò manos ü con otra cosa algu na polucion acordandote en ella de algun hombre?

R.

P. As tenido alguna polució co los carnales, quando nue les ò estas sentada en algu na parte

R.

P. Aucis os hechado alguna vez vna sobre otra, jugando como hombre y muger por via de burla y juego en algu na parte?

R.

P. As burlado te con alguna mugr ò con algun hombre, con tocamientos suçies de soneços tocando à tus par tes ò ella ati por tu manda do, ò estado durmiendo as palpado y tocado a alguna por donde tu venisteatener alguna polucion?

R.

¶ A todas estas preguntas que se preguntan en este sexto mandamiento a los vones, se puede, preguntar à las mugeres mudando los ge neros del manera, que se entie. di...j

FIG. 32. M. de León: sexual matters in the Mexican–Spanish Confessionary, 1611, folio 116.

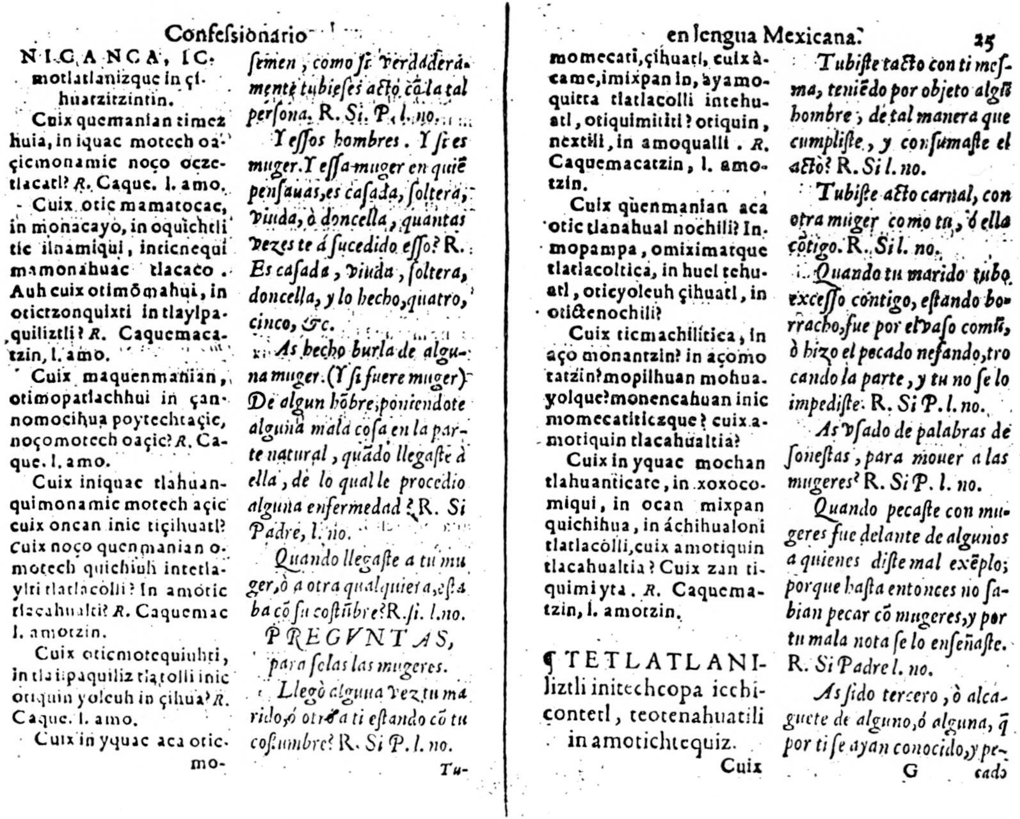

NICANCA, IC.
motlatlanizque in çe-
huatzitzintin.

Cuix quemanian timez-
huia, in iquac motech oa-
çicnonamic noço ocze-
tlacatl? R. Caque. l. amo.

Cuix otic mamatocac,
in monacayo, in oquichtli
tle ilnamiqui, inticnequi
mamonahuac tlacaco.
Auh cuix otimoꝫmahui, in
otictzonquixti in tlayapa-
quiltzli? R. Caquemaca-
tzin, l. amo.

Cuix maquenmanian,
otimopatlachhui in çan-
nomochua poytechpaçic,
noçomotech oaçic? R. Ca-
que. l. amo.

Cuix iniquac tlahuan-
quimonamic motech açic
cuix oncan inic tiçihuatl?
cuix noço quenmanian o-
motech quichiuh intetla-
ytiritlacolli? In amotic
tlacahualtiꝫ? R. Caquemac
l. amotzin.

Cuix in iyquac aca otic-
mo-

fimen; como ſe veriddderâ-
mentſ tubieſſes actoçarnal
perſona. R. Si. P. l. no.

Teſſos hombres. Y ſies
muger. Teſſa muger en quê
penſauas es caſada, ſoltera;
viuda, ò donçella, quantas
vezes ò ſuccidió eſſo? R.
Es caſada, viuda, ſoltera,
donçella, y lo hecho, quatro,
cinco, &c.

As hecho burla de algu-
na muger. (Y ſi fuere muger)
De algun hôbre, poniendote
alguná mala coſa en la parte natural, quâdo llegaſte à
ella, de lo quale proccedio
alguna enfermedad? R. Si
Padre, l. no.

Quando llegaſte à tu mu-
ger, ò a otra qual quiera, eſtâ-
ba cô ſu coſtûbre? R. ſi. l. no.

PREGVNTAS,
para ſolas las mugeres.

Llegô alguna vez, tu ma-
rido, ò otra ti eſtando cô tu
coſtumbre? R. Si. P. l. no.

Tu-

momecati, çihuati, cuixä-
came, imixpan in, ayamo-
quita tlatlacolli intehu-
atl, otiquimiliti? otiquin-
nextli, in amoqualli. R.
Caquemacatzin, l. amo-
tzin.

Cuix quenmanian aca
oticilanahual nochilli? In-
mopampa, omiximarique
tlatiacolica, in huel tehu-
atl, oticyoleuh çihuatl, in
oiꝫꝫenochili?

Cuix ticmachilitica, In
açononantzin? in açomo
tatzin? mopilhuan mohua-
yolque? monencahuan inic
nomecaticzeque? cuixa-
motquin tlacahualtia?

Cuix in iyquac mochan
tlahuanicate, in xoxoco-
miqui, in ocan mixpan
quichihua, in achihualoni
tlatlacolli, cuix amotiquin
tlacahualtia? Cuix zun ti-
quimiyta? R. Caquema-
tzin, l. amotzin.

¶ TETLATLANI-
liztli initechcopa icchi-
contetl, teotenahuatili
in amotichtequiz.

Cuix

Tubiſſet acto conti meſ-
ma, teniêdo por objeto algû
hombre; de tal manera que
cumplieſſe, y conſumaſſe el
acto? R. Si. l. no.

Tu biſſe acto carnal, con
otra muger como tu, ò ella
côtigo. R. Si. l. no.

Quando tu marido tuuo
exceſſo côntigo, eſtando borracho, fue por el vaſo comû,
ò hizo el pecado nefando, tro-
cando la parte, y tu no ſelo
impediſte? R. Si P. l. no.

As vſado de palabras de-
ſoneſtas, para mouer a las
mugeres? R. Si P. l. no.

Quando pecaſte con mu-
geres fue delante de algunos
a quienes diſte mal exêplo;
porque haſta entonces no ſa-
bian peccar cô mugeres y por
tu mala nota ſe lo enſeñaſte.
R. Si P. l. no.

As ſido tercero, ò alca-
guete de alguno, ò alguna, q
por ti ſe ayan conocido, y pecado

G

FIG. 33. J. Alva: sexual matters in the Mexican–Spanish Confessionary, 1634, folio 25.

is clear that Christ's sacrifice and the Communion strike one of the deepest chords in the human psyche: human sacrifice and ritual anthropophagy, which are evidently among the most ancient and most central
of religious concepts. Jung found that it was not surprising to encounter
among the Aztecs the ritual of *teoqualo* or "god eating" recorded by
Sahagún (1565): the dough-like paste made out of seeds of *Argemone
mexicana* and moulded into the figure of the god Huitzilopochtli eaten
by the Indians, besides ritual anthropophagy. This interpretation confirms
that the cruel nature of the pre-Columbian mind manifested in bloody
rituals, human sacrifices and anthropophagy was able to find an outlet
in vicarious Catholic rituals which, therefore, became an intimate part
of the behavioural patterns of contemporary Spanish-American people.

The Core of pre-Columbian psychotherapy was spiritual catharsis,
called by the Colonial chroniclers confession, owing to its similarity with
the Catholic sacrament of penance. In fact the pre-Columbian catharsis
differed profoundly from the Catholic sacrament despite their external
rituals. Raffaele Pettazzoni (1883–1959) in his comparative studies on the
history of religions dealt in detail with the confession of sins among the
primitive people of America (1926) with a sound knowledge of sources,
considering the highly specialized field of early Americana and the
dimensions of his research. According to Pettazzoni the Eskimo held
taboo the hunting of whales and practised confession to appease Sedna
the queen of the sea. The Takulli practised confession when they fell
seriously ill. The Iroquois on the fifth and sixth day after the feast of the
New Year performed a ceremony which seemed like a confession of sins.
In respect of the Huicholes, Pettazzoni followed the information supplied
by Lumholtz (1902) on the annual expedition in search of *peyotl* buttons;
in order to preserve the state of ritual purity the Indians had to fast and
remain chaste; afterwards they had to declare all the sexual affairs they
had had during their lifetime and name the co-respondent. They used in
this confession a piece of string where each knot meant a lover. Once the
confession by the members of the expedition was finished, the headman
collected all the strings and threw them into the fire to ensure the success
of the *peyotl* expedition. The women remained at home, but they too
made a confession and, like the men, the sins they confessed were their
sexual experiences. The sexual symbolism of the Huicholes extended even
to the sacred vases washed during the feasts of the New Year, which to
them represented the female sexual organs. Pettazzoni (1926) quotes
Preuss (1919) in respect of the Kagaba Indians near Santa Marta, Colombia, who also confessed when they wanted to get rid of diseases and
travails. Among them the sins were always sexual aberrations, incests,
sodomy, bestiality or sexual offences, rape, adultery and the like. About
the Tupinamba of Brazil, Pettazzoni quoted Las Casas (1542) who mentioned that the women used to confess among themselves the adulteries
they committed before the arrival of the tribal priest. Pettazzoni has also
surveyed certain marginal civilizations of Middle America, such as the

Otomies of Mexico, where the confession focused on sexual offences and inebriation. On the Mixtecs of central Mexico, Pettazzoni quotes Sahagún (1565) who believed they only confessed in time of serious illness. The Huaxtecs, in the coast of the Gulf of Mexico, around Veracruz and Tampico, an area repeatedly described as having a high incidence of sexual aberrations, Pettazzoni reminds us that the Indians there did not consider lewdness sinful.

The primary sources for the study of psychological catharsis in the great pre-Columbian civilizations quoted above are many. It was reported in the Maya area by Andagoya (1517), las Casas (1542), Landa (1570), Torquemada (1615), and Remesal (1619). The accounts of confession among the Aztecs are more detailed and begin with the pictographic descriptions in the Codex Magliabecchi (1565) and the texts of Sahagún (1565), Lopez Medel (1569), Mendieta (1596), Román (1575), Zorita (1575), Herrera (1601), Torquemada (1615), Vetancurt (1698) and Veytia (1775). The confession among the Incas is also very well documented with accounts by San Pedro (1559), Polo (1559), Santillan (1563), Sarmiento (1572), Molina (1580), Cabello (1586), Acosta (1590), Valera (1590), Huaman (1610), Murúa (1611), Arriaga (1621), Avendaño (1623), Cobo (1643) and Villagomez (1649).

The description of confession among the Aztecs by Sahagún (1565) gives some substance to the idea that the Mexican confession was a religious ritual similar to the Catholic penance: the Indian went to the soothsayer and asked for confession to Tlaelquani the goddess who provoked lust and also ate the filth of sins, or to Tezcatlipoca the *puto* or god queer. The Indians followed certain rituals of presenting a mat, sweeping the place, burning *copal*, had a steam bath in the *temazcalli*, took an oath touching the ground with the hand and recited to the soothsayer the sins they had committed. The way Sahagún described the Aztec confession very closely follows the ritual of Catholic confession, even to the point of accepting in the Aztec ritual the remission of sins, repentance, acknowledgement and restitution. In Sahagún's rendering of the Aztec confession the sinner addresses himself to Tlaelquani the eater of filth depicted in the Codex Tellerianus Remensis nos 17 and 21, Codex Borgia nos 10 and 64, and the Codex Vaticanus B nos 29, 87 and 91. The sins were all related to sexual aberrations, particularly sodomy or sexual excesses, Tlaelquani being the godess of lust or Mexican Venus, under the advocation of Tlaçolteotl.

Mendieta (1596) and the rest of the Mexican historians give a more medical description of the Aztec confession where all the religious connotations of Sahagún are absent. It should be kept in mind with regard to the Aztec confession that the Mexicans were outstanding for their hermeticism and, as Mendieta put it, whenever they did something wrong they did not allow even their father to know about it. Furthermore Mendieta clearly stated that the Aztecs did not show repentance in confession, neither were they afraid of damnation, they did not even believe in hell;

what they feared was that their evil action would be known and made public. With this background the description given in the chronicles of Aztec confession has a complete different meaning; in the first place the confessor was the physician who was called to cure a patient, and if the ailment was of minor importance only applied drugs, but if the patient was seriously ill, then he would tell the patient to confess the sins and insisted on actively searching the mind of the patient until he declared everything which for years had been troubling his conscience. This *yolme-laua* or vocal confession involved a very active participation by enquiry on the part of the physician and was the backbone of the whole medical treatment.

Lastres (1951) maintains that in ancient Peru the state of health was believed to be the result of the harmony between the individual and his god; thence the keeping of rites, the fasts during religious festivities, periodical sacrifices, abstention of taboos such as coitus, menstruation, salt and spices, and the periodical offerings to the sacred object or *huacas*. The anxiety felt by the Indian in the face of disease was related by him to psychic impurity, the breaking of taboos, or sinful acts, and he had to confess to get rid of them. All the descriptions of vocal confession or *ichurí* among the Incas are fairly consistent, and that by Polo (1559) is accurate despite the details of rituals found later in Murúa (1611), Arriaga (1621) and Cobo (1629). There were confessors for grave or lighter sins, and the ritual included the inspection of the entrails of a guinea pig, and the stoning of the back of the penitent until all sins had been declared. But all these details of ritual described in the accounts and quoted in this work have little relevance for the analysis of the principles involved in the spiritual catharsis among the pre-Columbian civilizations.

The pre-Columbian confession was the spiritual catharsis of the patient's conscious guilt by means of the word. The patients might be adult men or women, and younger people, particularly among the Mayas. The confessor was a physician, man or woman, highly respected in the community, with special training and experience, and was paid for this service. The patient resorted to confession under life problems, stress, illness and moral conflicts. The physician not only listened to the declaration of sinful acts, but actively searched into the mind of the patient and did not conclude the meeting until he was thoroughly satisfied that the patient had declared his most secret acts. The technique was to keep inquiring until the hidden experiences, precisely those the patient was trying to hide, became manifested. There was a well-established ritual around the transfer of guilt by words, complemented by penitence. Both Mayas and Aztecs incorporated into confession the cleansing of the body by the steam bath in the *temazcalli*; the Incas also completed the confession with *opacuna*, or bath in running water. European psychiatrists usually wonder at the ritual of baths in Spanish America by Indians whose external appearance and personal hygiene is very much below standard. The punctiliousness of the Indian about having his bath has little to do with personal hygiene, but it is related to the pre-Columbian ritual of purification, cleansing the body after spiritual catharsis.

The pschotherapy of the spoken word in the pre-Columbian civilization has a parallel with the same technique used in Classical Antiquity, which has been studied by Lain Entralgo (1970). He distinguishes in Plato three forms of speech—the magical, the rational, and the beseeching. All three are indeed found in pre-Columbian practices, although the last could be identified with prayer. The important thing to keep in mind is that the American Indians, like the Greeks, were able to cure by means of the word. Unfortunately, some critics of Lain Entralgo's work have interpreted it as a philological treatise on catharsis and a historical monograph on the art of persuasive talk, failing to understand its true meaning: this is that Greek culture kept using the word as a curative weapon of mental illness through the age of Plato and Aristotle. When scientific medicine was established at Cos under Hippocrates (460–377 B.C.), the use of the spoken word as a therapeutic method was dropped from medicine; instead the word entered the rituals of the Christian religion and remained there until the birth of psychiatry which brought it back into medicine. The spoken word was incorporated as a therapeutic agent when it became the main tool of psychoanalysis. The great find in pre-Columbian civilizations is that among them the spoken word never lost its therapeutic value, and fortunately it was preserved by the Catholic indoctrination of the Colonial period. Nowadays it is no stranger in Spanish America to current psychiatric practice.

The role of catharsis in pre-Colombian civilizations may be understood by bearing in mind the thesis on the social function of primitive medicine advanced by Ackerknecht (1958). He maintains that the most characteristic feature of primitive medicine is that it is almost completely based on magic, religious or supernaturalistic representations. As soon as a biological disorder or an ailment provoked by a sin of the patient rises above the level of normal behaviour, as soon as it is recognized by his society as a disease, it is dealt with in magico-religious terms. This method has been traditionally set aside by society, in the same way as society decides what is disease or what is aberration. Ackerknecht's idea, that disease becomes the most important sanction against a form of social behaviour in primitive societies, also applies to the problems of the pre-Columbian mind where the physician held the key to social control and his diagnosis became a kind of social justice.

From the observations of Ruiz de Alarcón (1629) it becomes apparent that one of the aims in the spiritual therapeutics of pre-Columbian civilizations was the idea of conciliation with oneself which has sometimes been mentioned by Jung (1939). The distress of the pre-Columbian mind at not being at one with oneself was resolved by the mechanism of confession and the individual reached internal harmony at the moment the interplay of time, place, attitude and the sanctioned ritual converged. The patient at the moment of the pre-Columbian confession was also demanding immediate answers to questions and problems that had been taking shape for the better part of his lifetime within the patterns of behaviour of the American civilizations. Kiev (1965) in his study of folk psychiatry recalls the psychological benefits of the church in the Middle Ages with its sanctuaries, sacred retreats, catharsis of the confessional and the expiation of sins through the purchase of indulgence; he joins Ackerknecht in the belief that it is quite possible that the therapeutic success of religion and primitive psychiatry was essentially due to the same basic mechanism of confession and suggestion which are so little understood.

We may wonder about an assessment of pre-Columbian psychotherapy five centuries after our first encounter and at a time when, despite our self-satisfaction, we who work in the field of basic medicine still look upon psychiatry as a very unscientific science. In fact it is my belief that the knowledge gained in fathoming the human mind both in health and disease is quite insufficient. In my view, pre-Columbian psychotherapy possessed the one pre-requisite factor for dynamic effectiveness by being emotionally mobile and therefore having the power to remove symptoms. Technically, pre-Columbian psychotherapy used the elucidative method of expression, as well as the inspirational approach capable of suppressing mental illness. The inspirational content of pre-Columbian psychotherapy was similar to the use of prayer in the Catholic Church which still persists in contemporary Spanish America, based on the acceptance of the superior power of Christ, the Virgin Mary or the Saints, and of their curative capabilities. The physician in pre-Columbian societies played very much the combined role of priest and physician in our society. The elucidative element of pre-Columbian psychotherapy included psychological analysis leading to the removal of symptoms by the discovery of their causes. The physician, having a key role in the community, could trace the historical development of the patient's personality and assess from his unique position the psychogenic and pathogenic bearing of that background in the relief of the patient's current life situation. Because of the close relationship between the physician and the individuals in pre-Columbian communities, the therapist was able to give emotional nurture to the patient, resulting in the identification of the anxieties and in their transference, which supplied much-needed spiritual strength to the mentally ill.

THE PRE-COLUMBIAN LEGACY

The conflicting factions within psychiatry have made it very difficult for the medical historian to accept evolutionary concepts, behavioural criteria or the advances in neurological research in the interpretation of historical surveys. Psychiatry still depends largely on ethical philosophy, though despite criticisms, psychology has been gradually assimilated into the field of behaviourism. Data objectively perceived is beginning to substitute data subjectively derived from introspective analysis, which is now being considered unsuitable for scientific methods. It is clear that the pre-Columbian civilizations left their imprint on the growing individual through cultural patterns which were well adapted to the realities of the physical and spiritual environment; these cultural patterns were inherited and self-preserved, and spread so long as the ecological and spiritual environment were maintained. Environment, we must not forget, may even influence genetics.

One hundred centuries ago, some archaeologists say two hundred and fifty, man invaded the American continent and survived by adapting his needs to the environment. During that long historical period he created communities, cities, adopted certain foods and drinks, developed techniques in pottery, clothing, metallurgy and architecture, established religions, family structures, medicine and political systems; in other words, he created the civilizations best suited to his needs. Some of his customs in respect of life and death, sex and drugs were in some ways different from those adopted by our Classical culture and were considered irrational by the Spaniards. After the Conquest a new culture was imported into America, and the pre-Columbian civilizations were indoctrinated into the Christian religion which aimed at basically changing their moral code. Many transformations also took place with more advanced techniques and new food, drink, clothing. Some customs, like anthropophagy and human sacrifices, disappeared altogether, polygamous marriages were reduced to monogamy, and cultural interchange was promoted by the introduction of writing and printing. Those three centuries of Christian acculturation of the pre-Columbian mind were critical for the shaping of the aboriginal aberrations into new behavioural patterns which were becoming adapted within the Colonial society, and which eventually produced the psychological characteristics of the Spanish-American mind. One century and a half after the Independence, Spanish America was again exposed to further technological and spiritual changes which in certain cases deeply affected the environmental conditions.

Contemplated in perspective through the eyes of medical history the evolution of the pre-Columbian mind seems like a gigantic exercise in conditioned reflexes, which we cannot resist correlating with data accumulated over the last century through the pursuit of experimental research in the biological sciences. There is evidence from neurophysiological and psychopharmacological studies that behaviour is in the greater part determined by the activity of nervous cells grouped in the limbic system and the hypothalamic areas of our brainstem. Leake (1970) indicates that two major centres are involved, one pertaining to self-preservation controlling the search for and intake of food, while the other controls the species preservation through sex drives. The centre for food intake is regulated by glucose levels, while the centre for sex drives is regulated by a more complex metabolic build-up. When the glucostat shuts off in the food intake centre, there is a feeling of satisfaction with muscular relaxation and often sleep, and when sexual drives are fulfilled with orgasm there is also a feeling of satisfaction with relaxation and sleep. The cultural environment of the individual may condition in many different ways the sense of satisfaction for both drives. This oversimplification of the biological processes involved in the drives for the mood of conditioned satisfaction may be illustrated by two theoretical examples drawn from pre-Columbian data. The Aztec's food was basically flat *tortillas* made of maize and chili; he ate that all through his life, as his forefathers had done for generations, and it is well known that eating habits are one of the most steadfast. If a Mexican tastes a European meal for the first time he will express a complimentary statement that it is *muy sabrosa* (very tasty); but the host must not be surprised if his guest when facing a European dish produces some chili to obtain the hot chili flavour which has conditioned his mood for food satisfaction through many centuries. The Mochica's favourite sexual aberration was heterosexual sodomy, as far as can be inferred from archaeological and historical evidence which indicate that it was practised for well over ten centuries. If he were to perform normal sexual intercourse with a beautiful woman, present knowledge on the pattern of physiological reflexes, and the experience of current psychiatric practice allow us to say that the Mochica would not find sexual gratification through normal coitus, and would complete his sexual experience by heterosexual sodomy which has conditioned his mood for sexual satisfaction through generations. As a postscript to these purported theoretical examples it must be pointed out that they are actual experiences. The occurrence of a Mexican woman in a European home taking some hot chilis out of her handbag to spice up some food has often been witnessed. The sodomitic experience was also frequently found in psychiatric practice, and many men find willing partners to perform anal coitus as their only way of obtaining sexual gratification.

Of course, oversimplification can be misleading, but we must acknowledge that the whole process of education is based on the transmission of behavioural, emotional and intellectual patterns, which become impressed upon our minds by the mechanisms of reward and punishment, repetition or suggestion, and we must remember that suggestion is the simplest form of conditioned reflex. What gives more relevance to this historical analysis of the aberrations in the pre-Columbian mind, reshaped under acculturation, but maintained by environmental conditions, is that these well-impressed patterns have neuronal mechanisms; the psychiatrist might wonder at Rodriguez Delgado's (1969) results on the physical control of the mind by electric stimulation of the brain, which is capable of altering at will the mechanisms of anger, hate, aggressiveness or territoriality.

The motivation involved in sex, food, drink or power drives are universal, but is shaped by cultural patterns. Sahagún (1565) believed that the fear of captivity and death at the hands of the enemies led the Aztecs to inebriation. Levi-Strauss (1961) explains the maniacal obsession with blood and torture among the Aztecs in terms of taming the fear of death. And Fernandez de Oviedo (1526) had no doubts about homosexual sodomy being contagious like an epidemic disease. But whereas the individual mechanism may be similar in man, the collective unconscious varies considerably between Europe and Spanish America. All the modules guiding the psychological analysis of the human mind were developed on the Classical tradition of Greek thought and, although they maintain universal value as the standards of our main cultural stream, they have considerable limitations in the assessment of Spanish-American psychological experiences and in current psychiatric practice there. One may recall the surprise of Kinsey in Peru when, after thinking he had exhausted the study of sodomy by his research in North America, he was confronted with the diversity of sodomy in pre-Columbian societies.

Psychoanalysis remains the basic therapeutic tool for scientific psychotherapy, but there is growing dissatisfaction with the results from psychoanalytical treatment based on the sexual theories of Sigmund Freud (1856–1939). The study of the pre-Columbian aberrations, through the testimony of historians for over three centuries and afterwards, indeed confirms the dominant role of sexual drives, but it also suggests the need for a more eclectic approach both to behavioural problems and to psychiatric practice in Spanish America. The approach used by Karl G. Jung (1875–1961), by giving a much greater role to religion as the integrative power of mankind, fits the pre-Columbian mind well. He considered libido as not just a sexual, but a creative energy or a spiritual yearning encompassed in the religion of the collective racial unconscious. Among the Mexicans, for instance, the archetype of the racial mother advanced by Jung (1939) seems to have much greater importance than the father image usually maintained by Freud (1949); this also seems to be clear in the ancient Peruvian civilizations. Jung points out that the relationship of the individual with the mother is immediate and deepest in the human conscience; the first instincts of the child and the last thoughts of the man are toward the mother.

The phylogenetic and ontogenetic development of the pre-Columbian mind can also be explored through Alfred Adler's (1870–1937) teleological concept of man, whose purpose is to dominate those in the environment as much as to dominate the environment itself. His individual psychology maintains that the basic driving force behind all human activity is the striving from a feeling of inferiorty towards one of superiority and perfection. The specific direction taken by this striving in the pre-Columbian civilizations was towards self-ideals shaped under the religious patterns of behaviour. The individual could not operate away from his social situation, since all his important life problems—food, sex, power—were in the end social problems. Ramos (1935), by accepting Adler's ideas, thought that the Mexican suffered an inferiority complex, a belief also maintained by Lopez Ibor (1954) about the Spaniard in respect of his technical and scientific inability.

tras llegué à mi mu-
ger; *sciencia*, y dos vezes.

7. MANDAMIENTO.

M. Nnoyolcuitia:ca za-
mach nitlachtequia,
oniquichtec ce huacax,
ihuã ce quaquähtla-
tilnqui; yepualpa,
ihuan matlacpa, ihuã
yexpa.

C. *Me confieffo que re-
petidas vezes hurto;
hurté una Baca, y un
Buey de tiro, manxo,
sciencia, y tres vezes.*

M. Oniccuili nohuampo
tomin, oniquixpachil-
huili yei pefo ce tla-
namaca, ano onicma-
cactlen qui namiquia-
ya, in tlein oniccò-
huilij; yepualpa ihuan
matlacpajihuan nacpa.

C. *Le arrebaté, ò rapi-
ñé à mi proximo, di-
nero, le efcondi; ò ef-
fos à un Mercader, ò
Vendedor, no le dilo*

que le correfpondia à
lo que le comprè; fi-
tenta y quatro vezes.

M. Oniccuilietiniz ce ci-
huatl,j payo qui malo-
loa;è ihuan icuëzoc-
ticarca onĩõntiquiz,
ye ica onĩpinauhti,
ihuan onicquixa alti,
yepualpa, tĩan cax-
topa.

C. *Le arrebaté à una mu-
ger fu payo, que tenia
cobijado, ò arrebofado,
y fus naguas, que efta-
ban tendidas, me las
atiecoxi violentamen-
te, ò me las arrebaté,
y con efto la abergon-
zè, y la hize enojar;
serena, y cinco vezes.*

M. Onictlatili nohuam-
po tlen niccuijuilia-
ya; nechtlatlanilaya,
ihuan ayocmo onicno-
cuiti, ihuan zantlapic
oritlaneltili;yepualpa,
ihuan caxtolpa, ihuan
ceipa.

C. *Le efcondi à mi pro-*

ximo lo q̃ le debia, me
lo pidiò, j ya no lo con-
feffè, y en vano juri;
serena, y feis vezes.

8. MANDAMIENTO.

M. Micepa oniciztla-
coc, onichicoitoc,onic
tlatlatac nohuampo;
yepualpa, ihuan cax-
tolpa, ihuan ocna.

C. *Muchas vezes mur-
muré à mi Proximo;
serena, y fiete vezes.*

M. Zanno onictecentla-
piquili ce nohuampo,
anozo onichiuh teteu-
tlapiquiliztli ica no-
ocnihua, immitech
onicclanqye zantlapic
temictiani tlatlacoli
ica ahulnemiliztli,
ihuan tlachtcquiliz-
tli, ihuan tetlachi-
huiliztli; yepualpa,
ihuancaxtolpa, ihuan
yexpa.

C. *Tambien levanté falfo
testimonio à un proxi-
mo mio, ò hize falzo*

testimonio con mis com-
pañeros, les impusé en
vano, ò fin caufa, ò
motivos, pecado mortal
de la fervia, y de la-
trocinio, y de echize-
ria, y ferenia, y ochove-
zes.

M. Notatzine, mooxitlã
cinco ni nezaninizziz-
pautlitzinohua, ca
onizalacacatica huetiz-
tlacaziliztli,yepaa pa,
ihuan caxtolpa, ihuan
nacpa.

C. *Padre mio à los pies
de Vmd. parefco, y
le manifiefto à Vmd.
que meni con grande
menira; ferena, y
nueve vezes.*

M. Nudexpuntia notla-
tlacol, onizzticcati ica
izzlacaztliztli tepiton,
nacpualpa.

C. *Manifiefto mi pecado,
ò publico mi culpa:
meni con menira le-
ve, ò pequeñas; ochen-
ta vezes.*

FIG. 34. C. C. Velazquez: sexual matters in the Mexican–Spanish Confessionary, 1761, pp. 12–13.

NOVENA
QUE EN CHARIDAD
DEVEMOS HAZER
AL GLORIOSO MARTYR
S. BONIFACIO,
Eficaz para alcanzar de Dios la
rostauracion de aquellos pobres, que
por sum? feria estan en pecado
mortal del inhonesto vicio.

COMPVESTA

*Por el Br. D. Joseph Manuel Garcia del Va-
lle, y Araujo, Presbytero de este Arzobispado.*

DEDICALA

A D. *Joseph Bernardo de Hogal* Ministro, è
impressor del Apostolico, y Real Tribunal de la Santa Cruzada en toda esta Nueva España, quien à su costa, y en su Imprenta, con licencia de los Superiores,
la imprime. Año de 1732.

Fig. 36. Woodcut of S. Boniface, Patron of
homosexuals, used in 1732.

Fig. 35. Novena to S. Boniface for homosexuals,
Mexico 1732.

NOVENA,

QUE EN CARIDAD

DEBEMOS HACER,

AL GLORIOSO MARTIR

S. BONIFACIO,

Eficaz para alcanzar de Dios la reparacion de aquellos pobres, que por su miseria estan en pecado mortal del inhumano vicio.

CONFUESTA

Por el Br. D. Manuel del Val'e y Araujo, Presbítero de este Arzobispado.

❧

MÉJ'CO: 1821.
Inprenta de D. Alejandro Valdés

Fig. 37. Novena to S. Boniface for homosexuals, Mexico 1821.

S. BONIFACIO. M...

Fig. 38. Woodcut of S. Boniface, still used in 1821.

DE LA DIFERENCIA ENTRE LO

TEMPORAL Y ETERNO

CRISOL DE DESENGAÑOS, CON LA ME

MORIA DE LA ETERNIDAD POSTRIMERIAS HV

MANAS, Y PRINCIPALES MISTERIOS DIVINOS

POR EL

P. IVAN EVSEBIO NIEREMBERG

DE LA COMPAÑIA DE

IESVS

Y TRADVCIDO EN LENGVA GVARANI

POR EL PADRE

IOSEPH SERRANO

DE LA MISMA COMPAÑIA

DEDICADO A LA MAGESTAD DEL

ESPIRITV SANTO

CON LICENCIA DEL EXELENTISSIMO

SEÑOR

D. MELCHOR LASSO DE LA VE

GA PORTO CARRERO

Virrey, Governador, y Capitan general del Peru

Impreſſo en las Doƈrinas Año de M.D.CC.V.

FIG. 39. Guaraní edition of J. E. Nieremberg's *Differences* . . . , 1705, with special engravings depicting suffering in hell.

Fig. 40. Mexican Virgin of Guadalupe appearing in P. de Horta *Treatise on Epilepsy*, 1763.

the new arrivals from the mother country Spain, the *aplatanarse* (to become "bananas") is well known. In our own time Gamio (1931) has discussed the psychological problems of cultural adaptation of the Mexicans in the United States of America, and these problems have also been examined by Paz (1950) in respect of the *pachucos* and *chicanos*. The recent study by Kiev (1968) on over two million Mexicans in the totally different cultural environment of the United States of America proves once and for all the permanence of the pre-Columbian behavioural patterns, the role of cultural adaptation in mental illness and the maintenance of pre-Columbian trends in psychiatric treatment. At home, the alteration in the traditional patterns of community life in rural areas with agricultural and industrial advances, and in urban centres with the import of new ways of family life, an erosion of the intimate structure of Spanish-American life has taken place. This might well cause a great tradition to vanish and with it the growth of personal crises which cannot be solved by the well-established traditional rituals and will lead to the growth of mental illness in Spanish America.

There have been a number of studies in recent years on isolated communities still preserving some traces of pre-Columbian patterns. Despite the fact that Benedict's informants read newspapers, Devereux's confidante drove a car, or Nash's villagers listen to the radio, there can be no doubt that pre-Columbian ideas predominated in the mind of those Indians. Lewis's studies (1961) prove, on the other hand, the disintegration of the aboriginal mind under the conditions of modern urban life in Spanish America. After years of ethnological studies on certain aboriginal tribes of the North American South-West, Ruth F. Benedict (1887–1948) pointed out the great diversity of social solutions to the challenges presented by man's physical needs or his environment, which in the end lead to the building up of cultural institutions. The American tribes studied by Benedict (1935), like the great nuclear civilizations examined here, help us to gauge and understand the immensely important role of culturally conditioned behaviour. The life-history of the individual is first and foremost an accommodation to the patterns and standards traditionally handed down in his community. It is practically impossible for an individual to achieve a life of fulfilment and happiness without the support of the standards of the society in which he lives. The social dilemma of the individual whose congenital drives are not provided for in the institutions of his culture, concludes Benedict (1952), becomes of psychiatric importance when his behaviour is regarded as categorically abnormal in society.

Despite the abundance of early studies on the aboriginal civilizations of the New World it is difficult to analyse the pre-Columbian aberrations within the context of community life and family relations. The studies by Nash (1970) among the Maya-Tzental of Amatenango, Chiapas, Mexico and certain surviving customs among the Indians of Central and South America help to give a better picture of the place of the individual in pre-Columbian civilizations, and his behavioural crises, which have also been mentioned by Aguirre Beltran (1963). Nash believes that the key to the persistence of the Indians as a culturally distinct population lies in age-ordered hierarchies sanctioned by the ancestors and the elders, who act as their intermediaries. The reward for remaining within the social control system is security and the right to their guardianship, the sanction against violating the norms is exile or exposure to the evil spirits they hold at bay. Among the Maya-Tzental the household unit of the family, nowadays extended to collateral terms, particularly *compadrazgo* or godparenthood, is still the most important structural unit providing for economic cooperation, education of the young and sustenance of the aged. It provides the setting and personnel for the traditional rituals, both civil and religious, and it is called upon to resolve the life crisis of the group. It remains the resource base through the life of the individual, it provides the idiom for behaviour in a wider community, instils obedience by cultivating a sense of fear and shame in the child by the parent, and this relationship of respect and obedience between parents and children is expected to last throughout life. The *compadres* or ritual kin are, next to the parents, the most important pool from which to draw assistance during life crises. These are frequently brought about by sickness which is a sign of upset relations between the spirits or people and those of relatives, neighbours or places. Nash emphasizes that in the curative ritual the curers not only treat the disease but they also try to bring about spiritual readjustment by dramatizing the ill effects of animosity. The Maya-Tzental, like the Aztecs and the Incas, still consider that disrespect shown to parents was a serious violation of morality and the cause of sickness.

The research by Devereux over a long period (1937, 1951 and 1969) on the psychiatric problems of the Mohave indians in the United States of America have considerable relevance in the interpretation of the pre-Columbian mind, since many of the behavioural problems and aberrations, particularly of a sexual nature, such as incest, homosexuality, and mental illness developing under acculturation were described in pre-Columbian societies and are still prevalent among the Mohave. The Mohave informants were unable to formulate a general etiological theory of insanity, and they referred to a disorganized power or force, indicating that the man's knowledge exceeded his heart. The Mohaves also mentioned as causes of mental illness soul loss, ghosts, witches, charms, and indeed they considered disturbances of sexual instincts as sharply differentiated from mere perversions, aggressive impulses and external situations such as heartbreaks. Devereux's intent to classify systematically the Mohave neurosis and psychosis in terms of modern psychiatry proved to be extremely hazardous, and the native categories fitted the psychiatric realities of the tribe much better than the artificial case histories of patients in our own culture. Each culture has its basic theories and "type conflicts" as well as its "type defences" against them. The Mohave, like the pre-Columbian Indians, had their own conflict-ridden persons to whom they offered genuine supportive psychotherapy, and other types of treatment such as songs, massage, and hydrotherapy. Interesting, too, in Devereux's work is his discussion on the position of the insane in the Mohave Society.

Several attempts have been made to portray the Spanish-American character in terms of its spiritual past. The earliest, by F. García Calderón the distinguished Peruvian diplomat (1883–1953), written from Europe (1912), was particularly aimed at the analysis of political structures and made abundantly clear that in his view, despite the admirable letter of national characters with all sorts of natural rights, liberal suffrage, and representative assemblies, the cruel traditions of the Indian races had produced over-simplified and barbarous systems of government. Brazil has been conscious of its own process of racial assimilation and many ethnological studies dealing with its national character have been published, but the indigenous vein has been so diluted that the original Tupi-Guaraní stock has been submerged, not under the Portuguese influx, but by African arrivals. The work by Gilberto Freyre (1933) is related to this subject.

The survival of pre-Columbian behavioural patterns from the ancient civilizations in the Inca area was examined in Peru from the historical and psychiatric standpoint by Hermilio Valdizán (1885–1929) and Juan B. Lastres (1902–1960), and completed by the pharmacological contributions of Carlos Gutierrez Noriega (1906–1950). Valdizán (1915, 1917), like Lastres (1937), pointed out the heavy psychological burden of the Inca past, and Gutierrez Noriega (1947) added to the sexual perversions and habitual inebriation, the damage produced by centuries of addiction to coca.

The analysis of the Mexicans has fallen into the hands of the philosophers. Samuel Ramos (1897–1959) dared to publish a profile of man and culture in Mexico (1934) where he attributed the 19th-century Mexican mimetism with Europe to an underlying fear of inferiority. Although Ramos was not destructive toward the nationalistic vanity of the Mexican, he tried to show that Mexico's contemporary growth was the result of educators and administrators who created a Creole culture by adapting to the local circumstances the European cultural heritage which came mostly from 19th-century France. Years later Ramos, jointly with L. Zea and E. Uranga, examined anew (1951) the mind and problems of the Mexican. It was natural that Ramos's training in the classical academic tradition and the interest of his associates in themes of political philosophy lent little emphasis to the pre-Columbian past, and most problems were examined at the light of Mexico's political reforms from the middle of the 19th century. However, Ramos's moral integrity and philosophical training gave a profound meaning to his honest analysis of the Mexican mind. He stated his views, quoting the words of Justo Sierra (1842–1912), that history should deny itself emotion and concentrate on the stability of facts, on analysis, and on coordination of its dominant characteristics to achieve synthesis. Ramos believed that the task of giving the Mexican way of life a characteristic stamp lacked the point of departure it logically should have had: knowledge of the Mexican man. Until his character, his desires, his capabilities, and his historical vocation were defined, all projects for reviving the nationalist sense would be blind attempts doomed to failure. He was well aware that modern psychological doctrines show it is impossible to make a man's character intelligible without knowledge of certain childhood experiences definitively influential in the evolution of his soul; and he was convinced that we should go back to the beginning of Mexican history to find out whether some event could have projected the evolution of the Mexican soul into a determined orbit. Ramos insisted that the Mexican intellectuals should have the courage to be themselves and the humility to accept the life that fate had bestowed upon them, because the examination of the Mexican conscience had not been undertaken with the rigour, depth and objectivity that the case required. Only the man who had a passion for truth would have the moral strength also to carry out a dispassionate analysis of himself. The interesting feature of Ramos's essay is that he implicitly accepts in the Mexican character the allegedly aberrant tendencies of the pre-Columbian mind: he finds it awkward to express the sexual allusions in the *pelado*, and takes for granted the heritage of violence and cruelty he quotes from other writers. To him the most striking aspect of the Mexican character at first sight is distrust and susceptibility. These were clearly described by Sahagún (1565) and Mendieta (1596). What makes Ramos unintentionally a behaviourist, despite his philosophical training, is that he believes that the indigenous inertia and immutability was not the result of the Spanish conquest, and that as soon as the compulsion of acculturation ceased the Indian turned back to his old ways. He even went further in stating that so long as the Indian remains in his native environment the individual is subservient to a collective conscience which is steeped and consolidated in its tradition, and that all the strange elements of civilization are incompatible with his nature, because for the Indian the useful qualities of things only exist in proportion to their mystic relationship with all being. Ramos's message was that Mexican culture should continue to learn about European culture and to prepare the young Spanish-American generations by means of strict instruction aimed at discipline of the will and intelligence. Like José Enrique Rodó (1872–1917) in Uruguay, Ramos believed that Mexico was vulnerable to the materialistic influences of the United States of America which by the pacific means of finance and technology were in danger of making the Mexicans slaves of foreign interests.

The same aspect of the Mexican character has been examined with great literary beauty by Paz (1950), discussing firstly the cultural differences between the *pachuco* or Mexican in the United States of America and the North American of Saxon stock. Paz agrees with Ramos that the hermeticism of the Mexican, so perfectly described among the Aztecs by

Mendieta (1596), is one of the several recourses of his suspicion and distrust. Any reader will immediately establish parallels between the sexual drives in pre-Columbian Mexico and Paz's detailed analysis of the *macho*, the he-man, and the submissiveness of the woman. The study of the nostalgia for death in contemporary Mexican society is discussed through literary examples and religious festivities. Paz maintains that the Mexican of today, like the pre-Columbian Aztec, is familiar with death, jokes about it, caresses it, sleeps with it, celebrates it; it is one of his favourite toys, he even eats sweets representing death, *las calaveras*, and it is his most steadfast love. In Paz's view the Mexican's indifference towards death is fostered by his indifference towards life, because he views not only death, but also life as non-transcendent.

The anthropological problems of Spanish-American acculturation were clearly visualized early in this century by Manuel Gamio (1883–1960), who held the idea that the soul and body of the greater part of the population have Indian extraction and are still pre-Hispanic. He dismissed the idea that the Indians could ever be Europeanized and suggested that instead the population of Spanish extraction ought to Indianize a little to assist in a blending encounter. Deep in Gamio's idea (1916) flows the thesis later expressed by Jung (1939), that the human mind like its body has been the recipient of the phylogenetic history, in a collective unconscious. The ancestral experiences deposited by the racial past in the pre-Columbian mind have provided a living system of reactions, aptitudes and behaviour which determine the life of the individual in Spanish America in invisible ways. A realistic understanding of that psychic life is necessary to guide the cultural reorientation of Spanish America towards its own personality. Jung's conviction that the dilemma of modern man is rooted in his neglect of the psychic reality gives considerable backing to the great spiritual problem of Spanish America as conceived by Gamio. This thesis is also valid for the individual: Stein (1963) finds it increasingly difficult to view even the most severe non-organic psychic disturbances as a psychopathological process going on entirely within the individual. He feels rather that his patients suffer primarily from the disease of our time: namely from a loss of connection with soul and spirit, from the collective over-concretization of the soul and over-rationalization of the spirit. The only hope for the individual in Spanish America is to turn inward and search for what his pre-Columbian unconscious and his Spanish mind have to tell, because they are the only true sources of his spiritual life.

This study, started intentionally as an analysis of the aberrant behaviour of the pre-Columbian mind, has led to the insensible recognition of the new forms taken during almost five centuries of acculturation by sexual drives, the use of inebriating drugs, and the attitude to the finitude of life in Spanish America. The original veins of so-called irrationality in the pre-Columbian man are now identified as basic ingredients in the Spanish-American character; they are permanent spiritual values as long as the environmental conditions are preserved and the cultural inheritance is maintained. Individual happiness and social fulfilment with political progress can only be achieved by the harmony of these elements, because human life is guided and only has meaning when the mind is nourished by that spiritual source which it knows and identifies as its unique destiny.

BIBLIOGRAPHY

PRIMARY SOURCES

Acosta, José de. *De natura Novi Orbis libri duo et de Promulgatione Evangelii apud Barbaros sive de Procuranda Indorum salute libri sex.* Salamanca, Guillermo Foquel, 1589. 8°, 10 l. 640 p.

Acosta, José de. *Historia natural y moral de las Indias.* Sevilla, Juan de León, 1590. 4°, 2 l. 535 p. 18 l.

Acosta, José de. *The naturall and morall Historie of the East and West Indies translated into English by E. G[rimston].* London, Val. Sims, 1604. 8°, 3 l. 590 p. 7 l.

Aguero, Cristobal de. *Miscelánea espiritual en el Idioma Zapoteco . . . Confessionario en la mesma Lengua Zapoteca.* México, Vda. de Bernardo Calderón, 1666. 4°, 15 l. 68 f. 232 p.

Alphonso X (the Wise), *Siete Partidas.* Sevilla, M. Ungut y L. Polono, 1491. Fol., 430 l.

Alva, Bartolomé de. *Confessionario mayor y menor en Lengua Mexicana. Y pláticas contra çupersticiones de idolatría.* México, Francisco Salbago, 1634. 4°, 4 l. 51 f. 1 l.

Alva Ixtlilxochitl, Fernando de. *Obras historicas . . . publicadas y anotadas por Alfredo Chavero.* México, Secretaría de Fomento, 1891–1892. 4°, 2 vols.

Alvarez Chanca, Diego. [Carta al Cabildo de Sevilla] in *Colección de los Viages y Descubrimientos que hicieron por mar los Españoles . . .* , vol. I, pp. 198–224. Madrid, Imprenta Real, 1825. 4°, 1 l. 455 p. 1 map.

Andagoya, Pascual de. "Establecimientos de los Españoles en el Darien", in *Colección de los Viages y Descubrimientos que hicieron por mar los Españoles . . .* , vol. III, pp. 393–459. Madrid, Imprenta Real, 1829. 4°, xv, 642 p.

Andagoya, Pascual de. *Narrative of the proceedings of Pedrarias Davila in the provinces of Tierra Firme or Castilla del Oro, and the Discovery of the South Sea and the coasts of Peru and Nicaragua.* Translated . . . by Clements R. Markham. London, The Hakluyt Society, 1865. 8°, xxix, 88 p. 1 map.

Anghiera, Pietro Martire d'. *Opera Legatio Babylonica Oceani decas Poemata epigrammata.* Sevilla, Jacobo Cronberger, 1511. Fol. 74 f.

Anghiera, Pietro Martire d'. *De orbe novo decades . . .* [Preface by Antonio de Lebrixa.] Alcalá de Henares, A. Guillelmi, 1516. Fol., 64 f. 3 l.

Anghiera, Pietro Martire d'. *The decades of the Newe Worlde or West India* ... *Englysshe by Richarde Eden*. London, William Powell, 1555. 8°, 24 l. 1 map, 361 f. 1 l.

Arriaga, Pablo José de. *Extirpación de la idolatría del Pirú*. Lima, Geronymo de Contreras, 1621. 4°, 8 l. 142 p. 3 l.

Arriaga, Pablo José de. *The extirpation of idolatry in Peru*. Translated and edited by L. Clark Keating. Lexington, University of Kentucky, 1968. 8°, xxiv, 192 p.

Avendaño, Fernando de. "Relación del P. Fernando de Avendaño", in *Relaciones geográficas de Indias publicadas por M. Jimenez de la Espada*, vol. I, p. 205. Madrid, Academia de la Historia, 1881–1897. Fol. 4 vols.

Avila, Francisco. *Narrative of the errors, false gods, and other superstitions and diabolical rites in which the Indians of the province of Huarochiri* ... Translated by C. R. Markham. London, The Hakluyt Society, 1873. 8°, 4 l. xx, 220 p. illus.

Bandera, Damian de la. "Relación general de la dispusición y calidad de la provincia de Guamanga llamada San Juan de la Frontera y de la vivienda y costumbres de los naturales della", in *Relaciones geográficas de Indias publicadas por M. Jimenez de la Espada*, vol. I, pp. 96–103. Madrid, Academia de la Historia, 1881–1897. Fol. 4 vols.

Bandera, Damian de la. "Relación del origen e gobierno que los Ingas tuvieron y del que había antes de que ellos señoreasen a los indios deste reino ...", in *Colección de libros y documentos referentes a la Historia del Perú*, 2ª serie, vol. III. Lima, Imp. y Libreria Sanmartí y Cia., 1920. 4°, xii, 184 p.

Baptista, Juan. *Confessionario en Lengua Mexicana y Castellana*. México, Melchior Ocharte, 1599. 8°, 2 l. 112 f. 2 l.

Barrionuevo, Jeronimo de. *Avisos 1654–1668. Precede una noticia de la vida y escritos del autor por A. Paz y Meliá*. Madrid, Imprenta Tello, 1892–1894. 8°, 3 vols.

Benzoni, Girolamo. *La historia del Mondo Nuovo*. Venetia, Francesco Rampazetto, 1565. 8°, 4 l. 175 f.

Betanzos, Juan Díez de. *Suma y narración de los Incas que los indios llamaron Copacenna que fueron señores de la ciudad del Cuzco*. Publícala M. Jimenez de la Espada. Madrid, Manuel G. Hernandez, 1880. 4°, 12 l. 140 p.

Cabello de Balboa, Miguel. "Historia del Perú bajo la dominación de los Incas. [Miscelánea Austral]", in *Colección de libros y documentos referentes a la Historia del Perú*, 2ª serie, vol. II. Lima, Imp. y Libreria Sanmartí y Cia., 1920. 4°, xv, 191 p.

Calancha, Antonio de la. *Chronica moralizadora del orden de San Augustin en el Perú*. Barcelona, Pedro Lacavallería, 1638. Fol., 15 l. 922 p. 14 l.

Cárdenas, Juan de. *Primera parte de los problemas y secretos maravillosos de las Indias*. México, Pedro Ocharte, 1591. 8°, 8 l. 246 p.

Casas, Bartolomé de las. *Brevissima relación de la destruyción de las Indias*. Sevilla, Sebastian Trugillo, 1552. 4°, 54 l.

Casas, Bartolomé de las. *Entre los remedios que don fray Bartolomé de las Casas* ... *refirió por mandato del Emperador* ... *para reformación de las Indias. El Octavo*. Sevilla, Jacome Cronberger, 1552. 4°, 53 l.

Casas, Bartolomé de las. *Apologética historia de las Indias* ... ed. por M. Serrano y Sanz. Madrid, M. Bailly-Bailliere e hijos, 1909. 4°, 2 vols.

Casas, Bartolomé de las. *Historia de las Indias.* Ed. por A. Millares Carlo, estudio preliminar de Lewis Hanke. México, Fondo de Cultura Económica, 1951. 4°, 3 vols.

Castañeda, Pedro de. "The narrative of the expedition of Coronado . . .", edited by F. W. Hodge, in *Spanish explorers in the Southern United States.* pp. 273–387. New York, Barnes and Noble, 1953. 4°, xv, 411 p.

Castro, Cristobal de, y Ortega Morejón, Diego de. "Relación y declaración del modo que este valle de Chincha y sus comarcanos se gobernaban antes que hobiese Incas y despues de que los hubo hasta que los cristianos entraron en esta tierra. 1558", in *Colección de documentos inéditos para la Historia de España,* pp. 217–262. Stuttgart, Strecher und Schröder, 1936. 8°, xv, 262 p.

Cervantes de Salazar, Francisco. *Crónica de Nueva España.* Introducción de F. del Paso y Troncoso. Madrid, Hauser y Menet, 1914. 4°, lvi, 363 p.

Chi, Gaspar Antonio. "Relación sobre las costumbres de los Indios [de Yucatán]", in *Diego de Landa, Relación de las cosas de Yucatán.* Translated by Alfred M. Tozzer. Cambridge, Mass., Peabody Museum, 1941. 4°, xiii, 394 p. 1 l. illus.

Cieza de León, Pedro de. *Parte primera de la Chronica del Perú.* Sevilla, Martin de Montesdoca, 1553. Fol., 10 l. 84 f.

Cieza de León, Pedro de. *Segunda parte de la Crónica del Perú* . . . Publicala M. Jimenez de la Espada. Madrid, Manuel G. Hernandez, 1880. 4°, 12 l. 279 p.

Cieza de León, Pedro de. *The Incas* . . . Translated by Harriet de Onís. Edited . . . by Victor W. von Hagen. Norman, University of Oklahoma Press, 1959. 8°, lxxx, 397 p. 1 l. illus.

Clavigero, Francisco Javier. *Storia antica del Messico.* Cesena, Gregorio Biasini, 1779–1781, 4°, 4 vols.

Clavigero, Francisco Javier. *The history of Mexico* . . . *translated by Charles Cullen.* London, G. G. J. and J. Robinson, 1787. 4°, 2 vols.

Cobo, Bernabé. *Historia del Nuevo Mundo.* Ed. M. Jimenez de la Espada. Sevilla, E. Rasco, 1890–1895. 4°, 4 vols.

Codex of the Bacabs. *Ritual of the Bacabs.* Ed. by Ralph L. Roys. Norman, University of Oklahoma Press, 1965. 8°, xxix, 193 p. illus.

Codex Badianus. *The Badianus manuscript (Codex Barberini Latin 241) Vatican Library; an Aztec Herbal of 1552.* Introduction, translation and annotations by Emily Walcott Emmart. With a foreword by Henry E. Sigerist. Baltimore, The Johns Hopkins Press, 1940. 4°, xxiv, 341 p. illus.

Codex Badianus. *Libellus de medicinalibus Indorum herbis* . . . *Estudio, texto y versión* . . . *Francisco Guerra.* México, Vargas Rea y Diario Español, 1952. 4°, xii, 258 p. illus.

Codex Chimalpopoca. *Códice Chimalpopoca. Anales de Cuauhtitlan y Leyenda de los Soles. Traduccción directa del nahuatl por* . . . *Primo Feliciano Vazquez.* México, Imprenta Universitaria, 1945. Fol., xxii, 166 p. facs.

Codex Magliabecchi. *Libro de la vida que los Indios antiguamente hazian y superticions y malos ritos que tenían y guardaban.* Ed. by Zelia Nuttall. Berkeley, University of California, 1903. 4° oblong, xix, p. 80 l.

Codex Mendoza. *Codex Mendoza, the Mexican manuscript known as the Collection of Mendoza and preserved in the Bodleian Library Oxford.* Edited and translated by James Cooper Clark. London, Waterlow and Sons, 1938. Fol., 3 vols.

Codex Quauhtinchan. *Historia Tolteca-Chichimeca. Anales de Quauhtinchan.* Versión preparada y anotada por Heinrich Berlin en colaboración con Silvia Rendón. Prólogo de Paul Kirchhoff. México, Antigua Librería Robredo, 1947. 4°, 147 p. 2 l. illus.

Codex Ramirez. "Relación del origen de los Indios que habitan esta Nueva España segun sus historias", in *Crónica Mexicana de H. Alvarado Tezozomoc*, pp. 17–149. México, Ireneo Paz, 1878. 4°, viii, 712 p. illus.

Colombo, Fernando. *Historie del S. D. Fernando Colombo nelle quali s'ha particolare, & vera relatione della vita & de fatti dell'Ammiraglio D. Christoforo Colombo suo padre . . . tradotte . . . Alfonso Ulloa.* Venetia, Francesco de' Franceschi Sanese, 1571. 8°, 20 l. 247 f.

[Conquistador Anónimo]. "Relatione di alcune cose della Nuova Spagna . . .", in *Colección de documentos para la Historia de México.* Ed. J. García Icazbalceta, vol. I, pp. 368–398. México, J. M. Andrade, 1858. 4°, 2 vols.

Cortés, Hernan. *Cartas de Relación.* México, Editorial Porrúa S.A., 1960. 8°, xxiii, 264 p. 3 l. map.

Díaz del Castillo, Bernal. *Historia verdadera de la Conquista de la Nueva-España.* Madrid, Imprenta del Reyno, 1632. Fol., 6 l. 254 f. 6 l.

Durán, Diego. *Historia de las Indias de Nueva España y Islas de Tierra Firme.* México, J. M. Andrade y F. Escalante, 1867–1880. 4°, 3 vol. atlas.

Escobar, Jerónimo de. "Relación . . . sobre caracter e costumbres de los Indios de la provincia de Popayan", in *Colección de documentos inéditos relativos al descubrimiento, conquista . . . de América y Oceanía*, vol. 41, pp. 438–492. Madrid, Manuel G. Hernandez, 1884. 8°, 556 p. 3 l.

Fernandez de Echeverría y Veytia, Mariano José. *Historia antigua de Méjico . . . la publica con varias notas y un apéndice el C. F. Ortega.* Méjico, Juan Ojeda, 1836. 8°, 3 vols.

Fernandez de Oviedo, Gonzalo. *Oviedo de la Natural hystoria de las Indias.* Toledo, Remón de Petras, 1526. Fol., 52 f. 2 l.

Fernandez de Oviedo, Gonzalo. *La Historia general de las Indias.* Sevilla, Juan Cromberger, 1535. Fol., 4 l. 193 f. 1 l.

Fernandez de Oviedo, Gonzalo. *Historia general y natural de las Indias, Islas y Tierra Firme del Mar Océano.* Publícala . . . J. Amador de los Rios. Madrid, Real Academia de la Historia, 1851–1855. Fol., 4 vols.

Fernandez de Oviedo, Gonzalo. "Historia general y natural de las Indias. Ed. . . . de J. Perez de Tudela", in *Biblioteca de autores españoles . . .*, vols. 117 to 121. Madrid, Ediciones Atlas, 1959. 4°, 5 vols.

Fernandez de Piedrahita, Lucas. *Historia general de las Conquistas del Nuevo Reyno de Granada.* Ambers, Juan Bautista Verdussen, 1688. Fol., 10 l. 599 p.

García, Gregorio. *Origen de los Indios de el Nuevo Mundo, e Indias Occidentales.* Valencia, Pedro Patricio Mey, 1607. 8°, 12 l. 535 p. 12 l.

García del Valle y Araujo, José Manuel. *Novena a San Bonifacio.* Móxico, José Bernardo de Hogal, 1732. 16°, 16 l.

Garcilasso de la Vega, Inca. *Primera parte de los Commentarios reales que tratan del origen de los Incas, reies que fueron del Perú . . .* Lisboa, Pedro Crasbeeck, 1609. Fol., 10 l. 264 f.

Garcilasso de la Vega, Inca. *Historia general del Perú.* Córdoba, Viuda de Andrés Barrera, 1617. Fol., 8 l. 300 f. 6 l.

Gumilla, José. *El Orinoco ilustrado, historia natural, civil, y geográfica de este gran río.* Madrid, Manuel Fernandez, 1741. 4°, 20 l. 580 p. 10 l. illus.

Gutierrez de Santa Clara, Pedro. *Quinquenarios o Historia de las Guerras civiles del Perú (1544–1548) y de otros sucesos de las Indias.* Madrid, Victoriano Suarez, 1904–1929. 8°, 6 vols.

Gutierrez de Santa Clara, Pedro. "Quinquenarios; o Historia de las guerras civiles del Perú", in *Biblioteca de autores españoles* ..., vols. 165–167. Madrid, Editorial Atlas, 1963. 4°, 3 vols.

Hernandez, Francisco. *Quatro libros de la naturaleza y virtudes de las plantas y animales ... en la Nueva España.* Ed. ... F. Ximenez. México, Vda. de D. López Davalos, 1615. 4°, 5 l. 203 f. 7 l.

Hernandez, Francisco. *Rerum medicarum Novae Hispaniae Thesaurus.* Roma, Vitalis Mascardi, 1628. Fol., 14 l. 950, 90 p. 3 l. illus.

Hernandez, Francisco. *Opera ... ed. C. Gomez Ortega.* Madrid, Herederos de Ibarra, 1790. Fol., 3 vols.

Herrera, Antonio de. *Historia general de los hechos de los Castellanos en las Islas y Tierra Firme del Mar Océano.* Madrid, Juan Flamenco y Juan de la Cuesta, 1601–1615. Fol., 9 parts in 4 vols.

Huaman Poma de Ayala, Felipe. *Nueva corónica y buen gobierno.* (Codex péruvien illustré.) Paris, Institut d'Ethnologie, 1936. 4°, xxviii, 1178, p. 2 l.

Isabel de Portugal. "La Reyna ... [Cédula contra el Pulque, ques lo proprio que Balché]." *Anales del Museo Nacional de México*, **6**: 37, 1892.

Landa, Diego de. *Relation des chosse de Yucatan ... texte espagnol et traduction française ... par l'abbé Brasseur de Bourboug.* Paris, Arthus Bertrand, 1864, 4°, 3 l. cxii, 516 p.

Landa, Diego de. *Landa's Relación de las cosas de Yucatan,* a translation edited with notes by Alfred M. Tozzer. Cambridge, Mass. Peabody Museum, 1941. 4°, xiii, 394 p. 1 l. illus.

León, Martin de. *Camino del cielo en Lengua Mexicana.* México, Diego López Dávalos, 1611. 4°, 12 l. 160 f. 7 l.

Lima, Concilio Provincial. *Doctrina Christiana y Catecismo para instrucción de los Indios.* Lima, Antonio Ricardo, 1584. 4°, 8 l. 84 f.

Lima, Concilio Provincial. *Confessionario para los Curas de Indios con la instrucción contra sus ritos ...* Lima, Antonio Ricardo, 1585. 4°, 4 l. 27 f.

Lima, Concilio Provincial. *Tercero Cathecismo y exposición de la Doctrina Christiana, por Sermones.* Lima, Antonio Ricardo, 1585. 4°, 8 l. 215 f.

Lizárraga, Reginaldo de. *Descripción y población de las Indias ... prólogo por Carlos A. Romero.* Lima, Imprenta Americana, 1908, 4°, 2 l. viii, 209 p.

López de Cogolludo, Diego. *Historia de Yucathan.* Madrid, Juan García Infanzón, 1688. Fol., 14 l. 760 p. 16 l.

López de Gómara, Francisco. *Historia general de las Indias.* Zaragoza, Agustín Millán, 1552. Fol., 4 l. 122 f.

López de Gómara, Francisco. *La Conquista de México.* Zaragoza, Agustín Millán, 1552. Fol., 139 f. 1 l.

López Medel, Tomás. "Relación", in *Landa's Relacion de las cosas de Yucatán.* Ed. by A. M. Tozzer. Cambridge, Mass., Peabody Museum, 1941. 4°, xiii, 394 p. 1 l. illus.

López de Velasco, Juan. *Geografía y descripción universal de las Indias recopilada ... desde el año de 1571 al de 1574, publicada ... por Don Justo Zaragoza.* Madrid, Est. Tipográfico de Fortanet, 1894. 4°, xvi, 808 p. map.

Matienzo, Juan. *Gobierno del Perú. Obra escrita en el siglo XVI.* Buenos Aires, Cía. Sud Americana de billetes de banco, 1910. 4°, x, 219 p.

Mendieta, Jerónimo de. *Historia eclesiástica Indiana; obra escrita a fines del siglo XVI ... publica ... J. García Icazbalceta.* México, F. Díaz de Léon y S. White, 1870. 4°, xlv, 790 p.

México, Inquisición. *Nos los Inquisidores ...* México, E. Martinez, 1616, Fol., 2 l.

México, Real Universidad. *Informe que ... haze ... sobre los inconvenientes de la bebida de el Pulque.* México, s.n., 1692. Fol., 18 l.

Molina, Alonso de. *Confessionario mayor, en Lengua Mexicana y Castellana.* México, Antonio de Espinosa, 1565. 4°, 121 f. 3 l.

Molina, Cristobal de. "Relación de las fábulas y ritos de los Incas", in *Collección de libros y documentos referentes a la historia del Perú,* vol. I. Lima, Imp. y Librería Sanmartí y Cía. 1916. 8°, xxxi, 215 p. 1 l.

Molina, Cristobal de. *An account of the fables and rites of the Incas ... translated ... by Clements R. Markham,* in pp. 1–64. London, The Hakluyt Society, 1873, 8°, xx, 220 p.

Montesinos, Fernando. "Memorias antiguas historiales y políticas del Perú", in *Colección de libros españoles raros o curiosos, vol. XVI.* Madrid, Miguel Ginesta, 1882. 8°, xxxii, 259 p. 2 l.

Motolinia, Toribio de Benavente. *Historia de los Indios de la Nueva España.* Estudio crítico ... por Edmundo O'Gorman. México, Editorial Porrúa S.A., 1969. 8°, 256 p.

Muñoz Camargo, Diego. *Historia de Tlaxcala.* Publicada y anotada por Andrés Chavero. México, Secretaría de Fomento, 1892. 4°, 278 p. 4 l.

Murúa, Martin de. *Historia general del Perú, origen y descendencia de los Incas.* Introducción y notas de Manuel Ballesteros Gaibrois. Madrid, A. Góngora, 1962. 4°, 2 vols. illus.

Nieremberg, Juan Eusebio. *De la diferencia entre lo temporal y eterno ... traducido en Lengua Guaraní por el Padre Joseph Serrano.* [Loreto] Doctrinas del Paraguay, 1705. Fol., 5 parts.

Nóbrega, Manuel do. [Lettera] in *Diversi avisi particolari dall' Indie di Portogallo ricevuti, dall' anno 1551, fino al 1558.* Venetia, Michele Tramezzino, [1558]. 8°, 8 l. 286 f.

Nuñez Cabeza de Vaca, Alvar. *La relación que dió ... de lo acaescido en las Indias.* Zaragoza, Agustín de Paz y Juan Picardo, 1542. 4°, 66 l.

Nuñez Cabeza de Vaca, Alvar. *La relación y comentarios del Governador ... scriptos por Pedro Hernandez.* Valladolid, F. Fernandez de Córdova, 1555, 4°, 114 f. 2 l.

Nuñez Cabeza de Vaca, Alvar. *The narrative of Alvar Nuñez Cabeça de Vaca,* translated by T. Buckingham Smith. Washington [G. W. Riggs], 1851. Fol., 138 p. 8 maps.

Oliva, Giovanni Anello. *Historia del Reino y provincias del Perú, y de sus Incas reyes, descubrimiento por los españoles ... publicado ... por J. F. Pazos Varela y L. Varela Orbegozo.* Lima, Imp. de S. Pedro, 1895. 4°, xxxi, 217 p.

Oré, Luis Jerónimo de. *Symbolo Catholico Indiano.* Lima, Antonio Ricardo, 1598. 4°, 8 l. 192 f.

Ortiz, Tomás. "Dixo lo siguiente, acerca de los hombres de Tierra Firme que era Caribes", in A. Herrera, *Historia general ... Decada III Libro VIII, Capítulo X,* pp. 312–313. Madrid, Juan Flamenco y Juan de la Cuesta, 1601–1615. Fol., 9 parts in 4 vols.

Pané, Ramón. [Relación de Fray Ramón acerca de las antiguedades de los Indios, las cuales con diligencia, como hombre que sabe el idioma de estos, recogió por mandato del Almirante.] in *Fernando Colombo, Historie* . . ., ff. 134–138. Venetia, Francesco de' Franceschi Sanese, 1571. 8°, 20 l. 247 f.

Pauw, Cornelius de. *Recherches philosophiques sur les Americaines, ou Mémoires interessants pour servir à l'histoire de l' Espèce humaine.* Berlin, George Jacques Decker, 1768–1769. 8°, 2 vols.

Pellicer de Ossau y Tovar, José. "Avisos históricos 1640–1647", in A. Valladares de Sotomayor, *Semanario eruditio*, vols. 31–33 (1790). Madrid, Blás Ramón y Antonio Espinosa, 1787–1791. 4°, 34 vols.

Peña y Montenegro, Alonso de la. *Itinerario para Parochos de Indios.* Madrid, J. Fernandez de Buendía, 1668. 4°, 29 l. 563 p. 42 l.

Peña y Montenegro, Alonso de la. *Itinerario para Parochos de Indios.* Lyon, Joan Ant. Huguetan y Cía., 1678. 4°, 32 l. 848 p. 66 l.

Pizarro, Hernando, "A los magníficos señores, los señores Oydores de la Audiencia Real de Su Magestad, que residen en la ciudad de Sancto Domingo". in *Colección de libros y documentos referentes a la historia del Perú.* 2ª serie vol. III pp. 165–180. Lima, Imp. y Librería Sanmartí y Cía., 1920. 4°, xii, 188 p.

Polo de Ondegardo, Juan. "Informaciones acerca de la religión y gobierno de los Incas", in *Colección de libros y documentos referentes a la historia del Perú*, vol. III–IV. Lima, Imp. y Librería Sammartí y Cía., 1916. 4°, xxxvi, 208 and vi, 204 p.

Ponce, Alonso. *Relación breve y verdadera de algunas cosas de las muchas que sucedieron . . . en las provincias de la Nueva España . . .* Madrid, Viuda de Calero, 1873. 8°, 2 l. 548 p.

Raleigh, Walter. *The History of the World.* London, W. Stansby for W. Burre, 1614, Fol., 32 l. 555, 669 p. 28 l. illus.

Ramirez, Baltasar, "Descripcion del Reyno del Piru, del sitio, temple, provincias, obispados y ciudades. De los naturales, de sus lenguas y trage . . . (1597)", in *Quellen zur Kulturgeschichte des prä-Kolumbischen America*, pp. 1–122. Stuttgart, Strecher und Schröder, 1936. 8°, xv, 262 p.

Ramos Gavilán, Alonso. *Historia del celebre santuario de Nuestra Señora de Copacabana y sus milagros, e invención de la Cruz de Carabuco.* Lima, Gerónimo de Contreras, 1621. 4°, 7 l. 432 p. 4 l.

Ramusio, Giovanni Battista. *Primo volume [-terzo] delle navigationi et viaggi . . .* Venetia, Heredi di L. Giunti, 1550–1574. Fol., 3 vols.

Remesal, Antonio de. *Historia general de las Indias Occidentales y particular de la Governación de Chiapa y Guatemala.* Madrid, Francisco Angulo, 1619. Fol., 5 l. 796 p.

Román y Zamora, Jerónimo. *Repúblicas del mundo divididas en XXVII libros.* Medina del Campo, F. del Canto, 1575. Fol., 3 vols.

Ruiz de Alarcón, Hernando. "Tratado de las supersticiones y costumbres gentílicas que hoy viven entre los indios, naturales de esta Nueva España", *Anales del Museo Nacional de México*, **6**: 123–224, 1892.

Sahagún, Bernardino de. *Historia general de las cosas de Nueva España.* Mexico, Ed. Pedro Robredo, 1938. 4°, 5 vols.

Sahagún, Bernardino de. *Florentine Codex. General history of the things of New Spain.* Translated from the Aztec into English ... by A. J. O. Anderson and C. E. Dibble. Santa Fé, New Mexico, School of American Research, 1950. Fol., 10 vols.

Salinas, Buenaventura de. *Memorial de las historias del Nuevo Mundo Piru: Méritos y excelencias de la ciudad de Lima* ... Lima, Gerónymo de Contreras, 1630. 4°, 7 l. 304 p. 2 l.

Sanchez de Aguilar, Pedro. *Informe contra Idolorum cultores del Obispado de Yucatan.* Madrid, Vda de J. Gonzalez, 1639. 4°, 8 l. 124 f.

Sanchez de Aguilar, Pedro. "Informe contra Idolorum cultores del Obispado de Yucatan", *Anales del Museo Nacional de México,* **6:** 13–122, 1892.

[San Pedro, Juan de]. "Relación de la religión y ritos del Perú hecha por los primeros religiosos agustinos que por allí pasaron para la conversión de los naturals [Huamachuco]", in *Colección de libros y documentos referentes a la historia del Perú,* vol. XI pp. 1–56. Lima, Imp. y Librería Sanmartí y Cía., 1918. 4°, xxxii, 176 p.

Santa Cruz Pachacuti, Juan de. "Relacion de antiguedades deste reyno del Perú ...", in *Tres relaciones de antiguedades peruanas,* pp. 231–328. Madrid, Ministerio de Fomento, 1879. 8°, xliv, 328 p.

Santa Cruz Pachacuti, Juan de. "Relación de antiguedades deste reyno del Perú", in *Biblioteca de autores españoles* ..., vol. 209, pp. 279–320. Madrid, Ediciones Atlas, 1968. 4°, lxxiv, 324 p.

Santillán, Hernando de. "Relación del origen, descendencia, politica y gobierno de los Incas", in *Tres relaciones de antiguedades peruanas,* pp. 1–136. Madrid, Ministerio de Fomento, 1879. 4°, xliv, 328 p.

Santillan, Hernando de. "Relación del origen, descendencia, política y gobierno de los Incas", in *Biblioteca de autores españoles* ..., vol. 209, pp. 97–149. Madrid, Ediciones Atlas, 1968. 4°, lxxiv, 324 p.

Sarmiento de Gamboa, Pedro. *Historia de los Incas.* 2ª ed. Buenos Aires, Ed. Emecé, 1943. 8°, 185 p.

Sepúlveda, Juan Ginés de. *Apologia pro libro de Justis belli causis.* Roma, Valerium Doricum Ludovicum frates Brixienses, 1550. 8°, 19 f. 5 l.

Sepúlveda, Juan Ginés de. *Democrates alter, sive de Justis belli causis apud Indos.* Traducido por M. Menendez y Pelayo. Madrid, Boletin de la Real Academia de la Historia, **21:** 257–369, 1892.

Serra, Angel. *Manuel de administrar los Santos Sacramentos a los españoles y naturales de esta provincia de Michoacan.* México, Maria de Benavides, 1697. 4°, 12 l. 127 f. 4 l.

Serra, Angel. *Manual de administrar los Santos Sacramentos a los españoles y naturales de esta provincia de Michoacan.* México, José Bernardo de Hogal, 1731. 4°, 6 l. 138 f. 4 l.

Simón, Pedro. *Primera parte de las Noticias historiales de las Conquistas de Tierra Firme en las Indias Occidentales.* Cuenca, Domingo de la Iglesia, 1627. Fol., 9 l. 671 p. 20 l.

Spain, Laws. *Recopilación de la Leyes destos Reynos, hecha por mandado ... del Rey Philippe Segundo.* Alcalá de Henares, Juan Iñiguez de Lequerica, 1581. Fol., 2 vols. 1 Index.

Toledo, Francisco de. "Informaciones acerca del Señorio y Gobierno de los Incas hechas por mandado de Don Francisco de Toledo Virey del Perú 1570–1572", in *Colección de libros españoles raros o curiosos,* vol. XVI, pp. 177–259. Madrid, Miguel Ginesta, 1882. 8°, xxxii, 262 p.

[Toledo, Francisco de]. "Parecer acerca de la perpetuidad y buen gobierno de los Indios del Perú ... a Don Juan Sarmiento, Presidente del Consejo de Indias", in *Colección de libros y documentos referentes a la historia del Perú*, serie 2ª, vol. III, pp. 145–164. Lima, Imp. y Librería Sanmartí y Cía., 1920. 4°, xii, 184 p.

Torquemada, Juan de. *Iª–IIIª Parte de los veynte y un libros rituales y Monarchia Indiana con el origen y guerras de la Indias Occidentales, ...* Sevilla, Mathias Clavijo, 1615. Fol., 3 vols.

Ulloa, Antonio de. *Noticias Americanas: Entretenimientos phisicos-históricos ...* Madrid, Francisco M. de Mena, 1772. 4°, 13 l. 407 p.

Valadés, Diego. *Rhetorica Christiana ad concionandi et orandi usum accomodata*. Perugia, Petrum Jacobum Petrutium, 1579. 4°, 10 l. 375 p. 8 l. illus.

Valera, Blás. "Relacion de las costumbres antiguas de los naturales del Pirú", in *Tres relaciones de antiguedades peruanas*, pp. 137–227. Madrid, Ministerio de Fomento, 1879. 8°, xliv, 328 p.

[Valera, Blás]. "Relación de las costumbres antiguas de los naturales del Pirú", in *Biblioteca de autores epañoles ...*, vol. 209, pp. 151–190. Madrid, Ediciones Atlas, 1968. 4°, lxxiv, 324 p.

Vasconcellos, Simão de. *Chronica da Companhia de Jesu do Estado do Brasil*. Lisboa, Henrique Valente de Oliveira, 1663. Fol., 8 l. 188, 528 p. 6 l.

Velasquez de Cárdenas, Carlos C. *Breve práctica y regimen del Confessionario de Indios en Mexicano y Castellano*. México, Bibliotheca Mexicana, 1761. 8°, 12 l. 54 p.

Vespucci, Amerigo. *Lettera di Amerigo Vespucci delle isole nuovamente trovate in quattro suoi viaggi*. [Firenze, Gian Stefano, 1505.] 4°, 16 f.

Vetancurt, Agustin de. *Theatro Mexicano, descripción breve de los sucessos exemplares ... del Nuevo Mundo Occidental de las Indias*. México, Viuda de Ribera, 1698. Fol., 3 parts.

Villagomez, Pedro de. "Exhortaciones e instrucción acerca de las Idolatrías de los Indios del arzobispado de Lima", in *Colección de libros y documentos referentes a la historia del Perú*, vol. XII. Lima, Imp. y Librería Sanmarti y Cía., 1919. 4°, xii, 293 p.

Vitoria, Francisco de. *Obras ... Edición crítica por el P. Teófilo Urdanoz O.P.* Madrid, Editorial Católica, 1960. 8°, viii, 1386 p. 5 l.

Zárate, Agustin de. *Historia del descubrimiento y conquista del Perú, con las cosas naturales que señaladamente allí se hallan y los sucesos que ha avido*. Anvers, Martin Nucio, 1555. 8°, 8 l. 273 f. 7 l.

Zorita, Alonso de. "Breve y sumaria relación de los señores y maneras y diferencias que había de ellos en la Nueva España", in *Colección de documentos inéditos relativos al descubrimiento, conquista ... de América y Oceanía*, vol. II, pp. 1–126. Madrid, Imprenta de Quirós, 1864–1884. 4°, 42 vols.

Zorita, Alonso de. "Historia de la Nueva España (Siglo XVI)", in *Colección de documentos referentes a la historia de América*, vol. IX. Madrid, Victoriano Suarez, 1909. 8°, cx, 534 p.

SECONDARY SOURCES

Ackerknecht, E. H. "Psychopathology, Primitive Medicine and Primitive Culture." *Bulletin of the History of Medicine*, **14**: 30–67, 1943.

Ackerknecht, E. H. "Natural diseases and rational treatment in Primitive Medicine." *Bulletin of the History of Medicine*, **19**: 467–497, 1946.

Ackerknecht, E. H. "Primitive medicine's social function", in *Miscellanea Paul Rivet*, vol. I, pp. 3–7. México, Universidad Nacional Autónoma de México, 1958. 8°, 2 vols.

Acosta Saignes, Miguel. *Tlacaxipeualiztli. Un complejo Mesoamericano entre los Caribes*. Caracas, Universidad Central, 1950. 4°, 50 p. illus.

Adler, Alfred. *What life should mean to you*. Ed. by Alan Porter. Boston, Little, Brown and Co., 1931. 8°, 5 l. 300 p.

Adler, Alfred. *The individual psychology of A.A*. Selections by Heinz Ansbacher and Rowena Ansbacher. New York, Basic Books, 1956. 8°, 526 p. illus.

Aguirre Beltran, Gonzalo. *Medicina y Magia. El proceso de aculturación en la estructura colonial*. México, Instituto Nacional Indigenista, 1963. 8°, 443 p. 2 l.

Allen, Clifford E. *The sexual perversions and abnormalities*. London, Oxford University Press, 1940. 8°, xii, 193 p.

Bacci, Andrea. *De thermis . . . libri septem*. Venetia, Vincentium Valgrisium, 1571. Fol., 32 l. 509 p.

Bailey, Flora L. "Some sex beliefs and practices in a Navaho community." *Papers Peabody Museum American Archaeology and Ethnology*, **40** (2): 1–108, 1950.

Balsalobre, Gonzalo de. "Relación de las idolatrías del Obispado de Oaxaca." *Anales del Museo Nacional de México*, **6**: 225–260, 1892.

Barrett, Ward. *The sugar hacienda of the Marqueses del Valle*. Minneapolis, University of Minnesota Press, 1970. Fol., 4 l. 152 p. illus.

Becerra de León, Berta. *Bibliografía del Padre Bartolomé de las Casas*. Habana, Sociedad Económica de Amigos del País, 1949, 8°, 67 p.

Benedict, Ruth F. *Patterns of Culture. An anthropological study of the Zuñi, Dobu and Kwakiutl tribes*. London, G. Routledge & Sons, 1935. 8°, xii, 290 p.

Braden, Charles S. *Religious aspects of the Conquest of Mexico*. Durham N.C., Duke University Press, 1930. 8°, xvi, 344 p. illus.

Bromberg, Walter. *The Mind of man. A History of Psychotherapy and psychoanalysis*. New York, Harper and Brothers, 1959. 8°, xxi, 344 p.

Burchard, Edward M. L. "Mystical and scientific aspects of the psychoanalytic theories of Freud, Adler and Jung." *American Journal of Psychotherapy*, **14** (2): 289–307, 1960.

Bushnell, Geoffrey H. S. *Peru*. London, Thames and Hudson, 1956. 8°, 207 p. illus.

Calderón de la Barca, Frances E. I. *Life in Mexico, during a residence of two years in that country*. Preface by W. H. Prescott. London, Chapman and Hall, 1843. 8°, xiv, 437 p.

Cámara Barbachano, Fernando. "Culturas contemporáneas de México." *América Indígena*, **7**: 165–171, 1947.

Capitan, L. "Les sacrifices humaines et l'anthropophagie rituelle chez les anciens mexicains." *Journal de la Societé des Americanistes,* **12**: 211–217, 1920.

Caso, Alfonso. *The Aztecs; people of the sun.* Illustrated by Miguel Covarrubias, translated by Lowell Dunham. Norman, University of Oklahoma Press, 1958. 8°, xvi, 125 p. illus.

Castiglioni, Arturo. *Adventures of the Mind.* New York, Alfred A. Knopf, 1946. 8°, xviii, 428, v p. 1 l. illus.

Clements, F. E. "Primitive concepts of disease." *University of California Publications in American Archaeology and Ethnology,* **32**: 185–252, 1932.

Danzel, Theodor Wilhelm. *Zur Psychologie der altmexikanischen symbolik,* Eranos Jahresbericht, Zurich, pp. 211–239, 1938.

Dávalos Hurtado, E. y Romano, A. "Las deformaciones corporales entre los Méxicas." *Revista mexicana de estudios antropológicos,* **14**: 79–101, 1956.

Deleito y Peñuela, José. *La mala vida en la España de Felipe IV.* Madrid, Espasa Calpe S.A., 1948. 8°, xi, 251 p.

Devereux, G. "Institutionalised homosexuality of the Mohave Indians." *Human Biology,* **9**: 498–527, 1937.

Devereux, G. "The social and cultural implications of incest among the Mohave Indians." *Psychoanalytic Quarterly,* **8**: 510–533, 1939.

Devereux, George. "Primitive Psychiatry." *Bulletin of the History of Medicine,* **8**: 1194–1213, 1940.

Devereux, George. *Reality and Dream. Psychotherapy of a Plains Indian . . .* Psychological tests edited and interpreted by Robert R. Holt. New York, International Universities Press [1951]. 8°, xxi, 438 p.

Devereux, George. *Mohave ethnopsychiatry: The psychic disturbances of an Indian tribe.* Washington D.C., Smithsonian Institution Press, 1969. 8°, xvi, 597 p. illus.

D'Harcourt, Raoul. *La médecine dans l'ancien Perou.* Paris, Librairie Maloine, 1939. 8°, 4 l. 242 p. illus.

Díaz Infante, Fernando. *Quetzalcoatl. Ensayo psicoanalítico del mito Nahua.* Prólogo de Angel Ma. Garibay K. Veracruz, Cuadernos de la Facultad de Filosofía, Letras y Ciencias (no. 18), 1963. 4°, 93 p. 2 l. illus.

Dietschy, H. "Die medizin der Azteken." *Ciba Zeitschrift,* **4** (42): 1438–1469, 1937.

Ehrenwald, Jan. "The return of Quetzalcoatl and doctrinal compliance. A case study of Cortés and Montezuma." *American Journal of Psychiatry,* **14** (2): 308–321, 1960.

Esteve Barba, Francisco. *Cultura Virreinal.* Barcelona, Salvat Editores, 1965. 4°, xi, 1019 p. illus.

Fanchamps, A. "Des drogues magiques des Aztèques à la thèrapie psicholytique." *Acta psychotherapeutica et psychosomatica,* **10**: 372–374, 1962.

Fenton, William N. "Iroquois suicide. A study in the stability of a culture pattern." *Bulletin of the Bureau of American Ethnology,* **128** (14): 79–136, 1941.

Ford, C. S. and Beach, F. A. *Patterns of sexual behaviour.* Introduction by F. A. E. Crew. London, Eyre & Spottiswoode, 1952. 8°, 307 p.

Freud, Sigmund. *An outline of Psychoanalysis.* Translated by James Strachey. New York, Norton Publ., 1949. 8°, 127 p.

Frezier, Amedée F. *Relation du voyage de la Mer du Sud aux côtes du Chily et du Pérou fait pendant les années 1712, 1713 & 1714.* Paris, Nyon, Didot et Qillau, 1732. 4° xvi, 298, 63 p. illus.

Friedrich, Paul. "Assumptions underlying Tarascan political homicide." *Psychiatry,* **25** (4): 315–327, 1965.

Gamio, Manuel. *Forjando Patria.* (Pro nacionalismo). México, Ed. Porrúa Hermanos, 1916. 4°, viii, 328 p.

Gamio, Manuel. "Trascendencia política de la Antropología en América. Río de Janeiro." *XX Congreso Internacional de Americanistas,* 1922. **2**: 297–305, 1922.

Gamio, Manuel. *The Mexican immigrant, his life-story.* Chicago, The University of Chicago Press, 1931. 8°, xiii, 288 p.

Gantt, W. H., Pickenhain, L. and Zwingmann, Ch. *Pavlovian approach to Psychopathology. History and perspectives.* Leipzig, Pergamon Press, 1970. 8°, vi, 341 p. illus.

García Calderón, Francisco. *Les démocracies latines de l'Amerique.* Preface de Raymond Poincaré. Paris, E. Flammarion, 1912. 8°, 2 l. 383 p.

Gimenez Fernandez, Manuel. *Bartolomé de las Casas.* Sevilla, Escuela de Estudios Hispano-Americanos, 1953–1960. 4°, 2 vols.

Goldman, Irving. *The Cubeo Indians of the Northwest Amazon.* Urbana, University of Illinois Press, 1963. 8°, 305 p. illus.

Gomez de Quevedo, Francisco. "Sueño de la Muerte (1622)" in *Sueños y discursos de verdades descubridoras de abusos, vicios y engaños.* Barcelona, Esteban Liberos, 1627. 8°, 8 l. 136 p.

Guerra, Francisco. *Libellus de medicinalibus Indorum herbis.* Estudio texto y versión. México, Vargas Rea y Diario Español, 1952. 4°, xii, 258 p. illus.

Guerra, Francisco. *Historiografía de la Medicina Colonial Hispano-Americana.* México, Abastecedora de Impresos, 1953. 4°, 324 p.

Guerra, Francisco. "Lo americano en la medicina." *La Prensa Médica Mexicana,* **18**: 176–180, 1953.

Guerra, Francisco. "Visao historica da Medicina do Continente Indigena e Colonição das Americas." *Imprensa Medica,* Lisboa, **17**: 715–726. 1953.

Guerra, Francisco. "La Medicina colonial americana. Tesis religiosas y políticas." *Revista de la Sociedad Venezolana de Historia de la Medicina,* **9** (23): 75–84, 1961.

Guerra, Francisco. "Medical colonization of the New World." *Medical History,* London, **7**: 147–154, 1963.

Guerra, Francisco. "Maya medicine." *Medical History,* London, **8**: 31–43, 1694.

Guerra, Francisco. "La política imperial sobre las drogas de las Indias." *Revista de Indias,* Madrid, **26** (103): 31–58, 1966.

Guerra, Francisco. "The influence of disease on race, logistics and colonization in the Antilles." *Journal of Tropical Medicine and Hygiene,* **69**: 23–52, 1966.

Guerra, Francisco. "Drugs from the Indies and the political economy of the sixteenth century." *Analecta Historica-Medica,* **1**: 29–54, 1966.

Guerra, Francisco. "Aztec medicine." *Medical History,* London, **10**: 315–338, 1966.

Guerra, Francisco. "Mexican phantastica. A study of the early ethnobotanical sources on hallucinogenic drugs." *British Journal of Addiction,* **62**: 171–187, 1967.

Guerra, Francisco. "The role of religion in Spanish American medicine", in *Medicine and Culture,* pp. 179–188. London, Wellcome Institute of the History of Medicine, 1969. 8°, vi, 321 p.

Guerra, Francisco. "Aztec Science and Technology." *History of Science,* **8**: 32–52, 1969.

Guerra, Francisco. "Acculturation of the concept of disease in Ancient Mexico." Bucharest, *XXII International Congress of History of Medicine,* 1970. (In press.)

Guerra, Francisco. *La medicina en la America Precolombina.* Barcelona, Editorial Salvat S.A., 1971. (In press.)

Guerra, F. y Olivera, H. *Las plantas fantasticas de México,* Diario Español, 1954. 4°, 124 p. illus.

Gutierrez Noriega, Carlos. "Alteraciones mentales producidas por la coca." *Revista de Neuro-Psiquiatría,* Lima, **10**: 145–176, 1947.

Guyon, René. *The ethics of sexual acts.* Translated by J. C. and Ingeborg Flugel. Introduction and notes by Norman Haire. New York, Alfred A. Knopf, 1934. 8°, xxii, 384, xxviii p.

Hanke, Lewis U. *The Spanish struggle for Justice in the conquest of America.* Philadelphia, University of Pennsylvania Press, 1949. 8°, xi, 217 p. illus.

Hanke, Lewis U. *Bartolomé de las Casas. An interpretation of his life and writings.* The Hague, Martinus Nyhoff, 1951. 4°, 6 l. 104 p. illus.

Hanke, Lewis U. *Aristotle and the American Indians. A study in race prejudice in the modern world.* London, Hollis & Carter, 1959. 4°, x, 164 p. illus.

Holland, William R. *Medicina Maya en los Altos de Chiapas. Un estudio del cambio sociocultural.* México, Instituto Nacional Indigenista, 1963. 8°, 4 l. iv, 321 p. illus.

Horton, Donald. "The function of alcohol in primitive societies: a cross-cultural survey." *Quarterly Journal Studies Alcohol,* **4**: 199–320, 1943.

Hrdlička, Aleš. *Physiological and medical observations among the Indians of Southwestern United States and Northern Mexico.* Washington, Government Printing Office, 1908. 4°, 460 p. illus.

Humboldt, Alexander von. *Essai politique sur le royaume de la Nouvelle-Espagne.* Paris, F. Schoell, 1811. 8°, 5 vols.

Janet, Pierre. *Les medications psychologiques. Études historiques psychologiques et cliniques sur les methodes de la psychotherapie.* Paris, F. Alcan, 1919. 4°, 3 vols.

Juan, Jorge y Ulloa, Antonio de. *Relación histórica del viage a la América meridional.* Madrid, Antonio Martin, 1748. Fol., 4 vols.

Jung, Karl G. *Modern man in search of a soul.* Translated by W. S. Dell and C. F. Baynes. London, K. Paul, Trench, Trubner & Co. Ltd., 1933. 8°, ix, 282 p.

Jung, Karl G. *The integration of the personality.* Translated by S. M. Dell. New York, Farrar and Rinehart Inc., 1939. 8°, 4 l. 313 p.

Jung, Karl G. *Psyche and symbol.* A selection of writings edited by Violet S. de Laszlo. Translated by C. Baynes anl F. C. R. Hull. New York, Doubleday Anchor Books, 1958. 8°, 363 p.

Jung, Karl G. *Psychology and Religion: West and East.* Translated by F. C. R. Hull, London, Routledge and Kegan Paul, 1958. 8°, xxiii, 699 p.

Kardiner, Abram. *The individual and his society.* The psychodinamics of primitive social organization ... with a foreword and two ethnological reports by R. Linton. New York, Columbia University Press, 1947. 8°, xxvi, 4, 503 p.

Karsten, Rafael. *Das altperuanische Inkareich und seine Kultur.* Leipzig, Brockhaus Verlag, 1949. 8°, 271 p. illus.

Keyserling, Hermann A. von. *Südamerikanische meditationen.* Stuttgart, Deutsche verlags-anstalt, 1932. 8°, 384 p.

Kierkegaard, Søren A. *The concept of dread.* Translated ... by Walter Lowrie. Princeton, Princeton University Press, 1944. 8°, xiii, 154 p.

Kiev, Ari. *Magic, faith, and healing. Studies in Primitive Psychiatry today.* New York, The Free Press, 1964. 8°, 475 p.

Kiev, Ari. "The study of Folk Psychiatry." *International Journal of Psychiatry,* **1**: 524–552, 1965.

Kiev, Ari. *Curanderismo. Mexican-American folk psychiatry.* New York, The Free Press, 1968. 8°, xiii, 207 p.

King, Edward. *Antiquities of Mexico.* London, Robert Howell and others, 1831–1848. Fol. 9 vols.

Kinsey, Alfred C., Pomeroy, W. B., and Martin, C. E. *Sexual behaviour in the human male.* Philadelphia, W. B. Saunders and Co., 1948. 8°, xv, 804 p.

Laín Entralgo, Pedro. *The therapy of the word in Classical Antiquity.* Edited and translated by L. J. Rather and J. M. Sharp. New Haven, Yale University Press, 8°, xxii, 253 p.

Lamb, Ursula. "Religious conflicts in the Conquest of Mexico." *Journal of the History of Ideas,* **17** (4): 526–539. 1956.

Larco Hoyle, Rafael. *Checan; essay on erotic elements in Peruvian art.* Geneve, Les Éditions Nagel [1965]. 4°, 146 p. illus.

Lastres, Juan B. "Las curaciones por las fuerzas del espíritu en la medicina incaica." *Revista del Museo Nacional,* Lima, **14**: 27–81, 1945.

Lastres, Juan B. "La 'citua' o 'coya raimi', fiesta purificadora del pecado-enfermedad." *Revista del Museo Nacional,* Lima, **25**: 233–256, 1956.

Lastres, Juan B. "Las causas de las enfermedades nerviosas en el antiguo Perú." *Revista del Museo Nacional,* Lima, **6**: 25–42, 1937.

Lastres, Juan B. *Historia de la medicina peruana. Medicina Incaica.* Lima, Imprenta Santa María, 1951. 4°, 3 vols.

Latrobe, Charles J. *The rambler in Mexico. MDCCCXXXIV.* London, R. B. Seeley and W. Burnside, 1836. 8°, viii, 309 p.

Leake, Chauncey D. "Mood, behavior and drugs." *Science,* **170**: 559–560, 1970.

Lejeal, Léon. "Rites phalliques, origine du théatre et des sacrifices humaines a Mexico." *Journal de la Societé des Americanistes,* **2**: 341–343, 1905.

León, Nicolás. "El culto al falo en el Mexico precolombino." *Anales del Museo Nacional,* Mexico, 2ª época, **1**: 278–280, 1904.

León Pinelo, Antonio. *Epitome de la Biblioteca Oriental i Occidental, Nautica i Geografica.* Madrid, Juan Gonzalez, 1629. 4°, 44 l. 186, xii p.

León Portilla, Miguel. *La filosofía nahuatl estudiada en sus fuentes.* Prólogo de Angel Ma. Garibay K. México, Instituto Indigenista Americano, 1956. 8°, xv, 344 p. illus.

Lévi-Strauss, Claude. *A world on the wane*. London, Hutchinson & Co. Ltd., 1961. 8°, 404 p. illus.

Lewis, Oscar. *The children of Sanchez: autobiography of a Mexican family.* New York, Random House, 1961. 8°, xxxi, 499 p.

Lima, Oswaldo Gonçalves de. *El maguey y el pulque en los códices mexicanos. Figuras de Honorina Lima.* México, Fondo de Cultura Económica, 1956. 8°, 278 p.

Lipschutz, Alejandro. *El problema racial en la conquista de América y el mestizaje.* 2ª ed. Santiago de Chile, Editorial A. Bello, 1967. 4°, 384 p.

Llaguno, José A. *La personalidad jurídica del Indio y el III Concilio Provincial Mexicano (1585),* México, Editorial Porrúa S.A., 1963. 4°, xxviii, 324 p. 1 l.

López Ibor, Juan José. *El español y su complejo de inferioridad.* 3ª ed. Madrid, Ediciones Rialp S.A., 1954. 8°, 194 p. 1 l.

Lumholtz, Karl S. *Unknown Mexico.* New York, C. Scribner's Sons. 1902. 4°, 2 vols. illus.

Lumholtz, Karl S. *Symbolism of the Huichol Indians.* New York, American Museum of Natural History, 1900. 4°, 228 p. illus.

McCarty, Joseph H. *Two thousand miles through the heart of Mexico.* New York, Phillips & Hunt, 1886. 8°, 288p.

Madsen, William. "Anxiety and witchcraft in Mexican American acculturation." *Anthropological Quarterly,* **39**: 110–127, 1966.

Martínez Cortés, Fernando. *Las ideas en la medicina nahuatl.* México, Prensa Médica Mexicana, 1965. 8°, 2 l. 110 p. 1 l. illus.

Mason, John A. *The ancient civilizations of Perú.* Harmondsworth, Penguin Books, 1969. 8°, xvi, 335 p.

Medina, José Toribio. *Historia del Tribunal de la Inquisición de Lima (1569–1820).* Santiago de Chile, Imprenta Gutenberg, 1887. 4°, 2 vols.

Medina, José Toribo. *La imprenta en México (1539–1821).* Santiago de Chile, Casa del autor, 1907–1912. 4°, 8 vols.

Menendez Pidal, Ramón. *El Padre Las Casas. Su doble personalidad.* Madrid, Espasa Calpe S.A., 1963. 8°, xvi, 410 p. illus.

Mora, George. "The history of psychiatry: a cultural and bibliographical survey." *International Journal of Psychiatry,* **2**: 335–366, 1966.

Morley, Sylvanus G. *The ancient Maya.* London, Oxford University Press, 1946. 8°, xxxii, 520 p. illus.

Muñoz y Manzano, Cipriano. *Bibliografía española de Lenguas Indígenas de América.* Madrid, Sucesores de Rivadeneyra, 1892. 4°, xxv, 427 p. 4 l.

Myerhoff, Barbara G. "The doctor as cultural hero: The shaman of Rincon." *Anthropological Quarterly,* **39**: 60–72, 1966.

Nash, June. "Death as a way of life: The increasing resort to homicide in a Mexican Indian Town." *American Anthropologist,* **69** (5): 455–470, 1967.

Nash, June. *In the eyes of the ancestors. Belief and behaviour in a Maya community.* New Haven, Yale University Press, 1970. 8°, xxiv, 368 p. illus.

Nieuwenhuis, A. W. "Principles of Indian medicine in American Ethnology and their psychological signification." Janus, *Archives internationales pour l'histoire de la médecine et de la géographie médicale,* **28**: 305–356, 1924.

O'Gorman, Edmundo. "Sobre la naturaleza bestial del Indio americano. Humanismo y humanidad. Indagación en torno a una polémica del siglo XVI." *Filosofía y Letras, México,* **1**: 141–159, 305–315, 1941.

Orozco y Berra, Manuel. *Historia antigua y de la conquista de México*. México, Gonzalo A. Esteva, 1880. 4°, 4 vols. atlas.

Pavlov, Ivan P. *Conditioned reflexes. An investigation of the physiological activity of the cerebral cortex*. Translated by G. V. Anrep. London, Humphrey Milford, 1927. 8°, xv, 430 p.

Pavlov, Ivan P. *Psychopathology and Psychiatry*. Selected works compiled by Y. Popov and L. Rokhlin. Moscow, Foreign Languages Pub. House [1962]. 8°, 543 p.

Paz, Octavio. *The labyrinth of Solitude. Life and thought in Mexico*. Translated by Lysander Kemp. London, The Penguin Press, 1967. 8°, 4 l. 199 p.

Pettazzoni, Rafaele. "La confessione dei peccati nell antiche religioni Americani." *Studi e matteriali di Storia delle Religioni, Roma*, **2**: 34–84, 163–229, 1926.

Ponce, Pedro. "Breve relación de los dioses y ritos de la gentilidad." *Anales del Museo Nacional de México*, **6**: 3–12, 1892.

Preuss, K. T. "Phallische Fruchtbarkeits-Dämonen als Träger des alt-mexikanischen mimischen Weltdramas." *Archiv fur Anthropologie, Braunschweig*, **29**: 129–188, 1903.

Pruyser, P. W. "Religion and psychiatry. A polygon of relationships." *Journal of the American medical Association*, **195**: 197–202, 1966.

Quintana, Gerardo. "Algunos aspectos de la medicina popular indígena." *Revista de Psiquiatría*, Lima, **4**: 296–302, 1923.

Ramos, Samuel. "En torno a las ideas sobre el Mexicano." *Cuadernos Americanos*, **10** (3): 103–114, 1951.

Ramos, Samuel. *El perfil del hombre y la cultura en México*. 3ª ed. México, Espasa Calpe S.A., 1951. 8°, 145 p.

Ramos, Samuel. *Profile of man and culture in Mexico*. Translated by Peter G. Earle. Introduction by Thomas B. Irving. [Austin] University of Texas Press, 1962. 8°, xx, 198 p.

Ricard, Robert. *La "conquete espirituelle" du Mexique*. Paris, Institut d'ethnologie, 1933. 4°, xix, 404 p. illus.

Rios, Fernando de los. "The religious character of Colonial law in the sixteenth century Spain." *Proceedings of the Sixth International Congress of Philosophy*, Cambridge, Mass. 1926. pp. 481–485 [1927].

Robertson, Donald. *Mexican manuscript painting of the early Colonial Period. The metropolitan schools*. New Haven, Yale University Press, 1959. 4°, xix, 234 p. illus.

[Rodriguez] Delgado, José M. *Physical control of the mind. Toward a psychocivilized society*. New York, Harper and Row, 1969. 8°, 280 p.

Romanell, Patrick. *Making of the Mexican mind. A study in recent Mexican thought*. Lincoln, Neb., University of Nebraska Press, 1952. 8°, ix, 213 p.

Rowe, John H. "The kingdom of Chimor." *Acta Americana*, **6**: 26–59, 1948.

Roys, Ralph L. ed. *Ritual of the Bacabs*. Norman, University of Oklahoma Press, 1965. 8°, xxix, 193 p.

Ruiz Moreno, Aníbal. *La lucha antialcohólica de los Jesuitas en la época colonial*. Buenos Aires, Editorial A. Moly, 1939. 8°, vii, 44 p.

Ruz, A. "El pensamiento Nahuatl respecto de la muerte." *Estudios de cultura Nahuatl*, **4**: 251–261, 1963.

Sandoval, Fernando B. *La industria del azúcar en Nueva España*. México, Universidad Nacional Autónoma de México, 1951. 4°, 222 p. illus.

Sartorius, Karl C. *Mexico. Landschaftsbilder und skizzen aus dem Volksleben.* Darmstadt, G. G. Lange, 1855. 4°, 4 l. viii, 364 p. illus.

Serna, Jacinto de la. "Manual de Ministros de Indios para el conocimiento de sus idolatrías y extirpación de ellas." *Anales del Museo Nacional de México,* **6**: 261–476, 1892.

Serrano y Sanz, Manuel. "Doctrinas psicológicas de Fr. Bartolomé de las Casas." *Revista de Archivos, Bibliotecas y Museos,* 3ª época, **17** (2): 59–75, 1907.

Simpson, Lesley B. *Many Mexicos.* 3rd ed. Berkeley, California, University of California Press, 1952. 8°, 349 p.

Sonenschein, D. "Homosexuality as a subject of anthropological inquiry." *Anthropological Quarterly,* **39**: 73–82, 1966.

Soustelle, Jacques. "Apuntes sobre la psicología y el sistema de valores en México antes de la Conquista", in *Estudios antropológicos publicados en homenaje al Dr. Manuel Gamio,* pp. 497–502. México, Universidad Nacional, 1956. 8°, viii, 713 p. illus.

Soustelle, Jacques. *Les quatre soleils. Souvenirs et réflexions d'un ethnologue au Mexique.* Paris, Librairie Plon, 1967. 8°, 340 p. illus.

Stein, Robert M. "Reflections on Jung's practice and concepts", in Michael Fordham, ed., *Contact with Jung,* pp. 172–175. London, Tavistock Publications Ltd., 1963. 8°, x, 245 p. illus.

Stoddard, H. L. "Phallic symbols in America." *American Antiquarian and Oriental Journal,* **27**: 281–294, 1905.

Theobert, H. "Amerikanische Phallus-Darstellung." *Verhandlungen der Berliner Gesellschaft fur Anthropologie,* **28**: 678–680, 1896.

Thompson, John E. S. *The rise and fall of Maya civilization.* 2nd. ed. Norman, University of Oklahoma Press, 1956. 8°, xv, 328 p. illus.

Thompson, Wallace. *The Mexican mind. A study of national psychology.* Boston, Little, Brown and Company, 1922. 8°, xvi, 303 p.

Trens, Manuel B. "Arte curativo de las enfermedades. Farmacia y hechicería. La brujería y el nahualismo en la Nueva España." *Boletin del Archivo general de la Nación,* México, **23** (4): 494–559, 1952.

Tylor, Edward B. *Anahuac. México and the Mexicans, ancient and modern.* London, Longman, Green, Longman and Roberts, 1861. 8°, 344 p. illus.

Uranga, Emilio. "Notas para un estudio del Mexicano." *Cuadernos Americanos,* **10** (3): 114–128, 1951.

Vaillant, George C. *The Aztecs of Mexico; origin, rise and fall of the Aztec nation.* Garden City N.J., Doubleday, Doran & Co. Inc. 1941. 8°, xxiv, 340, p. illus.

Valdizan, Hermilio. *La alienación mental entre los primitivos peruanos.* Lima, Universidad de San Marcos, 1915. 4°, 97 p.

Valdizan, Hermilio. "Los factores etiológicos de la alienación mental a través de la historia del Perú." *Crónica médica,* Lima, **34**: 221–236, 1917.

Veracruz, Alonso de la. *Speculum conjugiorum.* México, Juan Pablos, 1556. 4°, 686 p.

Von Hagen, Victor W. *The desert kingdoms of Peru.* Greenwich, Conn., New York Graphic Society Publ., 1965. 8°, 190 p. illus.

Wassen, S. Henry. "Anthropological survey of the use of South American snuffs," in *Ethnopharmacologic search for psychoactive drugs,* pp. 233–289. Washington D.C., Public Health Service Publication No. 1645, 1967. 4°, xxiv, 468 p. illus.

West, D.J. *Homosexuality.* 3rd ed. London, G. Duckworth & Co. Ltd., 1968. 8°, 304 p.

Wolfenden Committee. *Report of the Committee on Homosexual offences and Prostitution.* London, Her Majesty's Stationery Office, 1957. 8°, 155 p.

Zea, Leopoldo. "Dialectica de la conciencia en México." *Cuadernos Americanos,* **10** (3): 87–103, 1951.

ETHNOGRAPHIC INDEX

INDEX OF PRE-COLUMBIAN PROPER NAMES

INDEX OF PRE-COLUMBIAN WORDS

TOPOGRAPHIC INDEX

Conquistador Anónimo, 51, 124, 213, 255, 261, 262, 296
Correa, Pedro, 89
Cortés, Hernan, 51, 52, 85, 123, 217, 225, 231, 232, 233, 235, 243, 260, 261, 296
Cosa, Juan de la, 47
Council of the Indies, 3, 106, 130, 162
Covarrubias, Miguel, 303
Crew, Francis A. E., 303
Crockaert, P., 59
Cruz, Francisco de la, 224
Cruz, Martín de la, 82
Cullen, Charles, 295

D

Danzel, Theodor W., 275, 303
Dávalos Hurtado, E., 303
David, 19
Deleito y Peñuela, José, 228, 303
Dell, William S., 305
Devereux, George, 272, 286, 287, 288, 303
D'Harcourt, Raoul, 303
Diana, 151
Dianes, Hernando, 219
Díaz del Castillo, Bernal, 51, 52, 85, 123, 124, 204, 229, 255, 260, 261, 296
Díaz Infante, Fernando, 276, 303
Dibble, Charles E., 300
Dietschy, Hans, 303
Dioscorides, Pedacius, 136
Dominican Order, 3, 21, 52, 59, 68, 74, 102, 143, 161, 165, 173, 175, 235, 238
Drake, Francis, 129, 148
Dunham, Lowell, 303
Duran, Diego, 25, 140, 143, 144, 260, 296

E

Earle, Peter G., 308
Eden, Richard, 48, 49, 50, 294
Elizabeth I, Queen of England, 48
Emmart, Emily Walcott, 82, 295
Enriques, Pedro, 203
Ehrenwald, Jan, 276, 303
Escobar, Jerónimo de, 122, 123, 259, 262, 296

Esquilache, Prince of, 178
Esteve Barba, Francisco, 4, 303

F

Fanchamps, A., 303
Federmann, Nikolaus von, 223
Fenton, William N., 303
Ferdinand II, King of Aragón, 2, 44, 216, 221
Fernandez de Echeverría y Veytia, Mariano José, 101, 159, 209, 210, 211, 278, 296
Fernandez de Navarrete, Martín, 50
Fernandez de Oviedo, Gonzalo, 53, 54, 55, 56, 57, 67, 68, 70, 71, 72, 76, 107, 218, 255, 259, 260, 261, 265, 284, 296
Fernandez de Piedrahita, Lucas, 34, 202, 260, 296
Flugel, Ingeborg, 305
Ford, Clellan S., 272, 303
Fordham, Michael, 309
Francis I, King of France, 2, 53
Franciscan Order, 3, 21, 63, 64, 82, 112, 127, 132, 139, 140, 144, 152, 172, 187, 203, 235, 236, 237, 239, 242
Frederick II, King of Prussia, 207
Freud, Sigmund, 274, 284, 302, 303
Freyre, Gilberto, 288
Frezier, Amedée, 224, 304
Friedrich, Paul, 304

G

Galen, 71, 201
Galicia Chimalpopoca, Faustino, 100
Gálvez, Diego de, 91
Gamio, Manuel, 286, 290, 304
Gantt, William A. H., 304
Garcés, Julian, 3, 202
García, Gregorio, 161, 162, 261, 296
García Calderón, Francisco, 288, 304
García de Loaysa, C., 52, 106
García del Valle, José Manuel, 243, 296
García de Tobar, Francisco, 217
García Icazbalceta, Joaquin, 21, 51, 132, 296, 298
Garcilasso de la Vega, Inca, 161, 162, 163, 164, 165, 194, 200, 208, 209, 213, 261, 262, 296

SUBJECT INDEX

A

Abortion, 22, 23, 35, 38, 73, 80, 108

Acculturation, 5, 263, 264, 265, 266, 267, 268, 269, 270, 271, 273, 282, 285, 288, 289, 290, 291

Adultery, 23, 32, 33, 35, 37, 40, 73, 86, 104, 106, 131, 145, 147, 149, 154, 156, 157, 158, 160, 161, 167, 169, 171, 175, 176, 182, 183, 185, 186, 190, 204, 205, 206, 210, 215, 240, 262

Agriculture, 6, 7, 8, 9, 10, 12, 13, 15, 17

Air, 84, 179

Anger, 136, 163, 183, 184

Anthropophagy, 5, 14, 20, 29, 32, 41, 44, 45, 50, 52, 53, 54, 55, 61, 63, 64, 65, 66, 67, 80, 81, 85, 88, 89, 93, 94, 95, 96, 97, 99, 107, 108, 109, 110, 117, 118, 120, 122, 123, 124, 125, 126, 131, 155, 156, 173, 195, 203, 215, 217, 218, 219, 254, 259, 263, 282

Anxiety, 82, 114, 136, 185

B

Baptism, 40, 234

Bardaje, 43, 46, 55, 56, 66, 67, 71, 76, 85, 86, 91, 109, 123, 124, 127, 130, 133, 169, 173, 178, 190, 206, 222, 261, 263, 272

Bestiality, 24, 53, 98, 99, 163, 170, 195, 196, 200, 215, 222, 229, 237, 238, 239, 241, 261, 263, 272

Buba, 57, 114, 227, 241

C

Calendar, 8, 12, 14, 110, 117

Castration, 45, 66, 85, 141, 149, 188

Communion, 40, 41, 118, 144, 234, 277

Confession, 40, 41, 50, 74, 75, 102, 103, 104, 105, 106, 107, 112, 113, 125, 126, 128, 129, 131, 132, 133, 142, 143, 144, 145, 146, 147, 148, 152, 157, 158, 164, 165, 166, 167, 168, 169, 171, 174, 175, 176, 177, 190, 191, 192, 193, 194, 197, 198, 199, 203, 204, 205, 210, 234, 236, 237, 238, 277, 278, 279, 280

Conquistador, 107, 132, 162, 190, 219, 229

Curse, 38, 180, 204

D

Dancing disease, 106, 143, 166, 168

Decalogue, 39, 215

Disobedience, 18, 53, 81, 83, 158, 190, 195,

Divination, 133, 134, 135, 136, 140, 144, 150, 151, 181, 182

Divorce, 109, 235, 252

Dream, 66, 133, 135, 138, 150, 151, 171, 172, 201, 274

Drug, 5, 20, 25, 44, 45, 53, 72, 121, 134, 136, 149, 150, 152, 188, 202, 207, 244, 245, 260, 263

E

Epilepsy, 83, 84, 139, 171, 186, 197

F

Fast, 114, 124, 128, 129, 130, 147, 168, 174, 177, 194, 198

Fear, 82, 83, 84, 137, 138, 139, 186, 207, 284

Fornication, 22, 29, 31, 40, 62, 75, 111, 114, 119, 128, 131, 132, 142, 158, 159, 169, 170, 172, 176, 198, 207, 208, 220, 239, 240, 241

G

Giant, 8, 90, 99, 101, 131, 141, 142, 155, 165, 187, 188, 195, 209, 210

H

Hallucination, 64, 133, 134, 135, 136, 137, 151, 181, 243

Hallucinogenic, 45, 46, 64, 69, 87, 111, 112, 116, 133, 136, 144, 149, 181, 206, 244, 255

Hanging, 87, 108, 129, 177, 178, 191, 206, 214, 248, 253

Hell, 40, 41, 112, 129

Hieroglyph, 7, 10, 12, 14, 111, 128, 159, 210

Homicide, 20, 23, 29, 31, 34, 25, 37, 38, 40, 41, 54, 64, 65, 73, 75, 104, 106, 107, 117, 126, 128, 147 148, 156, 167, 174, 175, 192, 205, 208, 210, 215, 216, 217, 221, 223

Homosexuality, 22, 54, 61, 101, 112, 223, 224, 228, 229, 238, 263, 271, 287

Human sacrifice, 5, 14, 17, 30, 44, 54, 62, 63, 65, 66, 80, 85, 87, 97, 107, 108, 117, 118, 119, 120, 121, 124, 125, 126, 133, 148, 156, 173, 202, 204, 253, 254, 259, 260, 263, 268, 269, 273

I

Incest, 5, 20, 23, 24, 34, 36, 37, 39, 61, 63, 72, 80, 90, 93, 99, 107, 109, 122, 127, 148, 149, 153, 155, 156, 160, 196, 199, 206, 215, 220, 221, 228, 235, 239, 240, 262, 263, 287

Inebriation, 5, 20, 23, 24, 25, 35, 51, 52, 53, 57, 64, 82, 87, 89, 96, 97, 98, 106, 108, 109, 110, 111, 119, 122, 133, 134, 137, 140, 151, 160, 169, 181, 182, 183, 200, 201, 206, 207, 210, 212, 225, 226, 237, 238, 242, 245, 246, 247, 248, 249, 250, 251, 255, 261, 263, 265, 272, 288

Insanity, 137, 138, 287

Irrationality, 1, 2, 4, 5, 60, 63, 68, 79, 107, 108, 201

J

Jealousy, 19, 126, 238

L

Lesbian, 23, 162, 206, 236, 237, 238, 257

Lie, 30, 33, 37, 38, 40, 53, 128, 169, 171, 175, 265

Liquor, 225, 226, 246, 247, 250, 251

Love, 19, 28, 29, 39, 40, 136, 137, 161, 183, 184, 185, 186, 187, 270

Lust, 25, 26, 29, 40, 43, 51, 56, 77, 86, 136, 140, 153, 158, 161, 172, 178, 179, 185, 186, 187, 189, 210, 211, 224, 229, 239, 243, 246, 270

M

Madness, 116, 134, 135, 137, 171, 179, 180, 197

Matrimony, 40, 81, 109, 158, 173, 175, 183, 196, 206, 226, 234, 235, 238

Medicine, 18, 27, 46, 71, 74, 82, 83, 84, 85, 110, 111, 114, 131, 134, 136, 143, 149, 151, 152, 165, 179, 181

Mental Stupor, 83, 84, 137

Morals, Aztec, 21, 22, 23, 24, 25, 26, 27, 28, 29, 30

Morals, Maya, 30, 31, 32, 33

Morals, Inca, 34, 35, 36, 37, 38, 39

Morals, Spanish, 215, 216, 217, 218, 219, 220, 221, 222, 223, 224, 225, 226, 227, 228, 229, 230

Mushroom, 64, 112, 116, 117, 133, 134, 135, 144, 244

Mutilation, 11, 30, 110, 111, 133, 157, 188, 258

Myth, 276, 277

O

Obedience, 18, 143, 144, 167, 287

P

Penance, 40, 41, 110, 111, 114, 130, 132, 147, 158, 176, 190, 193, 234

Poisoning, 22, 23, 36, 38, 72, 87, 104, 105, 117, 190, 192, 205, 228, 251

Political disease, 82, 83

Polygamy, 55, 85, 88, 93, 122, 133, 153, 155, 174, 176, 198, 199, 234, 235, 252, 282

Procurer, 24, 36, 116, 160

Prostitution, 25, 26, 38, 86, 109, 119, 128, 138, 148, 154, 171, 262

Psychotherapy, 5, 181, 274, 275, 276, 277, 278, 279, 280, 281, 284

AP